THE MECHANICS' INSTITUTE REVIEW
ISSUE 3 AUTUMN 2006

The first Mechanics' Institute in London was founded in 1823 by George Birkbeck. 'Mechanics' then meant skilled artisans, and the purpose of the Institute was to instruct them in the principles behind their craft. As Birkbeck College, the Institute became part of London University in 1920 but still maintains one foot in the academy and one in the outside world.

D0265860

The Mechanics' Institute Review
Issue 3 Autumn 2006

The Mechanics' Institute Review is published by MA Creative Writing, School of English and Humanities, Birkbeck, Malet Street, Bloomsbury, London WC1E 7HX

ISBN 0-9547933-3-1 / ISBN 978-0-9547933-3-3
Foreword © Julia Bell, 2006
Contents © the individual Authors, 2006
English translation of 'Lost Bearings' © Celia Hawkesworth, 2006
Illustrations © the individual Artists, 2006
Cover image © Photolink/Getty Images, 2006
Cover drawing © Kit Jilly Ding, 2006

Project Director: Julia Bell

Editors:
John Braime
Jonathan Catherall
Christine Hsu
Laura Peters
Amy Popovich
Victor Schonfeld

The Editorial Board would like to thank Russell Celyn Jones, Anne-Marie Whiting, Mary Fox, Emma Forsberg and Sue Tyley for making this project possible.

For further copies or information, please contact Anne-Marie Whiting, MA Creative Writing, School of English and Humanities, Birkbeck, Malet Street, Bloomsbury, London WC1E 7HX. Tel: 0207 079 0689. Email: a.whiting@bbk.ac.uk

Website: www.bbk.ac.uk/mir

Printed and bound by Antony Rowe Ltd., Bumpers Farm, Chippenham, Wiltshire

Cover design and typesetting: Emma Forsberg

The Mechanics' Institute Review is typeset in RotisSerif

Table of Contents

List of Illustrations

FOREWORD
Julia Bell

At a recent PEN event on digital copyright there was much discussion and gnashing of teeth about the future of the book in an age of instant digital information. The new Sony Reader (iPod for the text generation) was heralded for a short while as the replacement of the book. But amongst some of its design flaws it has been discovered that it can't be dropped in the bath, or read in the glare of hot sun while wearing sunglasses, and is the uncomfortable size of a large B-format paperback.

While the argument for digital music players was won the moment digital music files became possible – all those clunky CDs and records slimmed down into something as elegant as an iPod – the evolution of the .doc or .txt file has not meant the end of the published book. Instead, it seems, it has led to a proliferation of them. Gabriel Zaid, in his thought-provoking little tract *So Many Books* (Sort of Books, 2004), suggests that even if no more books were ever published it might take over 250,000 years for us to acquaint ourselves with the fifty million titles ever published. 'Simply reading a list of them (author and title) would take some fifteen years.'

In this library of Babel where there are more books than readers to read them, it seems inevitable that reference books will lose out to Google, already the greatest gatekeeper of knowledge the world has ever known, and on whose pages you can uncover vertiginous amounts of information about almost anything on the entire planet. Reading novels and stories on the other hand, that old-school activity, handling ink on paper, bound between a card cover, is still best achieved in an easy chair, or on the train to work, or on the beach. As Allen Lane discovered when he founded Penguin, the pocket-sized paperback book is the most efficient delivery mechanism for novels and stories. It's portable, scuffable, tactile and convenient. In between its pages, with the sand and the biscuit crumbs, is a highly personal relationship between the reader and the author, mediated by typography.

Maybe Generation Next will have their stories downloaded direct from the matrix, but for now, more than ever, we exist in a world of text. The revolution in technology hasn't meant the end of the book as product; instead it has meant that the means of producing books has become cheaper and easier. Anyone with a few hundred quid, a basic computer set-up and access to print-on-demand can produce a book. Which means that for all the talk of homogenization, it's never been easier to be your own publisher and the potential for an exciting and enriching small-press culture has never been greater. The big headache for small presses isn't the production of books, it's the distribution.

Which brings in a whole other debate about the dominance of profit-driven corporations on our cultural lives. The tight margins within which high-street retailers operate, the constant pressure on the big publishers to hit their bottom lines mean that, as Robert McCrum continually attests in his *Observer* columns, there have never been so many over-hyped and under-written books on the shelves before. Standards, he would have us believe, disappeared the moment that advances started making headline news and those commonest of readers, Richard and Judy, got in on the act of promoting both books and their authors.

Maybe so. Maybe *Labyrinth* by Kate Mosse is just another example of this literary democracy where successful people add novel writing to their repertoire of skills. Although this is not such a new phenomenon; if one thinks back to Disraeli, popular novel writing has often been an added source of income for politicians and public figures – think Jeffrey Archer, Anne Widdecome, Prue Leith, even Edwina Currie . . . The exiled Croatian writer Dubravka Ugresic, in her collection of essays on writing and reading *Thank*

You for Not Reading (Dalkey Archive, 2003), mourns this storming of Parnassus by the 'novel-writing chauffeurs' and 'literary tycoons' who have created an identity crisis for the vocational or literary writer.

In such a culture, where a book is just a part of a wider portfolio – the film, the DVD, the video game, the CD – it is hard for writers to find a sense of integrity in the text. In both Harry Potter and *The Da Vinci Code* it's the concepts that matter more than the writing. Easily digestible, transferable into other media, and lazily derivative, the books that achieve commercial success seem to depend on telling stories we have vaguely heard before, rather than challenging assumptions and pushing the form.

So much we know. What is unknown is how, with access to the democracy of the Internet and cheap printing, writers and readers will fight back. There are already interesting examples out there. The Friday Project, a new Internet/print venture, headed up by ex-buyer Scott Pack, intends to change the way we buy and read books. Or Hari Kunzru's experimental print/Internet magazine *Mute* (www.metamute.org). What's certain is that the revolution will happen in a more diverse and democratic manner than simply with the birth of a new kind of screen from which to read text.

The Mechanics' Institute Review is in its own small way a part of this too. Edited each year by members of the Birkbeck MA Creative Writing cohort and printed in short runs, the magazine offers a forum, often for the first time, to new work by new writers. Issue 3 is bigger and bolder and includes this year new fiction by established authors who have collaborated or associated with our MA, as well as some carefully selected and edited work from across the range of MA and diploma courses. The writing in this year's issue is, we think, diverse, interesting, challenging, exciting. I hope that you will find the same to be true. The book is dead. Long live the book.

SHOES THAT MATCH
Maggie Womersley

Alison was halfway through buying a pair of purple suede ankle boots when the ward sister rang to say that her mother had died that morning. The boots were beautiful but extremely expensive; they had seduced her the night before as she walked home from the hospital, her mother's goodnight kiss still faint on her cheek. Early that morning, in the first blank moments of consciousness, it was the boots she had thought of first, and how she could have them if she set off early and went the long way to the hospital. They would go perfectly with her new charcoal suit, she reasoned, a justification still too fragile to assuage the guilt that fluttered when she told the shop assistant she would take them in a size six.

It was while the woman at the cash desk was wrapping each boot individually in black tissue paper that Alison's phone had rung. She listened intently at first when she realized it was the hospital, her heart beating ferociously as it always did when she was frightened, but then as the meaning of the first words sunk in, something inside her clicked off like a switch. She found she could no longer understand the trails of words coming down the line so she simply waited for them to finish, and when they did, said 'Thank you,' and rang off. Meanwhile the shop assistant had placed the carefully wrapped boots heel to toe in a large pink shoebox, which she then tied with a ribbon, taking more care than you might if you were packing the most fragile glass baubles in the world.

'Cash or credit, madam?' she said to Alison in a voice like honey poured over velvet.

'My mother just died,' replied Alison before she could help herself. The shop assistant's smile slid from her face. 'She died in her sleep about an hour ago. I was on my way to the hospital to see her. I only stopped off on the way to buy these.'

They both looked down at the shoebox. A noise like a gurgle or a whimper bubbled from the shop assistant's throat. She seemed to be suffering some kind of attack. Her mouth contorted and a criss-cross of lines appeared on her forehead. Alison watched fascinated and numb at the same time, as the woman's eyes darted around the shop, desperately hunting for something. The manager, perhaps, or maybe that security guard by the shop door.

'It's all right,' said Alison holding out her credit card. 'She didn't suffer.'

Alison walked out of the shop in a daze. She was in Covent Garden and it was ten thirty on a wet Wednesday morning. There were people everywhere and taxis streaming up and down the Seven Dials, but suddenly she couldn't hear the city's sounds above the deafening row of silence building in her head. Over her shoulder was the cardboard carrier bag with its slim silken ropes for handles, the boots inside bouncing gently against her hip as she walked. They felt lighter than she'd expected, but then maybe she just couldn't feel them properly. Despite the fact that she was wearing thin-soled trainers she no longer had any sense of the pavement beneath her feet. In fact, she had the uncanny impression that she was floating just millimetres above it, unanchored and impossibly light. She held out her hand to the mast of a nearby lamppost, as if trying to stop herself being borne away like a piece of flotsam on the tides of passers-by.

'I should find somewhere to sit down,' she thought to herself. 'I'm probably in shock.' Sharply she turned off the busy street and into a quiet alley.

Each year when Alison was a child her mother had bought her one pair of sturdy lace-up shoes for the winter and one pair of sandals with a buckle for the summer. The black lace-ups came from the school-uniform shop and looked like boys' shoes. They made her feet feel like hooves and caused her ankle socks to slip down so that her heels rubbed when she walked to school. Even Alison's father commiserated with her when he saw them.

'They won't let the rain in, by golly,' he said, when she put on her new school uniform for the first time. He started to laugh but the laugh had become a cough and he'd turned away from her to spit up into a hankie while Alison's mother rubbed his back.

The sandals were a different story, soft leather with a wave pattern of tiny holes punctured into the toe. They were for the holidays, for outdoor summer days and no socks at all. Alison was allowed to choose them herself from her mother's catalogue, a floppy doorstep of glossy pages where little girls' shoes were cast in romantic adventures involving parties in tree houses and day-trips to London. It was to a pair of light-blue T-bar sandals on the feet of a grown-up-looking child in a party dress that Alison, at the age of seven, first lost her heart.

She was thirty-eight now and the love affair had matured but not mellowed. The only difference these days was that she bought her shoes from expensive boutiques. She lived alone and had little else to spend her money on, and besides, she liked to look the part at the advertising agency where she worked. Even so, her clothes shopping had grown into something of a ritual over the years, with shoes in particular an expensive and guilt-edged obsession. They seemed to multiply behind her back, burrowed away in their shoeboxes and covertly stashed in cubbyholes around her flat.

At the end of the alley Alison found a church built of red brick squatting between two modern blocks of offices. One side of the church was so close to the new building that only a child could have squeezed along the gap between them, but on the other there was a small patch of churchyard. There were some benches here, mostly wet from the rain, and without slowing her mysterious weightless pace, Alison made for the furthest and most sheltered one.

Alison's mother Jean had not been a particularly pretty woman in her youth but she did have a kind smile and soft brown wavy hair. Until Alison was about ten her mother stayed at home and looked after the house and the small family's needs. Then when Alison's dad had to leave the factory because of his lungs she got a part-time job in the village shop where she wore a pink and white checked overall with her normal clothes underneath. Alison knew deep down that she loved her mother, but while she was growing up she could never quite shake off a niggling sense of disappointment in her. It shadowed her thoughts before she fell asleep at night, and whispered meanly when she went out with her mother in public. It had a lot to do with what her mother wore; clothes that were neither fashionable nor completely out of date, just achingly dull. Sensible skirts and corduroy slacks that were mute on the subject of their wearer, unless to say quietly, 'Excuse me, this person would rather you don't notice her at all.' She didn't really use make-up either, just a quick dab of coral lipstick or a barely-there stroke from the stub of an eyebrow pencil.

If she had been honest with herself Alison would have admitted that what she really wanted was for her mother to be more glamorous. For both her parents to be something special, something louder than they were. She went through a phase of wishing they had fallen in love in a terribly romantic passion, like the characters she was starting to read about in books. It stung her to think they had just met at the factory dance and decided, Why not? They were just plain old Jean and quiet Eddie, Mr and Mrs Ordinary; Mum and Dad.

In the churchyard droplets of rain from the leaves of a yew tree dripped on to Alison's head. Noticing the rain reassured her that she hadn't gone completely numb. Perhaps she wasn't going to lose it after all. She thought she should think about her mother and brace herself for the tears she knew she ought to be crying. She took a deep breath and set about remembering how her mother had looked the night before. One of those dreadful, chattery nurses had been propping her up on a pile of stiff pillows. She had seen her mother's eyes swim into focus over the plump nurse's shoulder and watched her slowly smile in a way that Alison realized now with a pang of remorse was a kind of apology. At the time, the only thought in her head had been that the faded old nightie her mother was wearing was one Alison had given her more than ten years before.

'Why are you wearing that old thing?' she said when the nurse left them alone. 'I'll bring you a new one tomorrow.'

'Don't bother, love,' said her mother in a weak voice. 'I like this one. It's still got plenty of wear left in it.' That was ironic, thought Alison to herself, then waited for the inevitable wave of guilt to swallow her up.

One summer evening when she was eleven, Alison had crept into her parents' bedroom to touch her mother's lipstick. She could hear her parents talking to the next-door neighbour at the bottom of the garden so she knew she wouldn't be disturbed. The lipstick was lying in a china dish on the dressing table, covered by a thin coating of dust. Alison picked it up and pulled off the lid which gave a pleasing pop as it came. It smelt like crayons. Then concentrating on the mirror she drew the waxy coral over her lips and pressed them together like she had seen women on the TV do.

The face looking back at her from the mirror was of a gawky, sullen child with a tense expression. Her hair, like her mother's, was brown and kinked. She had the same eyes too, a greeny-grey-brown. Nothing eyes, she thought angrily as she studied them. She pulled at her hair which was in bunches; the style made her look younger and she decided that she didn't like it that way any more. She pulled out the rubber bands and ran her mother's comb through the tangles trying to pull the curls straighter. In the reflection of the mirror her parents' wardrobe caught her eye; one of the doors had been left open just a chink. Checking through the window that her parents were still engrossed in their chat, she walked across the room to the wardrobe and opened the door just a little more. Inside were her mother's things: beige blouses and brown corduroy skirts mainly, and tucked to one side her almost-smart winter coat. There were a couple of long dresses that Alison could vaguely remember seeing her mother wear at Christmas or for parties, and a collection of droopy-looking cardigans. On the raised wooden floor there was a pair of brown everyday shoes, some plain black courts, and an old pair of Scholl sandals. The smell of mothballs haunted the gloom. Alison let out a sigh of boredom. Nothing to get excited about in there, nothing to run her fingers through or touch against her cheek. She thought of the fine coloured clothes that filled the slippery pages of the catalogue. Rainbows of jumpers, patterns and prints on skirts and dresses, long leather boots with stacked heels, open-toe sandals with ankle straps. Why didn't her mother ever order any of those things? She was about to close the door when something at the very back of the wardrobe floor caught her eye.

In the hospital Alison's mother had been given a room to herself. Secretly Alison thought this was probably a bad sign; that the cancer gnawing away at her mother's bones was going to win the war. Alison was her only visitor all that week and she tried to go every morning on her way to work and each evening when she finished. In the office everybody knew. They said things like: 'Take as long as you need' and 'Of course you must spend time with her'. Even Julian, her boss, had taken her to one side and asked if she needed a few weeks off.

'No,' she said firmly, 'I'd rather work right through it if you don't mind.' And Julian had nodded and patted her shoulder as if he understood.

The evenings were the worst, listening to the sounds of the hospital echo in the long chilly corridors, and trying to think of things to chat about. It seemed pointless talking about much anyway as her mother seemed to drift between wakefulness and sleep.

Once, though, she murmured: 'You look so smart tonight, dear. You shouldn't waste your best things coming here to see me.' Alison didn't tell her that those were the normal clothes she wore for work, and that there was a whole room at her flat dedicated to storing clothes just like them, and some much finer.

'Those weren't the shoes you were wearing yesterday,' her mother had said vaguely, moving her head from side to side on the big pillow.

'No, Mum, these are different ones. They match this bag. Look.' She held out her handbag for her mother's drowsy eyes to focus on.

'Your father bought me some beautiful shoes once.' The words quickened Alison's heartbeat and she looked down sharply at her mother, but it was too late: the drip feed of drugs was taking her under again, and she slept fitfully. Alison sat with her for another twenty minutes, studying the hollow-cheeked face, wondering what her mother had meant. When she left she tiptoed so that the steel tips of her heels made no sound on the hospital's cold linoleum floor.

The shoes that Alison found at the back of her parents' wardrobe were nothing like the ones her mother normally wore. They were the most exquisite and sophisticated pair of stiletto heels Alison had ever seen and she couldn't quite believe she had found them in her own home. It was like spotting an exotic peacock among a flock of old chickens: black patent leather glittering in the evening light, and soft midnight-blue panels of suede that yearned to be stroked. The shoes were slender and sleek, with toes that went to perfect unscuffed points, and tapering heels that were at least four inches high. The soles of the shoes were smooth and unmarked; they had obviously never been worn. Either not at all, or only in here on the bedroom carpet, thought Alison as she inhaled their pristine leather smell. These had not come out of the catalogue, she was sure of that.

Quickly she kicked off the sandals she was wearing and shyly introduced first her left, then her right foot into the shoes. She felt the sharpened end of the pointed leather toes squeeze her feet together in a tight but not unpleasant clasp. The shoes fitted her perfectly, their ultra-thin leather straps fastened by tiny buckles that were a fiddle to do up. She had sat on the bed to put the shoes on and now she wobbled as she attempted to stand up straight. She felt her whole body propelled unsteadily forward, as though her legs were afraid to trust the support of the shoes. As she found her confidence she let her weight rock back over her heels until she felt herself connected safely to the floor. Then she looked up and was amazed to see how much taller she'd become. She could see right out into the garden now without having to stand on tiptoe, as far as the back gate where the top of her mother's head was visible nodding along to what was being said by the neighbour. Slowly, and using the footboard of the bed for balance, Alison turned and took a few steps forward until she was standing directly in front of the full-length mirror on the wardrobe door.

When Alison saw her reflection in her parents' bedroom mirror she was overwhelmed by the sight of her childish sun-browned legs transformed into elongated limbs of womanliness. The muscles in her calves were stretched taught and she fell in love with the way her slim ankles extended away from the round shiny heels of the shoes. She twisted her body to check every angle and lifted her skirt to see how the shoes affected her knees and thighs. Then she practised walking and found that she wiggled. Sucking in her stomach and pushing out her chest, she worked on the wiggle some more, parading up and down in front of the mirror. At last she heard her parents coming up the garden path towards the house and quickly removed the shoes, thrilling at the way her toes sprang back into shape. Carefully she positioned them back exactly where she had found them, then left the bedroom carrying her old sandals by their straps, walking on clouds.

In the churchyard Alison opened the bag and took out the shoebox. She was wondering if the shoes at the back of the wardrobe had been the ones her father had bought. She had planned to ask her mother about it today during the visit.

'Mum,' she would have said, 'did Dad buy you those beautiful patent-leather shoes you kept at the back of the wardrobe?' Then she would have followed that bombshell with, 'So why didn't you wear them?' and then, 'Well, why didn't you just throw them away?' She shivered violently and then opened the shoebox. Tissue paper rustled in the breeze.

That summer, when she had fallen in love with her mother's secret shoes, Alison stole every opportunity she could to pay them a visit and put them on. She tried wearing them with socks, with a pair of her mother's stockings, and finally she secretly shaved her legs in the bath and wore the shoes with just a slick of baby oil on her shins, something she had read about in a magazine. A change came over her. It was still only the school holidays but she shunned her friends and preferred to stay indoors.

'Why don't you go out for a bike ride?' her mother would suggest, or, 'Go and see who's down at the playground.' But Alison just sighed and spent the long summer afternoons watching old films on the TV, or up in her room with the curtains drawn, reading novels.

Her excitement at finding the shoes had turned to brooding over why they were hidden away in the first place. From her bedroom window she watched her mother potter around in the garden wearing a shapeless shift dress she'd made herself in half an hour, her feet squat like two fat boats in brown brogues she'd had for years. 'She can't wear them,' thought Alison to herself. 'She's got nothing to wear them with and nowhere nice to go in them.'

Alison held the purple boots in her hands as if they were the bodies of roosting birds and might suddenly fly away. However gorgeous they might be to look at and touch, Alison knew from experience they would not be comfortable to wear for long. Boots like these were designed for taxi rides and soft hotel carpets, or for short tip-tapping distances across the marble foyers of expensive restaurants. Like so many of the shoes Alison had coveted and collected, they were not really designed for walking in at all. She took off her trainers and put the boots on, savouring the pleasure and pain of tight leather and vaulted arches. She stood up in them and walked a few steps up and down in front of her bench, getting to know their language, the bite of them.

At the end of that summer Alison celebrated her twelfth birthday with a small tea party. All her friends arrived wearing shorts and T-shirts as it was still so hot. They ate sandwiches and crisps and a homemade cake that vaguely embarrassed Alison, then out in the garden played childish party games that her father organized. Alison did not really enjoy herself even though everyone else seemed to. After the other girls had gone home and her parents were snoozing in deckchairs she crept upstairs and made straight for her parents' wardrobe. The shoes were there as usual, and she eagerly pulled them on to her feet, but this time something wasn't quite right. The shoes felt tighter than before and her big toes were crushed uncomfortably close. She could hardly get her heels to go down into either shoe, and she couldn't do the buckles up at all. When she walked in them now, she hobbled. 'They don't fit me any more!' she wailed at herself in the mirror. 'They don't fit.' She kicked them off in a storm of rage and grief, then fled to her bedroom where she wept noisily on her bed before falling asleep.

Alison took bigger steps away from the bench in the purple boots. She could feel her little toes beginning to pinch a bit already, but she was quickly getting used to the way the boots held her. She picked up her handbag and walked out of the churchyard with the careful foot-conscious steps that women who regularly wear heels know all about. She left the trainers behind on the bench.

On around the fifth day that Alison had visited her mother in the hospital she found a curtain pulled around her bed. She had heard noises coming from behind the curtain but was too nervous to go forward and take a look. The carnations she was carrying slipped through her limp fingers and fell to the floor. Then suddenly a plump brown hand ripped back the curtain with a shriek of nylon on steel.

'It's only your daughter, Mrs Daniels,' boomed a loud voice with a Caribbean lilt. 'Here, girl, perhaps you can help your mother out here.'

Rooted to the spot, Alison stared at the sight before her. There was a basin of hot water resting on a nightstand nearby, while the nurse was holding out a flannel and a big bar of pink soap.

'I was just washing your mother's feet. She's been saying they were cold so we thought we'd get the circulation going for her a bit. You can have a go too now you're here.'

Alison moved forward as though in a dream. She could see where the nurse had lifted away the bed covers and exposed her mother's feet and for one panicky moment she thought she might be sick. Her mother's toes had grown gnarled and twisted like claws, and the nails were brown and coarse like dull tortoise shell. They seemed to belong to another creature altogether. With her mouth dry and her breath catching in her throat Alison wordlessly took the flannel and began to lift one of the feet away from the bed. It felt cold and the flesh slightly spongy. She hadn't seen her mother's naked feet for nearly thirty years and to her knowledge she had never in her life touched them. She began to rub the flannel feebly up and down the yellow, papery sole and around the purple skin and knotted joint of the heel.

'That's right, girl, nice and firmly. We've got to get that blood charging through those veins. Now, I'll take your lovely smart handbag from you and these beautiful flowers. Oh, they look pretty, don't they, Mrs Daniels? I'll be back with some tea in just one minute, and then we'll do your pills.'

Alone in the tent-like enclosure of the hospital screens Alison and her mother stared at one another, the same frozen horror distorting both their faces. Neither of them spoke.

The shoes were never mentioned by Alison or her mother, even though Alison knew her mother must have found them lying sprawled and dishonoured on the bedroom floor. A few weeks later when the two of them cleared out all the cupboards in the house looking for jumble, Alison noticed with a nervous twist in her stomach that the shoes were no longer in the wardrobe. It would always be with a vivid and quite crushing sense of shame that she remembered them as she grew up.

It took Alison about forty minutes to walk to the hospital and by the time she got there the boots were ruined. The rain had stained tidemarks as high as the instep and the suede had been scuffed off completely in places. One of the heels had caught in a cobble and was now desperately loose, wobbling like a broken tooth. A searing pain throbbed through Alison's ankles and she could feel a warm squelch between her toes that she guessed was probably blood. As she had walked through the puddled streets, with rainwater streaking down her face, she had been relieved to feel the pain in her feet throb and build. It grounded her.

There was nobody in the corridor outside her mother's room so Alison let herself in quietly and approached the bed. The piles of pillows had been taken away, and the machines that had flashed and crowded around the bed before were now silent and pushed back to the wall. Her mother's body lay narrow and straight on the bed, a white sheet and a thin green blanket tucked tightly around her stillness. Alison looked at her mother's face, which appeared quite peaceful, then she walked to the end of the bed and holding on to the metal frame she used her left foot to push off the right boot, and her bare bloodied toes to ease off the left one. Immediately she felt smaller, shorter and less gangly. The cool hospital floor soothed the soreness and the shredded skin, and released the constriction that had started in her feet but spread all over her body like a thousand tightening knots. Once again she was the small girl who had crept into her mother's bedroom to play with a lipstick, and opened a wardrobe. She put out her hands and held her mother's feet through the blankets, rubbing them gently up and down, as if now she knew what to do to warm them. Putting her palms to their soles, she gently pressed the toes back and forth, before rubbing the ankles and around the heels.

'I'm so sorry about the shoes,' she said out loud, as the hot relief of tears came at last.

MONKEYTIME
John Braime

I am a monkey wrangler. I'm an expert in training monkeys to put on clothes, to smile for the camera, to ride bicycles, to entertain. Over the years I've had some very fine clients: circuses, TV companies, advertisers – people with money, influential people, nice people. Of course, the phone doesn't ring so much these days. That's the fault of the bloody do-gooders. What they don't understand is that everyone likes a monkey. The monkeys are happy, the punters are happy, so I can't see what the problem is. And I'm good at the work, one of the best. Dave says it's because I've a close affinity with them, and it's true – me and the monkeys get on. I have one myself. His name is George. He's got his own keys – I hear him coming and going in the mornings when I'm lying in bed. As the work isn't exactly rolling in, and Wendy's no longer here to nag me, I don't have to rise too early. I'm not sure what George gets up to in the mornings. He's been neglecting his duties, that's for certain – I've not had my morning cuppa in bed for ages. Sometimes I worry that he'll leave one day and not come back.

I used to go to all the parties, and nice-looking ladies would ask me: 'What is the difference between a monkey, a chimp, and an ape?' I didn't tell them. Said they could look it up in the library if they were interested. Differences don't matter to me – I'm equal opportunities as they say. In fact sometimes I'll be listening to a person, and for a moment, all I can see is a monkey in front of me. I reply in chimp language, and they look at me strangely, and I realize my mistake.

But never mind. It's daytime. I walk downstairs, go into the kitchen. I look at the letters, or rather, I look at the writing on the envelopes and put them under the ceramic pig. It's in the same place Wendy left it, on the shelves by the back door. I think about ringing Dave. He's the man, he's the one with the contacts. I don't know why I've not been in touch. It's been such a long time. He could help me. I pick up last night's *Southern Evening Echo*. There has been an audacious theft from the city art gallery. The robbers somehow avoided activating the alarms, though no one can say how. 'Police say that the robbery was painstakingly planned and faultlessly executed, and are not ruling out international organized crime.' That's what the paper says.

I turn to the back page and sip my tea. PG Tips. I'm an old sentimentalist. I helped train some of the chimps in the ads, back in the seventies, back when I was a young lad apprenticed to Walter Prideaux. Of course, they won't have chimps on telly these days. That's why the work has all dried up. It's only the occasional private client now, and the odd circus here and there, and some of them won't use animals any more. Wendy used to tell me it was my fault, that I should be more proactive. I think she'd been reading one of her books again. That's where she got that idea.

'You don't understand, things aren't like they used to be,' I said. I did feel a bit guilty on George's account though. If I don't work, he doesn't, and he can't look after himself.

He comes lolloping in on his knuckles. In his idleness, he's been picking up bad habits. *Where was my tea this morning?* I ask, though he pretends he doesn't understand. He wasn't always like this. He used to be an affable chimp, but he's all sullen now, engrossed in his little monkey world. Perhaps I should decorate. That might make George happier. This house, it's become tatty. The wallpaper makes flappy tongues at me, and the floorboards rattle. I swear it's like walking on a xylophone.

Time passes, but I never pay that much attention to it. If I watch the clock enough it stands still. Then it starts going backwards, and I go back with it. I'm not much interested in the future. There doesn't seem to be that much of it, not compared with how much past we've got. I watch everything reversing, faster and faster, through the years, the lines converging, humans and chimps becoming one. I told Wendy about it once. 'We're just the same you know. We're all one. People should remember that.'

'That's why I like you,' she said.

'What?'

'You're not like those others. You've a big heart. Everyone's the same to you. You're like Princess Diana.'

'Thanks.'

We were in the Red Lion. It was during our early days, and we'd had a bit to drink. We sat there talking all evening, until the landlord kicked us out. 'Don't you have a home to go to?' he said. 'Yes,' I replied.

At the bus station it was the usual drunken crowd. A girl was screaming and shrieking at another girl. Neither was wearing enough clothes. I would never let my chimps go out wearing that little, and they've got the advantage of hair. A young lad in a smart shirt was getting involved. The first girl told him to go and give the second girl a slap. Over in the corner, two youths were trying to extricate a Mars Bar from a vending machine, using a wire coat hanger.

'Don't do that,' I said.

'I'm starving. I could eat a scabby donkey,' said the one with the wire. His friend just looked at me, saying nothing. They both appeared to be well fed, a bit on the fat side if anything, but perhaps their glands were to blame. I went over, took the wire, and poked out a couple of bags of crisps.

'You're a talented man,' said Wendy, as we got on the number 16.

'Oh, you'll find I'm good at lots of things.'

George is going out again. He's dressed in a scruffy sweater and some old tracksuit bottoms. I'm busy cooking myself eggs and gammon with oven chips. *Where are you off to?* I ask, over the sound of sizzling white. He gives a monkey shrug, and reaches for the door handle. Eggs and gammon used to be his favourite, that and apples. He's gone for days this time. I lose track of them, though I do know at one point I'm listening to a lady on Radio Solent telling me about the recent spate of jewellery thefts. 'Daring' is a word she uses. 'Meticulously' and 'planned', those are another two. She has a lovely voice, not dissimilar to Wendy's, who could tell you the ingredients of a packet of faggots in gravy sauce and still sound like she was reciting poetry. The day she told me she was leaving I could do nothing other than sit there and let her sweet voice fill up my ears with warm golden syrup. And the lady on Radio Solent is like that too. I sit and listen to her until the electricity runs out, and then I go down to the Spar and get topped up. By the time I've returned a different programme is on, a boring one about someone's holiday in the African savannah.

George returns at some point. *Where have you been?* I demand, but he merely gives me a sad look. I suspect he's depressed, but he won't tell me what's wrong. I throw some balls at him. *Come on, George, let's have a bit of fun,* I say. I throw a hoop at him. He used to be fond of that. He came second in the hula-hoop contest at the Association of Chimpanzee Trainers shindig a few years back. But now, he's not interested. He lets the balls fall to the ground. He lets the hoops fall to the ground.

I've trained lots of chimps in my time, got to know them pretty well. There was Jerry, who used to be so good on the bicycle. He went off to the Chipperfields. There was Marge, a little beauty – she liked wearing dresses and make-up. I asked Wendy if she could be her bridesmaid at the wedding, but she wouldn't have it. I think that hurt Marge. She was taken on as a photographer's assistant soon afterwards – good steady work for a chimp. And there was Mikey, who I met outside an arcade in Spain. He was in a cage. I went in and offered the manager four hundred euros. It cost twice as much to smuggle him back to Southampton. A local footballer bought him in the end. I later heard that when they transferred him to a club in the North, the footballer gave Mikey to that bloody monkey sanctuary in Dorset. Waste of a year's training.

Wendy was a Saints season-ticket holder, and when they got relegated, she left me, so I blame Harry Redknapp really. If he'd kept Southampton in the Premiership, everything would be all right. A man in a van came and took away her drum kit, her floral-print dresses, her Princess Di memorabilia, her astrology charts, and those cookery books I bought her but she never read. He took lots of other stuff too.

I first saw her at a gig in the Cricketers. She was beautiful. Beating and brushing away at the drums, keeping things moving in the Strumpeteers, the best all-girl trad jazz band in the South. Dave had said something like, 'I'd give that drummer one' or 'I'd like to bang her'.

I said, 'Dave, leave it. She's the one for me. She has such a beautiful smile.' I later learned that one of her previous husbands had been an orthodontist.

'You can have her then,' he said, grasping a pint of Adnams with one of his huge hairy hands, and then tipping it into that mouth of his. 'On a second look, she's a bit too thin for me. It'd be like shagging a skeleton.'

'Don't you talk about her like that.'

'Or what, Roger?'

'Anyway, she's not skinny. She's lithe.'

After the gig, I approached her and asked if she'd like to come and meet my chimps. She didn't, but we went out for a drink anyway.

Nine months later we were married. 'Fourth time lucky,' she laughed, and I laughed too. She had a good sense of humour, my Wendy. We honeymooned indoors, not leaving the house for a week. I cooked her dinner every night, and showed her some of my tricks, and we talked about everything life had in store for us. It was great. I'd sent George on a holiday of his own, got him out of the way, up to Mr Magenta's circus in North Yorkshire somewhere. Looking back, perhaps that's where he picked up his bad attitude. There are some real bolshy little so-and-sos in there. Magenta doesn't know how to keep his monkeys in order. Lets them run the show.

By the time George got back, Wendy had gone. The man in the van had taken everything, apart from that ceramic pig. I went down to the Citizens Advice to ask about a divorce. Turns out that I hadn't been married long enough. Had to wait until the spring.

It's the afternoon, a Wednesday – no, it's a Friday – and George is nowhere to be seen. He's having his nap I expect. I cook myself some egg dip and then spread blackcurrant jam on it. I'll turn things around. I pick up the phone and dial Dave's number. It rings five times and then I get Dave's answerphone.

'Hello, it's Roger here. I was wondering if you've any business.'

And then he is talking to me. 'Roger, you stupid cunt, didn't I tell you to never ever leave anything on tape about business?'

'Oh, sorry Dave, I forgot. Bit out of practice. Got any, though, have you?'

'Getting more difficult by the day. Just as many punters, but procuring the animals, that's the fucker.'

'Oh.'

'Looks like we're going to have to put you in a monkey suit and train you to do somersaults instead, Roger.' Dave makes a noise like dishwater going down a blocked sink. I can hear a lady giggling in the background.

'Who's that?'

'None of your business. Look, if you wanted to sell George back, there'd be a lot of takers. Mr Magenta regards him highly, and I know Peppo would be interested.'

'No, they can't have him. I'm a monkey trainer, not a dealer.'

'Well, why the fuck are we having this conversation then?'

Dave thinks that just because he knew George first, he's got rights over him, but he's mine, fair and square. 'He's a good little mover, this one,' he had said, patting the top of George's cage, just after he'd been shipped in. 'Found him on a disco boat in Bodrum harbour – that's in Turkey you know. He was entertaining the tourists. He does a good impression of John Travolta – he does all that seventies stuff.' George peered out, still sleepy from the tranqs. He had a sweet face, a pale grey sort of colour, and a wonky smile. We were in the cellar at Dave's place. He'd called me over as he was trying to put together a monkey dance troupe and wanted me to do the training.

Whilst Dave went travelling, on the lookout for other chimps, I got to work with George. He was a pleasure to teach. He picked things up really quickly, had a nice even temper. I was teaching him to juggle one day, when I noticed a scar on his ear. *How'd you get that?* I asked. He explained that a fat man had stubbed out a cigarette on him, back on the disco boat. *He was jealous of me,* said George. *I was dancing with his wife. He got really angry – I thought he was going to kill me. I went and hid behind the bar. My ear really hurt. A nice girl gave me some ice.*

After a couple of weeks of training, Dave told me the client had pulled out, that there'd be no monkey troupe, that he'd pay me for the work I'd done with George. I said, 'I've become rather attached to the old chap. He's been a lot of fun. Tell you what, you can write off the fee, and in return, I'll take him on, permanent.'

'Bung in £500 and you've got yourself a deal.'

That was some years ago and now it's a Wednesday, definitely, and I'm listening to the news on Radio Solent again, eating a couple of Findus crispy pancakes with a side serving of cabbage. The crime wave continues: a Securicor van was hijacked, the driver bludgeoned to death. Someone with enormous strength did this, judging by the state of the poor man's body. George comes in, accompanied by another chimp. *Who's that?* I say. *Where did he come from? Where's his owner?* They ignore me and lope towards the stairs. This newcomer is an East African, his long hair poking through his string vest. Temperamental buggers in my experience, though this one has buckteeth which lend him a comical appearance. Upstairs, they're grunting and chattering. You've got to be careful when you get monkeys together. Standards can drop. Mine are always taught to use the loo properly – that chimp on that poster they used to sell in Woolworth's was one of mine. Bert was his name. Also, I won't tolerate any noisy behaviour. *You're not in the jungle now,* that's what I say to them at the start of training, although not if they're ex-lab as it's a bit insensitive.

The next day another chimp arrives. This one is older. He's got a shovel-shaped face and grey hair on his back, and he's only wearing safari shorts. The day after that there are two females as well, in nylon nighties. I'm starting to get worried. The authorities will be on to me, saying I'm keeping the animals in cruel, cramped conditions again. They'd really throw the book at me this time. George strolls in. *George, we have to have a word,* I say. *This can't go on.* He picks an apple out of the fruit bowl, and strolls out of the house. It annoys me. He comes and goes, doing I don't know what, doesn't pay any rent, doesn't help with my costs. I've got my overheads.

Then it occurs to me. I ring Dave. He answers. I must have interrupted one of his jokes or something. I can hear that lady giggling in the background just like before.

'Dave, mate, you know you were talking about the shortage of business?'

'Look, Roger, I've told you, I haven't got any fucking animals. You're starting to get on my tits.'

'No, no, what I mean is, I've a house full of them here.'

'What?'

'There are four chimps, not counting George.'

'What? Where d'you find them?'

'Don't know. They just turned up. George invited them along.'

'Have you been drinking again?'

'No, they're here. Come over and have a look if you don't believe me.'

'I'm busy right now,' he says, 'with an important business meeting, but I'll be over tomorrow midday.'

'Bring the van and your tranquillizer guns.'

Later that evening, Shirley from next door comes around.

'Roger, it's getting too much, the racket that's coming out of this house. It's driving me nuts.'

'I'm really sorry. I didn't realize,' I whisper. 'It'll all be sorted by tomorrow. Just bear with me.'

'Why are you whispering?'

'Was I? Oh, sorry.'

'And what's that smell?'

'Is there a smell?'

'Yes. Is everything all right, Roger?'

'Everything's going to be all right, Shirley, I promise.'

That night, what sleep I do get is haunted by strange dreams. In one, I'm a giant cake. In another, I'm in a spaceship with George. He's the pilot. In a third, I'm disturbed by a noise in my wardrobe. I go to open the door, and find Dave in there with Wendy.

Morning comes and I eat fried eggs on toast. Five more chimps enter and are promptly ushered out of the kitchen by George. Under other circumstances, I'd say something. After breakfast I venture to the lounge to see what they're doing. I peek through the door. The newcomers have formed a perimeter around the three-piece suite. The old chimp is sat on the sofa with George and the two females. They're all looking at my video collection. Can't see what they'd want with *A Touch of Frost* or those aerobic videos I bought for Wendy. George has a mobile phone in one hand, and in the other, the old Speak and Spell I bought him from the car boot. One of the sentries glowers at me. I close the door and return to the kitchen. I look at my watch, just to get the time. I wonder whether Dave's van is going to be big enough.

I stare at the kitchen clock and make it spin backwards. I see all the old people, and then I make it spin forwards to the day when there will be no humans, no monkeys. Everything will be reduced to a couple of feet of rock. We'll all be gone. In the meantime, I simply want to make a difference in this world, leave a mark. Bring the monkeys and the humans together, that's what I do. I'm a sort of ambassador, and my house is an embassy. Monkeys are clever, and so are humans, so the world needs people who can relate to both parties. Of course, there are the killjoys who want to ruin it for everyone, to stop what I'm doing. I care more for monkeys than they do. They've probably never met one. They should leave me alone, go spend their time having a go at the zoos instead. I watch the monkeys in there sometimes, without any clothes or bicycles or pianos, and I think it's inhumane. I've considered organizing a petition.

Suddenly I hear movement within the house, and then the monkeys burst into the kitchen. They start filing out of the back door, whooping and grunting in that impolite way, which usually comes before some childish outburst or temper tantrum. They're led by old shovel face. Not one of them even glances at me. Dave is due in twenty minutes. *George,* I say, as he ambles past, the last in the line, *I'm sorry. Don't go. You and your friends can stay, I don't mind. We can live together. They seem like a nice bunch. I don't care where they came from. I don't care if they've got no owners. Please, George. Don't go.*

George closes the door behind him. He's left his keys on the table. I'm buggered. I'm going to look like a right idiot when Dave gets here, dragging him away from his giggling lady for nothing. I should have just let him have George when he wanted him. I'll bet they've made a real mess upstairs, and in the lounge. My videos will be all out of order, of that I'm sure.

I prod the key with my finger. It jangles. The thing is, I felt sorry for George. His story truly touched me, and I suppose that's been the root of my difficulties. If I'd been firmer with him, if I'd acted more like a professional, not been all soft like that idiot Mr Magenta, I'd not be in this mess. I should have known better. Now I've got nothing. I spend a while looking at the ceramic pig, sat on the pile of letters. The money from flogging all those monkeys would have come in handy too.

A while later, there's a knock at the door. 'That'll be Dave,' I say.

I look through the spy hole. It's three coppers. I panic. I don't think straight. They're sure to do me about the monkeys. Probably looking at prison, on account of my being banned from keeping animals. But then I realize I'm safe, aren't I? Maybe George knew this was coming. That's what he's done. He's taken his gang out, to hide somewhere, until the coast is clear. I'll make it up to him, for being such a doubting Thomas.

I open the door. I smile. 'Hello, officers,' I say.

'Roger Solomon?' one of them asks. Parked along the road are five police cars. Marksmen train their sights upon me. I stop breathing for a short while, and then start again. I nod. The noise of a helicopter slightly obscures what he's saying. I say, 'Pardon?'

'Roger Solomon, you are under arrest. Come quietly.'

'What for?'

'For aggravated burglary, grievous bodily harm, murder, and armed robbery.'

And then they push me to the floor. I graze my chin on the hallway carpet. They pull my arms behind me. They put the cuffs on.

I'm in the back of the police car. The chief inspector is stood outside, drumming his fingers on the roof. It's annoying. I consider complaining, but then I see Dave's van arriving. A WPC in a fluorescent jacket has stopped him. She's asking him to take an alternative route. He's scratching his beard – no doubt he's rather confused. He sees me, and raises one of his enormous eyebrows in an attempt to convey some information or a request to me. His hairy hands are gripping the steering wheel.

'Thought you'd put up more of a struggle, to be honest, big shot like you,' says the copper sat beside me.

'What? I'm just a monkey wrangler.'

'Aren't you just.'

I wriggle. My arms ache. They're not used to being in this position.

'I'm an expert in training monkeys.'

'Yeah, yeah, and the rest.'

'I train them to put on clothes, to smile for the camera, to ride bicycles, to entertain. I'm not a bank robber. You've got the wrong man.'

He stops talking for a bit, and then his colleague in the front says, 'You've got a lot of enemies, that's for sure. That's how we always get your sort. The tip-off.'

'Yeah,' says the one next to me, 'you're not so clever.'

I'm straining to look at his watch. If I could just look at it for a while, I could make the hands go back. I could make everything all right. I could shoo those other monkeys away. Put my foot down. Go back and train George properly. Go back and treat Wendy right. Go back and make everything perfect.

LOST BEARINGS
Dubravka Ugresic

I recently met a family, new neighbours of my mother's in the block of flats where she lives. They came to Zagreb from Mostar, a couple with two children – two boys – and their grandmother. Decent people, they were lucky: they somehow managed to sell their house in Mostar and buy a little two-room flat in Zagreb, at a time when that was still possible, before the first shells hit. They leapt on to the last train. They were lucky. The parents found jobs, while Granny's task is to make ends meet. She bakes Bosnian pies, and brings them to her neighbours to try. 'Try some,' she says. 'Don't worry, Bosnian pies come from paradise!' The family are vegetarians and followers of Sai Baba. That, the Sai Baba thing, came with the war as well. At least as far as Granny is concerned. She wouldn't have taken any interest otherwise. All religions are the same to her, and God's messengers are thieves. This is what happened. One day her washing machine packed up. They didn't have the money for a new one, and the man who came to fix it was a cheat, like all repairmen. Being without a washing machine with two children and three adults in the house is no joke. And then one night Granny dreamed a strange dream. A swarthy man with curly hair, small as a garden gnome, dressed entirely in an orange robe, came into her bedroom, pointed importantly into the air and said: 'Don't worry, Zdenka, your washing machine is working!' In the morning she remembered the dream, turned on the machine and – it worked! So, that's how she turned to Sai Baba. Because that garden gnome was the spitting image of Sai Baba . . .

Her grandsons are very different. The older one is a strong, healthy boy, who likes sport, while the younger one, the ten-year-old – ah, he's a worry, a real headache. Lately, the very devil seems to have got into him. He sticks to her like a burr and keeps on and on asking questions. He'll pick up a newspaper, point at someone's photograph and ask: 'Granny, is this a good or a bad person?' Or he'll be watching television: 'Granny, is this a good or a bad person?' He goes on and on all day long, as though obsessed. And there are people like flies: they move across the television screen, appear in the newspapers; you meet them on the stairs, in the lift, at school, in the street . . . 'Granny, is this a good or a bad person?'

Granny doesn't know what to do. 'Maybe it'll pass,' she says, but you can see by her face that she's not all that sure. 'Who knows, maybe Sai Baba is trying to send us some kind of message through him . . .' she says, shaking her head anxiously.

'Why do you think that?' I ask.

'Well, I don't know, other children aren't like that. No one in our family is like that. We're all "normal",' she says.

The little boy points stubbornly at the photograph of a man in the paper and asks: 'Granny, is this a good or a bad person?'

'That man's a film director. He's made some films. He's probably good . . .'

'But why is there a picture of the ruined bridge in Mostar beside him?'

'Because he ordered the bridge to be destroyed . . .'

'Because he was making a film?'

'No, because he was a soldier, a general. Generals give all sorts of orders, including destroying things.'

'Why did he destroy it?'

'Well, to protect his people, I suppose . . .'

'So he's a good man?'

'Well, yes, I suppose, he's a good man . . .'

'And who was he protecting them from?'

'From us, Muslims, but luckily for us our family wasn't there then.'

'And did we shoot at them?'

'No.'

'So what was he protecting his people from, if we didn't shoot at them?'

'He was a general. All generals protect their people.'

'And are generals good or bad people?'

'It depends. Some think they're good, some think they're bad . . .'

'What about the film director, the one who ordered the bridge in Mostar to be destroyed. Is he a good or bad person?'

'You can't divide people into good or bad.'

'Why not?'

'Because it's hard to be good the whole time, or always bad. You get tired . . .'

'Why do you get tired?'

'Because it's a hard business, constantly wondering whether you're good or bad . . .'

'And are we good because we're vegetarians?'

'That's not why . . .'

'So why are we vegetarians?'

'Because we like spinach pie . . .'

'And are we bad because we're Muslims?'

'We aren't even Muslims. I'm Croatian, your grandad was Muslim, your dad has a Muslim surname, and your mum's Serbian.'

'So what are we?'

'We're a vegetarian family.'

'So why was that film director who destroyed the bridge fighting the Muslims?'

'He didn't destroy it as a director, but as a general, and he wasn't fighting the Muslims . . .'

'Who, then?'

'The enemy.'

'So are we the enemy?'

'Well, no.'

'So why was he fighting?'

'Because he's a soldier.'

'So are soldiers good people or bad?'

'They're neither good nor bad . . .'

'And was our grandad good or bad?'

'Our grandad was a good man.'

'Our grandad was with Tito's partisans?'

'Yes, grandad was a partisan.'

'And were the partisans good people or bad?'

'They were good people.'

'Who were they fighting?'

'The Fascists, Hitler, the *ustashas* and the *chetniks* . . .'

'And was the man who destroyed the bridge in Mostar an *ustasha*?'

'He was a hero of the homeland war. You can read that in the papers . . .'

'But our grandad was a hero as well?'

'Yes, our grandad was a hero as well. Grandad was awarded an important partisan medal . . .'

'The man who destroyed the bridge and our grandad, they were both good people?'

'Yes . . .'

'If our grandad was alive, would the man who destroyed the bridge fight our grandad?'

'Well . . .'

'And would our grandad defend himself?'

'Grandad would be too old to defend himself . . .'

'Do heroes go to prison?'

'Heroes don't go to prison.'

'But why does it say here that the man who destroyed the bridge in Mostar ought to go to prison?'

'Where does it say that?'

'Here . . .'

'Well, maybe it's because there are good heroes and bad heroes.'

'And can a good hero be a bad person? And can a bad person be a good hero?'

'I don't know.'

'What about our grandad?'

'Our grandad was a good person and a good partisan.'

'So why doesn't it say anywhere in our reading book that the partisans were good people?'

'He'll drive me round the bend! I don't know what to do with him, what the devil has got into him! He keeps staring at the television, leafing through newspapers, always adding things up. I'm worried about him . . .'

'He'll get over it. Besides, no one talks about the war any more . . .' I say.

'I don't know . . . School confuses him, too. They're learning the new way there now. I've been wondering whether we should take him to Sai Baba. He'd probably know what to do . . . What do you think?' asks Granny anxiously.

'I don't know . . .' I say.

'Have another piece . . .' She offers me more pie.

'Your pies really do come from paradise . . .' I say, taking a piece.

'Ah, it was easy before. You knew what paradise was, and what hell was. But nowadays! How can you bring up your children and grandchildren, when you don't know what's what? And when you don't know who to ask . . .' She sighs.

'At least we know about the pies, and that's something . . .' I say.

Translated by Celia Hawkesworth

SHUT UP GRACE
Emma Henderson

A shadow made me start as my mother's face loomed towards me where I lay, spastic and flailing on the coarse rug, on the warm lawn, in the summer of 1947 – in an English country garden. My father was playing French cricket with John and Miranda, and I could hear a tennis ball: in his hand, in the air, on the bat. Sometimes I saw the balling arc or even the dancing polka dots on Miranda's dress as she raced after the ball, and John's dusty brown sandals and grey socks when the ball rolled on to the rug and he came to retrieve it.

My mother's breath was toffee-warm, and mingled with the oiliness of her flesh. She kissed me on the cheek, put a palm to my forehead, then scooped me up and tried to hug me, aimed to contain the dreadful flailing. She cooed and cuddled, I whimpered and writhed. We were both wet with sweat.

The next day, they clipped my tongue. A rip-roaring success. They got carried away: let's clean up the cleft to make her more palatable. Routine operations. All of them. All relative.

Lickety split. Spilt milk. Not Mother's. The nurses gave it to me, clean and cold, in a chipped enamel mug. My loosened tongue lapped feebly, flopping against the smooth inside. The mug upturned. Widen your eyes now – lids slit – oops-a-daisy, lazy eyes. Hold the mug yourself. Can't speak. Can't eat. Dead meat. A fresh start, Mrs Williams. Hospital beds, wet nurses, clean sheets, clean slates. Mother agreed and home we went. Again and again.

We were all confused. No one was prepared for the look in my eyes after the slit. So knowing. So many slits. My parents clutched each other and cried. Miranda and John peered curiously. I appeared unable to cry. But I could shit, so I did. It doesn't matter, they said. It's a miracle.

Not long afterwards, Miranda tied string around my tongue, my enormous, lolling tongue, with which I was learning – fast – to bellow, suck and yelp. Doctors and nurses, she said. Tut tut. I was in my cot, rolled rigid up against the side. A wonky foot had wedged itself between the bars. My face was squashed against the mattress, mouth open, tongue dry and loosely rubbing on the sheet; stench of starch, and little particles of dust tickling my cheek, prickling the inside of my nose.

'I'm going to make it better,' said Miranda, and wrapped the string systematically around my tongue. She worked away without a word, breathing heavily, her own pink, tip of a tongue flickering in the corner of her mouth. 'There.'

The ends of the piece of string were tied in a neat bow. Miranda stood back and surveyed her work critically. She must have been just six at the time; her eyes were level with mine – four small, set jellies.

'I'll tell you a story,' she said, backing towards the door. She had one hand on the handle and the other on the doorframe. I didn't want her to go. I wanted to hear the story. I grunted and knocked the side of my head against the bars of the cot. Miranda swung her torso backwards and forwards, again and again, holding both sides of the doorframe now. At the end of a forward swing, she suddenly stopped, taking all the weight with her arms. Shoulders pulled, elbows jutted, tendons strained.

Are you sitting comfortably?

I'm not. I'm straining too: to see in the darkness, hear in the silence. Tell.

'Once upon a time, there was a girl called Grace –'

A ski-jumper, a snow-bird in mid flight?

But someone shouted: 'Tea's ready. Come on, Miranda.' Then, 'Where's she got to, that child?'

Miranda pulled herself upright, backed out of the room and shut the door quietly behind her.

The string soon slipped off, as I tossed and dribbled. It fell down into the dark gap between cot and nursing chair and wasn't found until we moved house, several years on.

Miranda was the silk-haired love child, so the story goes, pretty as a pixie, naughty as a postcard. Solemn John came along too soon afterwards. Less than a year between them. Less than nothing now. John was the quiet one, the clever one. At the age of three, he added spectacles to his fat, flat face and began to read books. Later, at mealtimes, he would gaze at me, in those long periods while my parents finished eating and Miranda picked fussily at her food. Amazing gaze, I say: grey, steady, unblinking. Absolute, neutral.

The gaze of strangers wasn't neutral. After we moved to London in 1951, only when my mother was feeling particularly brave, or especially masochistic, outrageous or outraged, only then would she take me out for walks. I had learnt to walk, after a fashion. Without the support of another person, I tumbled and splayed, but with an arm, shoulder or palm to palm on either side, I managed to totter quite nifty-shifty along. We must have been an odd sight, my mother and I, she done up and efficient in her lightweight macintosh, home-sewn skirt and sensible shoes, me lopsided and limp, but buttoned nevertheless into my bristly blue coat, with its dark, soft collar, a matching beret on my head, and knitted, patterned, starry mittens hiding my hands.

After helping me down the steps to the pavement, Mother would stoop to hook an arm through mine; she drew me close with the other arm, and started to chant: 'Left. Left. I left my wife with forty-five children and nothing but gingerbread left. Left.'

Sometimes I slipped and broke the rhythm.

'And it served them jolly well right.' Hop-skip. 'Right.' Pause.

So began our deformed walk along the street. Often we paused. I needed a rest, she guessed, hop-skip. People stared, usually keeping their distance. She stared at the houses as we passed, or paused. What lay behind those doors? she sometimes wondered aloud. Why paint them at all?

'There's nothing wrong with wood, Grace.'

Those Popeye primaries – red, blue and yellow – she maintained she found silly; I think their frivolity was unbearable to her. She was supercilious about any whites – unimaginative, she said; such blankness frightened her. The only colour she openly envied was a dark, olive green. There were just three of these doors in our street, but we always seemed to stop by them and she would frequently tell me then about a journey she once made in Italy. Not all at once, of course, just snippets and images, but something warm and wistful would enter her voice as she talked, and gradually I was able to spread my own Mediterranean around me, heady and potent, whenever she began.

Once upon a time before the war, there was a very clever girl whose cleverness was marked, first by her mother then by the school her mother managed to send her to, aged four. Six, eight, ten, twelve, fourteen years passed by. At the age of eighteen, instead of going on to higher education, as school and mother had hoped, she became engaged to our father. But the next we know, she's off to Italy, leaving poor Father sharing flea-ridden digs with two violinists in Maida Vale. Why, one can only speculate. A final fling? I hardly think so. Her family trying to prise the lovers apart? Perhaps. She remains adamantly coy on the question. Not so coy, however, when it comes to the Italian trip itself. Driving around in an open-top car, both of them – she and the Isadora Duncan of a girlfriend she went with – scarves trailing, leaning, waving, whooping at the bemused Italian boys. It was early spring 1939. Adventures with spaghetti, language and wine. Other tastes – other tongues in your mouth, Grace. Tattered Penguin paperbacks; and two hungry English girls, giggling in the gondola on their way back from the Lido in Venice, so loudly and lewdly that the gondolier poled back to the landing stage and ordered them to disembark for their own safety. Florence, Rome, right down to Naples and beyond to Pompeii, where one of them lost a shoe somewhere in the volcanic ruins. Further even, a tiny fishing village with a luscious long name, Santa Maria di Castellabate, where they spent the night, sitting on the quayside, watching for dawn, chatting with a young man from Birmingham, of all places, an archaeologist, a field trip.

'Quite brilliant,' were the two words my mother always chose to end the story. Was she referring to the young man, or to the whole experience? Who knows? Now ended. A field day. Her only one.

She returned to England and married our father; Hitler invaded Poland; Miranda was conceived and born, then John, then me: all wrong. Not just not perfect, but damaged, deficient, mangled in body and mind. Mashed potato! Let's take her photato! What shall we do with the crumpled baby, early in the morning? Put her in the hospital with a nose drip on her, early in the morning. What shall we do?

Return to our own, pale-green front door. Shut it quick. Shut us up. Restrain me please. My fleece is black as ice.

Nobody openly pitied Mother. Everybody shunned. Intimacy dwindled. They stopped having sex. My London room adjoined my parents', my cot was against a wall, and on the other side of the wall was their big bed with its slippery eiderdown. When I couldn't sleep at night, I derived comfort from thinking about the head of their bed, framing and protecting them both. I was familiar with the sounds of sex and all the other sounds of bedroom farce and tragic triviality. Now, there was talking. My father's voice, grave, entreating, sometimes explaining; the response from my mother either yawning and bored – a tut-tut page-turning; or bitingly quick – capricious and vicious – which usually put an end to the talking, but prompted heavings, sighs and leaping waves of grief.

Bedtime, playtime, poo-time. You-time, me-time, teatime. Bread before cake. You before me. Bread and butter sprinkled with pink, sugary hundreds and thousands. Boiled egg and Marmite fingers. Soldiers, said John. Chicken and egg. Mother and daughter. How many eggs in the ovaries of a newborn female baby? Five million, I believe. Why was I the rotten one? Did they think I was contagious? Who can blame them?

For Christmas 1956, John, now fourteen, was given the *Concise Oxford Dictionary*, Miranda a red Baedeker guide to Europe. I received a baby swing. I was still tiny at ten, you see. The swing was hung in the doorway between the kitchen and dining room, and I hung there in it, day after day, the soles of my stiff leather shoes tapping and scuffing as I swung and jerked. She loves it, they said. She can see what's going on. It makes her feel a part of things. Apart from things indeed. My feet were cold and my toes in the inaccurately measured shoes bunched and scrotched. How I loathed that swing. The wooden bar at the back itched and irritated, and although I squirmed, my squirming merely slid me lower in the seat until the vertical bar between my legs thudded and bumped, flinging me floppy, sideways or forwards. Eventually my mother came to the rescue and sat me up again. When we had guests, she would place my hands on the ropes, moulding my fingers into curls and making empty triangles with my elbows. In my hair, which was blonder than Miranda's and curlier than John's – 'Your crowning glory, darling' – she would tie a bow of winter-velvet or satin-summer ribbon. Ha Ha the Clown, that's me. Let's knock her down. Or up. Ha! Ha!

The following summer started early and built itself a burning climax towards the end of August. On the Sunday before Bank Holiday, Mother cooked roast beef, despite the heat. And this little piggy had none. Roast beef, Yorkshire pudding, roast potatoes, runner beans and gravy. Her face was red and she flustered crossly around the kitchen; our cousins were coming to lunch. Father was in his creamy white study on the top floor, with Wagner oozing out under the door. John was in his bedroom. Miranda was in the garden, but the smell of burning brought her running, barefoot, through the open kitchen door.

I had fitted.

While the roast beef crisped itself to a cinder, I fitted. Again and again, convulsions battered my unresisting body. When they finally stopped, the charred remains of lunch were rattled from the oven, a note hastily penned and pinned to the front door for our cousins, and I was laid across the back seat of the car, while John and Miranda half crouched on the floor, half perched on the seat. My father sat in the passenger seat. My mother drove to hospital.

It's a mild sort of epilepsy, they said. Very mild in origin, but with the complications of being so spastic, and a mental defective to boot, it seems much worse than it is. Try not to worry, Mrs Williams. Relax. Think about the new baby.

For our mother, billowing, burdened camel, it was the final straw. Broken, she continued to struggle onwards, but she kept her head bowed now, eyelids down against the light.

I roared and I roared and I roared, but it didn't stop her from giving up. Not even when I roared so much that there was the crashing of glass, or six big, strong hands holding me down, and shit and piss in my knickers, on my legs and through the white, cotton socks, running all over the seat of the swing, then drip, drip, drippings on the tiles below, where my shoes turned the mess into strange and changing configurations of liquid and semi-solid.

Unbearable. Think of the others. Hopeless.

Off we went, one September afternoon, two months before my eleventh birthday. Just me this time, in the back of the car, propped upright with cushions and an old tartan rug, thin and holey. Father and Mother in the front, him puffy in a greenish overcoat; white, chicken-skin neck; sparse, straight, light-grey hair, badly cut, hanging like icicles on the collar of his coat. Her brittle now, and tweedy, pregnant, in a man's navy anorak, with a Paisley scarf, knotted at the jaw, tightly. Through the bobbling gap between the front seats, I could see her left hand, gripping the steering wheel tightly. The ring on her wedding finger had bitten into the flesh, making a wealy red line. All of us were silent for most of the journey. Occasionally my mother would look over her shoulder and ask if I was warm enough or if I needed weeing.

When we had left London behind and were heading north through dull, faded brown and orange countryside, my father produced a map and started to read out place names from it. Mother said there was no need for that, she knew the way; and pressed her lips so firmly together that they became a dark slit, screaming silence. I forced my eyes away from the rear-view mirror and towards the side window. Grey skies hurting my eyes. Grey smell of warm plastic and bananas. And nothing but gingerbread left, hop-skip. Nodding. Off her head. Deadhead the Rose Queen. Sleepy weepy. Don't cry.

'Wake up, darling. We're nearly there.'

Scarcely any traffic now. Scraggy, turfy fields on one side of the road, brick after brick of wall on the other, until we came to a pair of enormous black gates, set into the wall, a few yards back from the road. My mother turned the car and we stopped. A man – a dwarf – rotund, fairy-tale-like, except for the tell-tale shabby grey jacket and bleached corduroy trousers, too big; also, his face held no fairy-tale sparkle: it was puckered and pocked and whoever had shaved it had left unpleasant tufts and messy patches of brown bristle – this face appeared at the driver's window. My mother wound down the glass. My father picked up his briefcase from the floor.

'Williams,' he said, removing a letter from the briefcase; Mother took it from him, snatchy-swiftly, and passed it out of the window. The little man nodded, passed the letter back, then glanced at me, before pottering to the gates, easing them open and, one by one, pushing them wide enough apart to allow our car to pass through. I wanted to turn round, as you used to see children do, kneel on the back seat and wave a smile at the man. I wanted to be one of those children. But it was far too late for that. Dee-dum.

We drove slowly and quietly for another minute; greyness had come down from the sky, and our breath misted the windows. Then we stopped by a long, low, still building, with a corrugated-iron roof. There were eight windows, paintwork pale and cracked, a few steps, with a handrail, and a door at the end nearest to us.

'Here we are,' said my mother.

Here we are. Here we are.

She didn't turn and try to smile.

My father cleared his throat as if to say something, when the door opened and two figures came out, one tall and male, dressed in a dark shinny-shiny suit, the other tall, female and large, wearing a nurse's uniform. Car doors opened and closed. My case was taken from the boot and carried by the tall, suited man. My mother and the nurse manoeuvred me out of the back seat. I stood, wonky, uneasy, blinking. There were soft, chilly cheek-kisses from my father; a quick hug and neck-peck from my pushing-me-away-from-her mother.

It began to rain. My parents got back into the car. Hurry and blur. The nurse took my arm and I, unaccustomed to the stranger's gesture, tripped. The nurse stooped to help me up and I caught a glimpse over her shoulder of the car and of my parents in the car. Ghosts. Their eyes looked towards but not at me. The sound of the key turning in the ignition. My mother turned her head and began to back the car down the drive. Reversing.

So vivid is my memory of those final moments, that it is not hard to imagine myself reversing with them, going back, towards – and with the smallest of imaginative leaps, to – a very different life.

'Shut Up Grace' is an extract from the novel *Grace Williams Says It Loud*

ALMOST SHOOTING
AN ELEPHANT
T. C. Boyle

So we went in there with Meghalaya Cable, a subsidiary of Verizon (don't ask, because I couldn't begin to tell you; just think multinational, that's all), and put in the grid so these people could have colour TV and DSL hookups in their huts, and I brought a couple rifles with me. I like to hunt, all right? So crucify me. I grew up in Iowa, in Ottumwa, and it was a rare day when I didn't bring something home for my mother, whether it was ringneck or rabbit or even a gopher or muskrat, which are not bad eating if you stew them up with tomatoes and onions, and plus you get your fur. I had to pay an excess-baggage charge, which the company declined to pick up, but there was no way I was going to India without my guns. Especially since this leg of the project was in the West Garo Hills, where they still have the kind of jungle they had in Kipling's day. Or at least remnants of it.

Anyway, it was my day off and I was lying up in my tent, slapping mosquitoes and leafing through a back issue of *Guns & Ammo*, the birds screeching in the trees, the heat delivering one knockout punch after another till I could barely hold my head up. I wouldn't say I was bored – I was putting in a six-day working week stringing wire to one ramshackle village after another, and just to lie there and feel the cot give under my bones was a luxury. Still, it felt as if the hands of my watch hadn't moved in the last hour and as I drifted in and out of sleep the birds always seemed to be hitting the same note. I tried to relax, enjoy the moment and the magazine, but I was only waiting for the heat to let up so I could take my .22 and a jar of the local rice beer down the hill to the swamp and see what was stirring in the bushes.

I was studying the ads in the back of the magazine – a party in Wishbone, Montana was offering a classic Mannlicher Schoenauer carbine with a Monte Carlo stock for sale or trade, a weapon I would have killed for – when I heard the sound of footsteps approaching on the path up from the village. Flip-flops. You could hear them a mile away, a slap, a shuffle, another slap, and then a quick burst: *slap, slap, slap*. There was a pause and I felt the bamboo platform rock ever so slightly.

The birds stopped screeching, all of them at once, as if the point of contention, whatever it was, had slipped their bird brains. A smell of meat roasting over the open fire came wafting up the hill on the first hint of an evening breeze. In the sudden hush I heard the frogs belching in the ditch behind the tent and the faintest thumping strains of Lynrd Skynrd's *Free Bird* from a radio in one of the other tents.

'Randall? You in there?' came a voice just outside the front flap.

This was a female voice, and my hope (notwithstanding the fact that I was, and am, totally attached to Jenny, who I'm saving to buy a condo with in Des Moines) was that it was Poonam. Poonam was from Bombay; she wore tight jeans and little knit blouses that left her midriff bare and she was doing her Ph.D. thesis on the Garos and their religious beliefs. She'd been waiting for me with a bottle of gin and a plate of curry when I got off work two days earlier, and I have to admit that the sound of her voice – she spoke very softly, so you had to strain to hear – put me in a sort of trance that wouldn't seem to let up and I'd begun to entertain thoughts about what she might be like without the jeans and blouse. All she could talk about was her research, of course, and that was fine by me, because with the gin and the curry and the sweet soft music of her voice she could have been lecturing on the Bombay sewer system and I would have been rooted to the spot. (And what *did* the Garos believe in? Well, they called themselves Christians – they'd been converted under the British Raj – but in actuality they were animists, absolutely dead certain that spirits inhabited the trees, the earth, the creatures of the forest, and that those spirits were just about universally evil. That is, life was shit – rats in the granaries, elephants obliterating the fields, kraits and cobras killing the children the leopards hadn't made off with, floods and droughts and diseases that didn't even have names – and whoever was responsible for it had to be as malicious as a whole squad of devils.)

So I said, 'Yeah, I'm here,' expecting Poonam, expecting gin, religion and a sweet little roll of belly flesh I could almost taste with the tip of a stiff tongue going south, and who should part the flaps but Candi Berkee, my co-worker from New Jersey whose presence there, in my tent in the West Garo Hills, was a real testimony to Verizon's commitment to equal-opportunity employment.

'Hi,' she said.

''S up?' I said.

She gave a sort of full-body shrug, her lips crushed together under the weight of her nose and the *Matrix*-style shades that never left her face, then ducked through the flaps and flopped down in my camp chair. Which was piled high with six or seven sedimentary layers of used socks, underwear and T-shirts I was afraid to toss on the floor for fear of what might wind up living inside them.

'I don't know,' she said, dropping her face as if she were emptying out a pan of dishwater, 'I'm just bored. This is a boring place. The most boring place in the world. Number one. Know what I mean?'

It wasn't that she was unattractive – body-wise, she was off the charts – but there was something about her that irritated me, and it went beyond the fact that she was forever whining about the heat, the mosquitoes, the food, the tedium and anything else she could think of. For one thing, she was a militant vegetarian who regarded anyone who even thought of hunting as the lowest of the low, a step below the average Al Qaeda terrorist ('At least they *believe* in something'). For another, her taste in music – Britney, Whitney and Mariah – was as pathetic as you could get. The fact that she was in my tent was a strong indicator that everybody else must have gone into Tura, the nearest excuse for a city. Either that, or committed suicide.

I didn't respond. The cot cupped my bones. She was wearing shorts and a bikini top, and there was a bright sheen of sweat on her exposed flesh that made her look as if she'd been greased for the flagpole event at the county fair. The birds started in again, screech, screech, screech.

'You want to smoke out?'

She knew I had pot. I knew she had pot. Everybody had pot. The whole country was made out of it. I was about to beg off on the grounds that I had to keep my senses sharp for putting bullets into whatever might be creeping down to the river to sneak a drink, be it muntjac or macaque, but thought better of it – I was in no mood for a lecture.

'Nah,' I said finally, sucking all the enthusiasm out of my voice. 'I don't think so. Not today.'

'Why not?' She shoved her sweat-limp hair out of her eyes and gave me an accusatory look. 'Come on, don't be a pussy. Help me out here. I'm bored. Did I tell you that? Bored with a capital B.'

I don't know whether the birds cut off before or after the sound of a second pair of approaching flip-flops came to me, but there it was – the slap, the shuffle, and then the give of the bamboo floor.

'Hello?' Poonam's voice. 'Hello, Randall?'

Poonam wasn't exactly overjoyed to see Candi there, and for her part, Candi wasn't too thrilled either. I'd been up front with both of them about Jenny, but when you're away from home and affection long enough, strange things begin to happen, and I suppose hunting can only take you so far. As a distraction, that is.

'Oh . . . hi,' Poonam murmured, shifting her eyes from me to Candi and back again. 'I was just –' She looked down at the floor. 'I was just coming for Randall, because the Wangala celebration is about to begin, or the drumming anyway – we won't see the dancing till tomorrow, officially – and I wondered if, well' (up came the eyes, full and bright, like high beams on a dark country road), 'if you wanted to come with me to the village and see what they're doing, the ritual, that is . . . Because it's, well, I find it stimulating. And I think you would too, Randall.' She turned to Candi then because she was graceful and pretty and she had manners to spare. 'And you too, Candi. You're welcome too.'

I'm no expert, but from what Poonam told me, the Garos have a number of celebrations during the year, no different from the puffed-up Christians of Ottumwa and environs, and this one – Wangala – was a harvest festival. Think Thanksgiving, but a whole lot more primitive. Or maybe 'rootsier' is a better word. Who are *we* thanking? God, supposedly, but in Ottumwa, it's more like Wal-Mart or Hy-Vee. The Garos, on the other hand, are doing obeisance to Saljong, god of fertility, who provides nature's bounty in the form of crops and fish and game. Of course, Poonam never did tell me what they would expect to happen if they didn't give their abundant thanks to this particular god, but I can guess.

Anyway, the three of us went down the hill to the village amidst the bird-screech and the smell of dung and cookfires, and Candi fired up a bowl and passed it round and Poonam and I took our turns, because I figured, Why not? The muntjacs could wait till tomorrow, and this, whatever it might turn out to be, was something different at least, not to mention the fact that Poonam was there at my side with her slim smooth limbs and the revelation of flesh that defined her hipbones and navel. 'Do you feel anything?' Candi kept saying. 'You want to do another hit? Randall? Poonam?' Half a dozen chickens fanned out across the path and vanished in the undergrowth. The sun enflamed the trees.

In the village itself – foot-tamped dirt, cane and thatch huts on raised platforms of bamboo, lurking rack-ribbed dogs, more bird-screech – people were preparing the evening meal in their courtyards. The smoke was fragrant, the smell of curry and vindaloo making my salivary glands clench and clench again. A pig gave us a malicious look from beneath one of the huts and I couldn't help laughing – the thing wouldn't have even come up to the hocks of one of our Iowa hogs.

'What are you talking, "drums"?' Candi said. 'I don't hear any drums.'

Overhead, the high-voltage wires bellied between the electric poles, at least half of which we'd had to replace with the new high-resin-compound model that resists rot and termite damage, and you wouldn't believe what the climate here can do to a piece of creosote-soaked wood stuck in the ground – but don't get me started. Just looking at the things made my back ache. Poonam was about to say something in response, something cutting or at least impatient – I could tell from the way she bit her underlip – when all at once the drums started up from the rear of the village where the bachelors had their quarters in the front courtyard of the headman's compound. There was a hollow booming and then a deeper thump that seemed to ignite a furious palm-driven rhythm pulsing beneath it. Children began to sprint past us.

Instantly I was caught up in the excitement. I felt like a kid at the start of the Memorial Day parade, the high-school band warming up the snare drums, the horses beating at the pavement in impatience and the mayor goosing his white Cadillac convertible with the beauty queens arrayed in back. I'd heard some of the local music before – my best bud in the village, Dakgipa, played a thing like an oversized recorder, and he could really go on it too, knocking out the melodies to *Smells Like Teen Spirit* and *Paranoid Android* as if he'd written them himself – but it was nothing like the ferment of those drums. I glanced at Poonam and she gave me a smile so muscular it showed all her bright perfect teeth and lifted her right nostril so that her nose ring caught the light and winked at me.

'All right,' I said. 'Party time!'

And that was how it went. Everybody knew us – the Garos are not in the least bit standoffish or uptight or whatever you want to call it – and before long we were sitting cross-legged in the courtyard with plates of food in our laps and jars of rice beer in hand while the bachelors went at it on every sort of drum imaginable – the *Ambengdama*, the *Chisakdama*, *Atong dama*, *Ruga* and *Chibok dama*, the *Nagra* and *Kram*. And gongs. They were big on gongs, too. Candi wouldn't touch the food – she'd been down with one stomach ailment after another, right from orientation on – but she drained that beer as if she were at a kegger on Long Beach Island while Poonam sat beside me on a clump of grass with her flawless posture and sweet compressed smile.

At one point – and my recollection isn't too clear here, I'm afraid, after the weed and the beer, not to mention the flamingest curry I've ever yet to this day run across – Dakgipa came and sat with us and we made a date to go hunting the following day after work. Dakgipa spent all his free time out in the bush, snaring squirrels, bandicoots and the black-napped hare and the like, potting green pigeons in the trees and crow pheasants out in the fields, and he'd acted as a sort of guide for me, teaching me the habits of the local game and helping me tan the hides to ship back home so Jenny and I could stretch them decoratively over the walls of our condo-to-be.

There was a quid pro quo, of course – Dak was a Counter-Strike addict and all he could talk about was the DSL capability he hoped we were bringing him and the 10Base-T Ethernet network interface cards he fervently hoped and expected we'd hand out to go with the new modems we were seeding the village with. But that was OK. That was cool. He gave me the binturong and the masked palm civet and I gave him the promise of high-speed Internet.

It grew dark. The mosquitoes settled in for their own feast and the screeching day birds flew off to their roosts even as the night creatures took up the complaint, which sizzled through the quieter moments of the drummers' repertoire like some sort of weird natural distortion, as if the gods of the jungle had their amps cranked too high. I was aware of Poonam beside me – Dak was sounding out Candi on the perennial question of Mac versus PC – and the drums had sunk down to the hypnotic pulse of water flowing in its eternal cycle, everything gone calm and mellow. After a long silence, Poonam turned to me.

'Did you know the auntie of my host family was carried off by a *bhut* the other night?'

I didn't know. Hadn't heard. But Poonam's skin glowed in the light of the bonfire somebody had lit while I was dreaming the same dream as the drummers and her eyes opened up to me so that I wanted to crawl inside of them and for ever forget Jenny and Des Moines and the Appleseed Condo Corp Inc.

'What's a *bhut*?' I asked.

'A forest spirit.'

'A what? Don't tell me you actually –' I caught myself suddenly and never finished the thought. I didn't want to sound too harsh because we were just starting to have a real meeting of the minds and a meeting of the minds is – or can be, or ought to be – a prelude to a meeting of the flesh.

Her smile was softer, more serene than ever. 'It was in the form of a leopard,' she said. '*Bhuts* often take on the shape of that sneaking thief of the night. They come for adulterers, Randall, false-promisers, money-lenders, for the loose and easy. Some nights, they just take what they can get.'

I stared off into the fire, at the shapes that shifted there like souls come to life. 'And the auntie – what did she do?'

Poonam gave an elaborate shrug. 'They say she ate the flesh of the forest creatures without making sacrifice. But you'd have to believe, wouldn't you, to put any credence in a primitive speculation like that?' The drums flowed, things crept unseen through the high grass. 'Just think of it, Randall,' she said, shifting her hips so that she was facing me square on, 'all these people through all these aeons and when they go out to make water at night they might never come back, grandmother vanished on her way to the well, your childhood dog disappeared like smoke, your own children carried off. And you ask me if I *believe*?'

Maybe it was the pot, maybe that was it, but suddenly I felt uneasy, as if the whole world were holding its breath and watching me and me alone. 'But you said it yourself – it's only a leopard.'

'Only?'

I didn't know what to say to this. The fact was I'd never shot anything larger than a six-point buck on the edge of a soybean field and the biggest predators we had in Iowa were fox, bobcat and coyote, nothing that could creep up on you without a sound and crush your skull in its jaws while simultaneously raking out your intestines with swift knifing thrusts of its hind claws. That was a big 'only'.

'Would you hunt such a thing, Randall? In the night? Would you?'

Candi was deep in conversation with Dak when Poonam and I excused ourselves to stroll back up the hill to my tent ('Yes,' Dak was saying, 'but what sort of throughput speed can you offer?'). I'd felt so mellow and so – detached, I guess you'd call it – from Jenny that I found myself leaning into Poonam and putting my lips to her ear just as the drummers began leapfrogging up the scale of intensity, and the ground and the thatch and even the leaves of the bushes began to vibrate. It was hot. I was sweating from every pore. There was nothing in the world but drums. Drums were my essence, drums were the rain and the sunshine after a storm, they were the beginning and the end, the stars, the deeps – but I don't want to get too carried away here. You get the idea: my lips, Poonam's ear.

'Would you –' I began, and I had to shout to hear myself, 'I mean, would you want to come back to the tent for a nightcap maybe? With me?'

She smelled of palm oil – or maybe it was Nivea. She was shy, and so was I.

'Yes,' she whispered, the sound all but lost in the tumult around us. But then she shrugged for emphasis and added, 'Sure, why not?'

The night sustained us, the hill melted away. Her hand found mine in the dark.

For a long while we sat side by side on my cot, mixing fresh-squeezed lime juice, confectioner's sugar and tumblers of Tanqueray in my only glass and taking turns watching each other drink from it, and then she subsided against me, against my chest and the circulatory organ that was pounding away there – my heart, that is – and eventually I got to see what she looked like without the little knit blouse and the tight jeans and I fell away to the pulse of the drums and the image of a swift spotted *bhut* stalking the night.

I woke with a jolt. It was dark still, the drums silent, the birds and monkeys nodding on their hidden perches, the chirring of the insects fading into the background like white noise. Somewhere, deep in my dream, someone had been screaming – and this was no ordinary scream, no mere wringing out of fear or excitement, but something darker, deeper, more hurtful and wicked – and now, awake, I heard it again. Poonam sat up beside me.

'Jesus,' I said. 'What was that?'

She didn't say I told you so, didn't say it was a leopard or a *bhut* or the creeping manifestation of the Christian devil himself, because there was no time for that or anything else: the platform swayed under the weight of an animate being and I never thought to reach for my rifle or even my boxers. For an interminable time I sat there rigid in the dark, Poonam's nails digging into my shoulder, neither of us breathing – 'Jenny,' I was thinking, 'Jenny' – until the flaps parted on the grey seep of dawn and Dak thrust his agitated face into the tent.

'Randall,' he barked. 'Randall – oh, shit! Shit! Have you got your gun, your rifle? Get your rifle. Bring it! Quick!'

I could hear the birds now – first one started in and then they were all instantaneously competing to screech it down – and Poonam loosened her grip on my arm.

'What is it? What's the problem?' I couldn't really hear myself, but I have no doubt my voice was unsteady, because on some level – scratch

51

that: on every level – I didn't want to know and certainly didn't want to have to go off into the bush after whatever it was that had made that unholy rupture in the fabric of the night.

Dak's face just hung there, astonished, a caricature of impatience and exasperation, though I couldn't see his eyes (for some reason, and this struck me as maybe the oddest thing about the whole situation, he was wearing Candi's *Matrix* shades).

'The big one,' he said. 'The biggest bore you have.'

'For what? Why? What's the deal?' Though our entire exchange could have been compacted into the space of maybe ten seconds, I was stalling, no doubt about it.

His response, delivered through clenched teeth, completely threw me. I don't know what I'd expected – demons, man-eaters, Bangladeshi terrorists – but probably the last thing was elephants. 'Elephants?' I repeated stupidly. To tell you the truth, I'd pretty much forgotten they even had elephants out there in the bush – sure, they still used them to haul things, like telephone poles, for instance, but they were as tame as lap-dogs and no more noticeable or threatening than a big grey stucco wall.

I still hadn't moved. Poonam shielded herself from Dak – as if, in this moment of fomenting crisis he would have been interested in the shape of her breasts – and before I'd even reached for my shorts she had the knit blouse over her head and was smoothing it down under her ribcage.

What had happened, apparently, was that the wild elephants had come thundering out of the jungle at first light to ravage the village and raid the crops (all I could think of were those old Tarzan movies – I mean, really: *elephants*?).

'You're joking, right, Dak?' I said, reaching now for my clothes. 'It's like April Fools, right – part of the whole Wangala thing? Tell me you're joking.'

I'd never heard Dak raise his voice before – he was so together, so calm and focused, he was almost holy. He raised it now, though. 'Will you fucking wake up to what I'm telling you, Randall – they're wrecking the place, going for the granary, trampling the fields. Worse – they're drunk!'

'Drunk?'

His face collapsed, his shoulders sank. 'They got the rice beer. All of it.'

And so, that was how I found myself stalking the streets of the village ten minutes later, the very sweaty stock of a very inadequate rifle in my hand. The place was unrecognizable. Trees had been uprooted, the huts crushed, the carcasses of pigs, chickens and goats scattered like trash. Smoke rose from the ruins where early-morning cookfires had begun to swallow up the splinters of the huts, even as people ran round frantically with leaking buckets of water. There was one man dead in the street and I'd never seen a dead human being before, both sets of my grandparents having opted for cremation to spare us the mortuary and the open casket and the waxen effigies propped within. He was lying on his face in the dirt, the skin stripped from his back as if it were the husk of a banana, his head radically compressed. I couldn't be sure, but I thought I recognized him as one of the drummers from the previous night. I felt something rise in my throat, a lump of it burning there.

That was when the villagers caught sight of me, caught sight of the rifle. Within minutes I'd attracted a vengeful, hysterical crowd, everybody jabbering and gesticulating and singing their own little song of woe and me at the head of the mob, utterly clueless. The rifle in my hands – a 7mm Remington – was no elephant gun. Far from it. It packed some stopping power, sure, and I'd brought it along in the unlikely event I could get a shot at something big, a gaur or maybe even a leopard or (crucify me) a tiger. Back in Ottumwa I suppose I'd entertained a fantasy about coming down some sun-spangled path and seeing a big flat-headed Bengal tiger making off with somebody's dog and dropping him with a single perfect heart shot and then paying a bunch of worshipful coolies or natives or whoever they might be to skin it out so Jenny and I could hang it on the wall and I could have a story to tell over the course of the next thousand backyard barbecues. But that was the fantasy and this was the reality. To stop an elephant – even to put a scare into one – you needed a lot more firepower than I had. And experience – experience wouldn't hurt either.

The noise level – people squabbling and shouting, the eternal birds, dogs howling – was getting to me. How could anybody expect me to stalk an animal with this circus at my back? I looked round for Dak, hoping he could do something to distract the mob so that I could have some peace to prop myself up and stop the heaviness in my legs from climbing up over my belt and paralysing me. I'd never been more afraid in my life, and I didn't know what was worse: having to shoot something the size of a house without getting trampled to the consistency of onion-skin paper or looking like a fool, coward and wimp in the face of all these people. Like it or not, I was the one with the gun, the white man, the pukka sahib; I was the torchbearer of western superiority, the one with everything to prove and everything to lose. How had I gotten myself into this? Just because I liked to hunt? Because I'd potted a bandicoot or two and the entire village knew it? And this wasn't just one elephant, which would have been bad enough, but a whole herd – and they were drunk, and who knew what that would do to their judgement?

The crowd pushed me forward like the surge of the tide and I looked in vain for Dak – for a friendly face, for anybody – until finally I spotted him at the rear of the press, with Candi and Poonam at his side, all three of them looking as if they'd just got done vomiting up breakfast. I gave them a sick wave – there was nothing else I could do – and came round a corner to see two other corpses laid out in the street as if they were sleeping on very thin mattresses. And then, suddenly, the crowd fell silent.

There before me was an elephant. Or its truck-high back end, that is. It was standing in the ruins of a hut, its head bent forward as it sucked rice beer up its trunk from an open cask that somehow, crazily, had remained upright through all the preceding chaos. I remember thinking what an amazing animal this was – a kind of animate bulldozer, and it lived right out there in the jungle, invisible to everybody but the birds, as stealthy as a rat – and wondered what we'd do if we had things like this back home, ready to burst out of the river bottom and lay waste to the cornfields on their way to Kenny's Bar and Grill to tap half a dozen kegs at a time. The thought was short-lived. Because the thing had lifted its head and craned its neck – if it even *had* a neck – to look back over its shoulder and fan its ears that were like big tattered flags made out of flesh. Reflexively, I looked over my shoulder and discovered that I was alone – the villagers had cleared off to a distance of five hundred feet, as if the tide had suddenly receded. How did I feel about that? For one thing, it made my legs go even heavier – they were pillars, they were made of concrete, marble, lead, and I couldn't have run if I'd wanted to. For another, I began a grisly calculation: as long as the crowd had been with me, the elephant would have had a degree of choice as to just who it wanted to obliterate. Now that choice had been drastically reduced. Reduced, that is, to one.

Very slowly – infinitely slowly, millimetre by millimetre – I began to move to my right, the rifle at my shoulder, the cartridge in the chamber, my finger frozen at the trigger. I needed to get broadside of the thing, which had gone back to drinking beer now, alternating snorts with tearing up a patch of long grass behind the remains of the hut and beating it against its knees in a nice calm undrunken grandmotherly kind of way that lulled me for an instant. But really, I didn't have a clue. I remembered the Orwell essay, which *Guns & Ammo* reprinted every couple of years by way of thrilling the reading public with the fantasy of bringing down the ultimate trophy animal, and how Orwell said he'd thought the thing's brain was just back of the eyes when in fact a seasoned hunter would have let loose at the earhole – all right, fine – but I also remembered what he figured would happen if he missed ('I should have about as much chance as a toad under a steamroller'). My right arm felt as if it was in a cast. My trigger finger swelled up to the size of a baseball bat. I couldn't seem to breathe.

That was when the elephant gave a sudden lurch and swung round amidst the splintered bamboo and the tatters of thatch to face me head on. *Boom*: it happened in an instant. There the thing was, fifty feet away – four quick elephantine strides – stinking and titanic, staggering from one foot to the other like one of the street people you see on the sidewalks of San Francisco or New York. It seemed perplexed, as if it couldn't remember what it was doing there with all this wreckage scattered round it – and I had to credit the beer for that. Those fermenting tubs hold something like fifty gallons each, and that's a lot of beer by anybody's standards, even an elephant's. The term 'blind drunk' came to me then and the smallest ray of hope stirred in me: maybe, if I just stood rock still, the thing wouldn't see me. Or couldn't. Maybe it would just stagger into the jungle to sleep it off and I could save face by blowing a couple shots over its retreating butt.

But that wasn't what happened.

All at once the unreadable red-rimmed eyes seemed to seize on me and the thing threw back its head with one of those maniacal trumpeting blasts we all recognize, anybody who's got a TV, anyway, and then, quite plainly berserk, it came for me. I'd like to say I stood my ground, calmly pumping off round after round until the thing dropped massively at my feet, but that didn't happen either. Suddenly my legs felt light again, as if they weren't legs at all but things shaped out of air, and I dropped the gun and ran like I'd never run before in my life. And the crowd – all those irate Garo tribesmen, Dak and Candi and Poonam and whoever else was crazy enough to be out there watching this little slice of drama – they turned and ran too, but of course they had a good hundred-yard head start on me and even if I'd just come off a first-place finish in the 100 metres at the Olympics, the elephant would have caught up to me in a heartbeat and transformed me into a section of roadway and all the money my parents had laid out on orthodontics and tuition and just plain food would have been for nought. I hadn't gone ten paces before an errant fragment of what just an hour earlier had been a thatch roof caught hold of my foot and down I went, expecting imminent transformation (or pancakeization, as Poonam later phrased it, and I didn't think it was all that funny, believe me).

The elephant had been trumpeting madly but suddenly the high notes shot right off the scale and I lifted my fragile head to see what I at first thought was some sort of giant black snake cavorting with the thing, and I'll tell you the elephant was lively now, dancing right up off its toes as if it wanted to fly away with Dumbo. It took me a moment and then it came together for me: that was no snake – that was the high-voltage cable and that thing at the other end of it was the snapped-off bobbing remnant of a high-resin-compound telephone pole. The dance was energetic, almost high spirited, but it was over in an instant, and when the thing came down – the elephant, big as an eighteen-wheeler – the ground shook as if a whole city had collapsed.

There was dust everywhere. The cable snaked and snapped. I heard the crowd roar and reverse itself, a hundred feet pounding at the dirt, and then, in the midst of it all, there was that screech again, the one I'd heard in the night, and it was as if someone had slipped a knife up under my ribcage and twisted it. My gaze leapt past the hulk of the elephant, past the ruin of the village and the pall of smoke, to the shadowy architecture of the jungle. And there it was, the spotted thing, crouching on all fours with its eyes fastened on me, raging yellow, raging, until it rose on two legs and vanished.

This story originally appeared in the US in *Zoetrope* Winter 2004

POSTMODERN VENUS
Christina Papamichael

The photograph lay on top of the dresser. Black and white. 10 x 8. One corner weighted down by a pottery fruit bowl full of dried curling leaves. Jane pulled open the top dresser drawer, scooped up her folded underwear and walked back to the unmade bed. Scraps of silky material and under-wiring cascaded from her grip, sprawling across the double mattress in a way she'd never been comfortable enough to do. Nearly half a year after she'd moved in, it was still Adam's bed. His flat. Jane stared down at the hillock of possessions on the bed, saddened at how easy it was for her to gather her things together – books and CDs, pyjamas, pullovers. Nothing new. Nothing added to what she'd unpacked in those beginning days, after Adam had given her a set of keys.

A breeze buffeted one of the net curtains. The leaves rustled in the fruit bowl. Jane stood in front of the dresser and trailed the backs of her fingers across the dried foliage, letting the curled leaf edges tickle her skin. She prised the photograph out from under the bowl and stared at the image. Toes tensed, a foot clawed at crumpled white bedsheets. It was the first photograph Adam had ever taken of her. Just one foot caught kicking free of the bedclothes. Rubbing her face with her hands, Jane stamped down on the all too familiar feeling of bitterness that rose to choke her like unshed tears. How stupid she'd been not to realize earlier that one captured moment, one still frame would never be enough for Adam. Not for a man so fascinated by everything that each waking moment was unfinished, unless it could be moulded into art.

The first time Jane saw Adam, he was feeling up a tree. Palms resting flat against the wide, solid trunk of an oak, he'd stood utterly still as if drawing forth stillness from within the tree itself. Cutting across Hyde Park, running late to meet Beth, Jane hadn't slowed her stride to see if he was going to press his hands together in prayer position and bow, but that half-registered glimpse had stayed with her over lunch. Distracted, Jane had fiddled with her tomato and cheese toasted-sandwich, kept quiet as Beth had gone on about coincidence, synchronicity and karma. Watching thin threads of cheese break off between her oily fingers, she'd wondered what Beth had been reading.

'Life's not a bus,' her friend had said, before hopping on to the number 73. 'Another one won't come along if you just wait long enough.'

Fourteen months earlier a perfect stranger had saved Jane's life. Called for help, held her blood-slick hand, talked to keep her conscious. She'd survived the crash, but even on good days Jane still wondered if she was going to survive the recovery. Making her way back through the park, Jane was telling herself that walking was the best form of exercise and cursing the complaining ache in her muscles when she realized the man she'd noticed earlier was still staring, still focused on the same tree. His stillness was compelling.

It did occur to Jane that he might be confused, or even crazy. But she'd almost closed the distance between them before childhood mantras about strangers and dangers came rushing back to her, in her mother's voice – the one she still used when she was overly irritated with something Jane had done and was choosing to ignore the fact that her only child had been a legal adult for over a decade. But then, maybe it was easier to slip back into those outgrown roles if you'd spent weeks helping your grown child bathe. Changed dressings like you'd once changed nappies. Cooked, fussed and passed judgement on *everything.*

At the sound of dead leaves crunching softly underfoot, the loitering man turned his head and the focus of his attention.

'I'm crap with directions. Where are you heading?'

He'd spoken before Jane managed to string her words together. Before she'd figured out how to ask a stranger if he needed help. The repeated whirr-click of a shutter drew her attention to the fact that the man who'd been fondling a tree was holding a camera.

'I'm not lost,' she said. Relief that her impressions had been so wrong mingled with the knowledge that she was intruding. It was a dizzying cocktail.

'Curious?' he asked.

Jane shrugged her shoulders then nodded, more intrigued than reticent.

'Texture . . .' He paused. Reaching out with a dirt-streaked hand he touched the tree once again, fingers stroking the bark. 'Shows up real well in black and white. Think I'm going to do a series.' He curled his fingers into the shallow natural spaces in the wood. 'Trees shed their skin just like snakes, don't you think?' he asked. 'Only the old skin flakes away over time. Doesn't get peeled off in one go.'

Jane thought of a tree wriggling and shimmying against the sky, leaving a tubular shell-self standing in the park. Hollowed out. Gutted. An ant ran over the back of Adam's hand and down around his wrist. Then, as Jane watched, a woodlouse skittered across his fingers. She shuddered. He didn't move.

'Everything the tree's been through is written into the wood. Just like skin really. Wrinkles. Stretch marks. Liver spots. Nature's markings.' Adam sounded enthused.

As he turned back to look at her, Jane realized he was studying her as closely as he'd studied the tree, his gaze never drifting even momentarily. Despite her burgeoning discomfort, there was something compelling about this man's scrutiny. Compelling and unnerving. When was the last time she'd looked at herself that closely? When was the last time she'd wanted to?

She knew she probably shouldn't have accepted his four-word invitation for coffee. But, well, something about his energy, his vision, his sandy-blond head and even his shitty green anorak was enticing. It was surprisingly easy to fall into step beside Adam, dart across busy Bayswater Road and stop in at the first coffee shop they found. Easy to tell herself that if his hands didn't look visibly scrubbed when he got back to the table, she'd drink half her coffee and leave. No harm, no foul. No number. Just a mini-lecture from Beth, if Jane admitted that she'd let a strange man pick her up in the park. No doubt Beth would hark on about how Jane could have been assaulted; or else tell her that the park and the pub on a Friday night were much the same animal. Jane didn't plan on telling her mother how she'd met Adam. Nor that, for most of what could later be considered their first date, she hadn't known his name. When he had finally introduced himself, hands smelling of soap, fingers rubbed red raw, it had seemed somewhat fitting that Adam had been hugging a tree.

A casual comment from a night nurse had started Jane thinking about names and their meanings. About the irony of being tagged with her own name for the few hours that she'd been unconscious and unclaimed. A book of babies' names borrowed from the nurses' station on the maternity ward then found its way to her bedside. Pages loose, spine cracked, it had smelt of dust and sunshine. She'd looked up Jane: from the Hebrew, meaning gracious and generous, neither of which she felt on a good day. The second definition read: God is gracious. When she met Adam, Jane should have remembered she'd used up her quota of God's grace.

Over coffee, all she could focus on were his hands. His cuticles were cracked, broken, bleeding red grooves, somehow reminiscent of the tree trunk he'd put his hands up against. Adam tore a blueberry muffin into large moist crumbs and spoke easily. Jane struggled to fit words into something that resembled a conversation.

She wondered if the split skin stung, if his cuticles itched. She wanted to heal his fingers. She wanted to disinfect them, then put them in her mouth and suck on them. Later, when the man who'd fondled a tree asked her to dinner, she didn't think of saying no.

Adam was open to everything. Unflinching. Brave. Utterly unlike Jane. He'd snuck chocolate cake into the cinema on their fourth date, complete with chocolate sauce, cutlery and linen napkins. She'd been too embarrassed to eat the offering, accepting just one mouthful from his fork before handing over her portion and staring determinedly at the screen. Weeks later, when he'd lain down on carpeted hotel stairs, his legs and torso on the landing, head and shoulders on the steps, she'd tried, lying down next to him, willing herself to be enchanted. Dangling above them like translucent wisteria was a copiously ornate chandelier, its light illuminating breaks in an architrave. Adam talked about the interplay of light and shadow, about film stock, digital and flash photography. Jane slipped her trembling hand into his, and stared up at cracking, flaking paint and plasterwork. She'd wondered if Adam saw gold leaf where she saw vitiligo.

'There's more than one way to look at everything in this world,' Adam would say. It was his favourite phrase.

Four and a half months after they'd met, Jane moved back out of her mother's house and in with Adam.

'You're not ready,' her mother had said as she'd refolded all of Jane's clothes, taking them out of bin liners and placing them neatly in a suitcase. She'd even bubble-wrapped the pots and pans Jane took with her.

'It's not the first time I've lived with someone,' Jane said.

It wasn't, but Jane knew full well she'd been different then. Then, she wouldn't have had to fight not to shy away from Adam's touch. Now, sex was awkward, half dressed, half naked, half-hearted. At least for her. And it wasn't something Jane could bring herself to talk about. Not with Beth who'd want every awkward detail, nor with her mother who'd no doubt say that in her day sex had been less important, neatly glossing over the fact that her day had been the swinging sixties.

'Pushing your boundaries is a good thing,' Beth had said encouragingly, the day she'd helped Jane move in with Adam. 'And he's OK with everything, right?' Beth had whispered, her words half swallowed by the loud popping sounds of bubble-wrap being rubbed, then pressed between Adam's fidgety fingers.

'Right.' Jane knew her reply sounded weak but avoidance was so much easier than explanation. She clung to the fact that Adam had never asked her outright why she was so body conscious. He'd made a list: two columns of differences, stuck on the fridge. Abridged, it was simple. Unthreatening. Tea versus coffee. Meat versus vegetarianism. Words that simplified the dance of cohabitation every couple learnt. Adam revelled in the fact that they seemed to be complete opposites; teased Jane that he was an 'outie' where she was an 'innie'.

Adam would get out of the shower, dripping soapsuds still glued to the tuft of hair under one armpit, if some artistic idea had struck him. Jane carried her clothes into the bathroom, showered, dried and dressed with the door firmly shut. Adam slept nude. Jane slept in pyjama pants and a long-sleeve cotton T-shirt, even when she was hot. But he'd hold her anyway, waking when she pushed the duvet off in her sleep. Restless, she'd push against the sheets, burrowing, fighting, clawing. He'd watch the movement and the stillness, often with a camera in hand.

On the morning Adam surprised Jane with the photo of her bare foot, he handed it to her with a cup of tea. He'd made the tea black, forgetting that Jane took milk. Preoccupied, a toothbrush in his mouth, he'd stood naked at the end of the bed, then gone off to dress, muttering something about trees after a rainstorm. Adam's photos, which did well in coffee-table books, did even better as glossy cards sold in gift shops. But he hadn't had a breakthrough exhibition and that was what he was really after. That was what he'd talk about, or clam up about, depending on the day, depending on how the work was going.

Jane was still staring at a close-up shot of her heel, when she heard the front door bang shut. Alone, she slipped a hand into her pyjama bottoms and forced herself to touch her own skin, the right side of her belly, her thigh. Numb, creased, ropey, keloid tissue. Those scarred parts of her body that still felt utterly alien, that she nudged Adam's hands away from. Her heartbeat was strong in her ears and in her throat as she tried not to flinch from the feel. Dry-mouthed, her fingers trembling, Jane got up and headed for the bathroom.

The gouging scars wouldn't pale further, nor become less prominent. They would remain just as they were: parasitic earthworms that had burrowed into her skin and were lying dormant between feeds. Her stomach lurched. Jane turned away from her reflection. She felt queasy. Revolted.

She didn't realize she'd heard the front door again, until the bathroom door swung open abruptly. 'Jane, you OK?' Adam asked.

The question was posed to a woman half crouched on the floor, fumbling to tie her pyjama bottoms securely.

'Why doesn't this damn door lock?' Jane asked angrily.

'Do you want –' Adam asked, only to be cut off.

'No.'

'Don't you think –'

'No.'

She stood and pushed past him. It didn't matter what the questions actually were. Jane knew that her reply would have been the same.

Her scars hadn't healed quickly. Hadn't healed into neat, tidy, docile white lines that were barely visible. Black and green stitch-knots, which were supposed to have smoothly dissolved into each wound, had instead become infected, pulling and tearing at the skin they were meant to be sealing. Puss had seeped out between the stitches, just as blood and plasma had, in the first post-surgical days of gauze and Betadine. Like all of nature, healing was harsh.

She didn't remember the actual crash – skidding, hitting a tree, the driver's window shattering and the steering wheel breaking its way into her pelvis. All she could remember was pain, pain and screaming, screaming through clenched teeth, teeth slick with blood. Even after the surgery, she couldn't discern where her memories ended and her nightmares began. They'd bled into each other, in much the same way as her wounds.

She'd lost her right ovary. Lost it, as if some surgeon had just misplaced it, as if it had been misfiled with someone else's x-rays. They'd reconstructed her pelvis, focusing on bones and the metal screws fusing them together. All Jane could see were the gauzes and the bloody knot-infested flesh they covered. Months later a brief consultation with a cosmetic surgeon only promised more surgery without a guaranteed outcome. So Jane had done what was expected. Pretended that she was fine. Coping. Getting stronger. Grateful not to be further debilitated. Pushed too far, the pretence was fraying.

Jane lay down on the sofa and curled up into a ball. Moments later Adam's coat was covering her. He switched on a light, held out a postcard. Botticelli's Venus, her nudity partially hidden by her hair, stood on an oyster shell. Fat black felt-tip scars had been added to her torso.

'I want to photograph you,' Adam said quietly.

They stayed silent, almost still. Jane took the postcard, touched the man-made markings.

'Dressed. Only,' she'd said, finally.

It shouldn't have come as a surprise to Jane when Adam finally, openly, turned his artistic attention on her like a glaring spotlight. After all, she'd seen him scavenge doorknobs from houses that were being gutted, knew he'd salvaged two old travelling trunks, strapping them together to make a coffee table. And tree branches once rescued from the skip were now propped up in the kitchen by the side of the fridge, as if waiting for spring to transmute them back into a living tree. Adam's single-minded intensity shouldn't have shocked Jane, but it did.

He watched, followed, shadowed her, camera in hand. She'd thrown a kitchen towel at him when he'd tried to photograph her first thing in the morning, thrown an opened bottle of shampoo at the bathroom door when he'd tried to come in while Jane was in the bath. Theirs was a modern dance set to an almost silent score, the percussion beat audible every time the camera stuck its Polaroid tongue out at Jane.

Framed in white squares, the growing stack of Polaroids segmented Jane. A hand. An arm. Her elbow. The bits of skin she was happy to show to the world. Her nose, her chin, the curve of her cheek sloping down to her jaw-line. Her bitten lips. Intrigued, inspired, Adam was unrelenting.

'It's objectification,' Beth said, when Jane had called up in the middle of the afternoon, begging her to leave the office. Adam had turned the hundred or so Polaroids into a collage, gluing them down on to the kitchen floor. It was life-size. When Jane had gotten up to make coffee that morning, she'd found herself literally walking over her self. Her two-dimensional mouth was open, frozen in a silent shout.

'Actually it isn't objectification. It's fetishistic. Degrading. He's made you into something he can step on for Christ's sake!' Beth had yelled and passed judgement before she'd even seen the makeshift mosaic.

Two hours later she was standing on the jigsaw Polaroids of Jane's right hand, looking down at Adam's representation. 'That's what you get when you go out with arty blokes who might be strangely sexy, but are also dead weird,' she said caustically. Grabbing the nearest sharp knife, she crouched down ready to scrape the photographic paper up off the tiled, vinyl flooring.

'Don't!' Jane reached out to clasp Beth's wrist just before the knife met her two-dimensional calf. 'Do you think it's any good?' she asked.

'You're serious?' Gesticulating, Beth waved the knife around. Jane took a couple of steps back. 'You're planning to leave this here?'

'I said yes.' Jane spoke quietly. 'So, it's my problem, no?'

'Damn right you should have a problem with him walking on you!' Beth said.

'He's not walking on me,' Jane trailed off. 'It's art. Just like I'm not really screaming.'

Beth stared at her, one eyebrow rising. She tried to cross her arms, discovered she was still holding a kitchen knife and placed it on the counter.

'I was surprised,' Jane said, picking up the knife and sliding it into the nearest drawer. 'That's all.'

'Right.' Beth tapped the toe of her shoe against the skirting board. 'And what about everyone else who'll come in here? Anyone? The plumber?'

'And you slicing me up is less symbolic?' Jane asked, rubbing her face with her hands, trying to ignore the fact that she was still bra-less and in her pyjamas at two thirty in the afternoon. Everything still took up too much of her energy. All those little things she used to take for granted – brushing her hair, her teeth, rinsing out the bath, unloading the dishwasher. The tasks the physiotherapist had called 'the activities of daily living'. Things Jane had once done automatically and barely noticed.

'How could he push you like this?' Beth asked, as she watched Jane fill the kettle. 'You have told him, haven't you?'

Jane shook her head. 'Well, not outright. Not directly.' She pulled open a drawer and there, among cutlery and paintbrushes, spatulas and coins lay the postcard. 'Postmodern Venus,' Jane said handing it to Beth. 'By Adam Jardyn.'

'And you're staying?' Beth asked, holding the postcard carefully by its edges.

'Know anyone else who can show me how to hang upside down in a tree?' Jane asked, with a slight smile. 'And anyway, he agreed. He's only going to photograph me when I'm dressed.'

Nine weeks after moving in with Adam, everything still kept Jane awake at night. Her bed-mate's half-snores. His body heat. The clank of bathroom pipes. The creak of polished floorboards. And in the mornings, before the upstairs neighbour's children left for school, she'd hear *Chopsticks*, Chopin or Beethoven bashed out with fumbling, clumsy fingers. Jane bought packs of wax earplugs, rolled two little balls into fat sausages each night, then slid them into the small, shallow orifice of her inner ear. Still, the muffled slam of a piano lid regularly woke her before she was ready. Memories of lying in bed listless from exhaustion were all too recent. Jane told herself that was why she'd asked her doctor for sleeping pills. Ignored the mocking, shocked look from her Polaroid self when she slipped and took a pill during the day. Pharmaceutically fuelled, Jane's dreams were vivid, incongruous, surrealist. Remembered. She bit into piano keys, climbed stairs that folded down into each other, and when she stepped into a warm bath it always grew shallow beneath her. Each morning over breakfast, she gifted her dreams to Adam, unwrapping them with inadequate description. He didn't comment, not until the morning she told him she was sure she was bathing nightly in a baking tray.

'You sure that's what it is?' Adam had asked, dipping a buttery knife into the strawberry jam. 'A baking tray? Not a developing tray like the ones I've got in the darkroom?' He'd licked a blob of jam off his thumb, chewing on the fleshy pad in absent preoccupation. Something in his distant gaze had made Jane shiver.

The night Adam brought home his updated book, the prodigy upstairs was killing *Für Elise*. While Adam cooked, Jane looked through his portfolio. A spider's web stretched across broken brickwork. A woman struggling with her broken high-heel shoe. Jane's own foot curved in shadow against white sheets. Moments that had enraptured his attention. They'd missed the opening scenes of countless films and no longer made dinner plans because Adam was always late. He'd notice something, reach for his camera and then lose all sense of time. But on those indefinable occasions that Jane did or said something to capture his attention Adam would be utterly, intensely, focused upon her.

'And you really can't see you're objectifying?' she asked, turning past page upon page of leggy, digitally retouched women, fragmented naked torsos. Fashion photography and advertising paid well.

'It's not like my work is cutting edge. Bursting out into uncharted territory,' Adam said, adding a pinch of seasoning to the sauce he was stirring. 'Unfortunately.'

'Thighs and breasts and buttocks laid out in little viewfinder trays like slabs of meat at the butchers,' Jane said, turning the page.

'Do you think the *Venus de Milo* is objectified? Or Michelangelo's *Dying Slave*?' Adam asked, crossing over to the fridge, stepping on her cracked and broken photograph nose.

'That's sculpture. People used to fear that photographs could steal pieces of their soul.' Clumsy misplayed music flooded down into the kitchen, grew louder. Jane stared down at the damaged picture of her face looking up at her from the kitchen floor.

Adam dried his hands on a damp dishcloth. 'I want to show you something,' he said.

The photograph, once unrolled, took up a third of the living-room floor. A naked woman, her body elegantly twisted, stretched out across the overly large canvas, reaching forth with arms that had become tree branches. On the left side of her body, her skin was flaking and peeling away. It was tree bark.

'I want to frame your scars,' Adam said.

Incredulous, blood rushing in her ears, Jane wasn't sure she heard Adam clearly. 'Use somebody else's,' she said, shakily.

After Jane's refusal, Adam's cameras sat dreaming, defused on the hall table, the Leica nudged against the Polaroid, lenses nestled in sturdy cases, lens caps fastened. And as Adam's passion was once more an outdoor sport, Jane relaxed in the knowledge that he was no longer taking her picture. And when he started coming to bed late, or not at all, when Jane woke to find paint marks daubed on the legs of her pyjama bottoms, on pillow corners and across the duvet, she took it as proof that his focus had shifted.

In his search for texture, Adam was apparently marrying photography, paint and textiles. Scraps of chiffon, tulle and ribbon gathered under the coffee table like wind-blown leaves, loosely raked into a spreading pile. Books lay open on the floor, one on top of the other, their spines creasing. It didn't occur to Jane that the splayed books could remind her of butterflies pinned under glass until Adam brought home a true, dead specimen.

'It's not a butterfly, it's a moth,' he'd said, as he'd placed it on the kitchen counter next to the pasta jar. Jane had stared at the plump torso and the motionless feelers. Fragile wings, predominantly brown, yet with colourful markings, were affixed to a silk backing. 'Did you know some species lay their eggs in trees?' Adam had asked rhetorically.

Embalmed butterflies, cloth scraps, photographs and drawings all migrated when a friend lent Adam space in a studio. Relieved he'd found something else to occupy and fascinate his muse, Jane didn't question anything. Not about where Adam was working, nor the endless hours he was away. Beth did, rampantly.

'It's a con. A cover. He's filming porn on DV and uploading it online. Where's your boyfriend's souped-up laptop? We should run a search.' She'd come over on a rainy Sunday afternoon. As always, Adam was off creating.

'Search? For what?' Jane asked, pouring herself a glass of wine. 'His name and the word erotica?'

'His name at least,' Beth said. 'His portfolio might be up on the Web.'

'You want to see Adam's portfolio? Dig through the pile of things in the hall. I think it's propped up against the wall somewhere.' Jane waved her arm in that direction. 'There's an OK photograph of me in there too. Well, of my foot.'

'Your foot?' Beth asked.

Jane nodded, savouring a large sip of velvety wine. 'He took it months ago, while I was sleeping.'

'But you still don't think he's up to something?' Beth asked.

'Aside from whatever he's working on? Hardly. Ask him anything – if we're out of milk – anything, and somehow he'll end up telling you about parasites and predators. Camouflage. Nature's bloody markings and such. He thinks they're beautiful.'

Standing in the exhibition space the night before Adam's opening, Jane trembled with swallowed anger, swallowed screams. Before her, splayed across a series of black and white photographs a woman lay sleeping. Half covered, half naked. Shadows on her skin drew attention to scars that had been lit so they could clearly be seen. Worse still, exposed on the opposite wall, spread out across prints and installations in harsh, unflinching colour, were Jane's scars. Blown up and segmented, their details enlarged, they delineated geographical borders on maps, were sliced into by glass shards. In a third piece, a solitary butterfly was struggling to escape from a scar that had split apart, blood-splatter staining the dainty wings. Ironically, Adam had called the work *Boundaries*.

'How much would a picture of one ovary go for?' Jane tried to keep her voice level. 'How come you didn't ask my mother for my x-rays?' A sob came out as a broken laugh. Jane pressed the back of her hand to her mouth, to stop herself screaming.

'I think they're beautiful. Why can't you see that?' Adam asked urgently. His gaze sliding away from Jane, he paced rapidly. 'Do you want me to apologize?'

It wasn't hard for Jane to imagine how Adam had done it, how he'd gotten the chance. Her lover kneeling on the bed, the light from the hallway and the kitchen enough for exposure. Loosening the fabric tie that held up Jane's pyjama bottoms, rolling her over gently, so that they'd slip down as he half rolled her out of the duvet's clasp. Camera lens and human touch mapping her. The shutter snapping, slicing her into little-bitty frames. Just like a scalpel.

'I made it so easy for you, didn't I?' Jane said, scratching her forearm in nervous agitation. 'When I started taking those stupid pills. Did you wank as you took these?' she asked, her tone as bitter as the taste in her mouth. 'Camera in one hand, dick in the other? Bastard.'

'No! It wasn't like that!' Adam shouted, turning sharply to look at her.
'Really?'

'Jane . . .' Adam moved, taking a step towards her, his momentum stalling as she started and then backed away.

'How could you? I said no, Adam. Repeatedly.' Walking back over to the piece where a butterfly struggled to take flight, Jane reached out, her fingers tracing the tip of one wing. 'Prints, negatives,' she said. 'If you ever gave a . . .' She swallowed the excess of saliva pooling in her mouth. 'Burn them. Delete them. Please.'

Silence stretched thin between them, like an unspooled, exposed role of film, dry and brittle at its perforated edges. It was broken by the heavy clink of glassware and the tangy scent of wine. Jane looked back over her shoulder at the drinks table set up for opening night. She watched as Adam poured himself a glass of wine, drank it, then poured another. Watched as he finished that in two or three swallows, his Adam's apple juddering. Stubble-covered skin shielding healthy, vulnerable cartilage.

For a moment, Jane imagined herself wielding the bottle, swinging it, hitting Adam, bruising his temple, or his jaw. She wondered if a mouthful of blood would taste like success to him. If the glass would break, flecks and shards embedding themselves painfully in his skin, cutting, slicing, marring. Her fingers closed tightly, reflexively, into a fist and she could almost feel the narrow cylindrical bottle neck in her hand.

'It was always *only* about what you chose to see, wasn't it?' Jane asked, numbly.

'No, I –'

'Half the proceeds, Adam, and I want the one with the butterfly.'

MATISSE RED
Mariko Iwasaki

She roams the crowd in a daze.
Whispers float around her, like a radio in the distance.
She is buried.
Alone.
She doesn't know where to stand, which queue to join.
All she knows is that she needs to see her.
The woman she was never to meet.

A faint evening breeze fans through the temple like a casual passer-by, brushing the black and white drapes on the walls. The echo of wooden chimes fills the air.

The queue that Runa joined now approaches the main hall. The mixed odour of chrysanthemums, lilies and incense grows stronger and chokes her nostrils. As she turns the final corner, a priest in a plain black robe comes into view.

His chant grows louder and louder in tormenting rhythms, gradually transforming into a reproach: What are you doing here? What are you doing here?

Runa wants to step out of the queue and run.

Instead, she breathes in deeply, enters the hall, and looks up.

Yuji is there, in a black frame, on the altar-like table covered in white cloth, amongst flowers and lanterns, surrounded by sugar-coated cakes, a cup of water, and a bowlful of rice in which a pair of chopsticks stand.

How can this have happened?

Step by step, Runa approaches his photograph. A line of people before her bow and leave the queue, and it is her turn.

Close by, a woman sits sideways, motionless in the dark.

Yuji's wife.

It had been a good day, two years earlier, when Runa met Yuji.

Runa rushed towards the competition hall. Her hand trembled as she reached out for the brass door handle. Any minute they would be making the announcement.

The door was heavier than she expected. She stepped back to push it again, when a male hand, thick-palmed with square fingertips, appeared from behind. She turned to see its owner, then let out a small cry.

It was Yuji Furuya.

Runa had heard the legendary designer would also be competing to plan the top floor of a new forty-seven-storey building completed in southern Tokyo. Slightly taller than Runa, he glanced down at her and helped her in. His luxuriant hair with hints of white just above his ears was carefully combed down and shone as if to boast his success. A pin-striped collar, perfectly ironed, cupped his face.

'Thank you,' she mumbled and slipped into the hall.

The room steamed. Men and women in dark suits slid like snails through the packed space. They fanned themselves with competition programmes and bellowed over one another in anticipation. This was the first major competition since the decline in property prices. There were high hopes that the new skyscraper would boost the city, and eager interest in who would be chosen to put his stamp on the top floor.

Runa squeezed into a corner and turned around to drink in the atmosphere. People were shifting aside to create space for Yuji and his men, murmuring his name as he passed by. Runa followed him with her eyes, astonished at how one man could make a whole crowd turn to admire.

Twelve years into her apprenticeship, standing in a dark corner, was she in the right place? Her female friends, who had been as passionate with their dreams years before, had slipped away to quieter lives, some quitting their jobs as soon as they became pregnant. Their curious eyes had turned still like stones, their captivating charms vanished like smoke in mid air, caring only for the movements of their husbands and children. Runa had chosen to be here.

When every head in the competition hall turned to search for the winner, a female designer whom nobody had heard of, Runa's spine straightened, her face flushed. She drifted amongst them, receiving excited pats and offers of champagne. Countless business cards landed in her palms. For a moment she didn't know who she was.

It was then that the hand appeared from behind and beckoned her. The same hand she had seen earlier.

'I'm impressed by your work, Miss Saeki,' Yuji said, offering his handshake, a rare gesture for a man of his age. So confident. His eyes looked down at her keenly. 'It's a shame that you won and we lost, but what can I say? Your work has probably opened up a completely new trend.'

'Has it?' Runa took his hand hesitantly. 'In what way?'

'Your use of colour, the way you combine bright red with light blue, is imaginative, original. A vibrant piece of work, Saeki-san.'

Runa took a closer look at the man. She searched for a hint of frustration at losing the contract to a girl twenty years younger than him. His dark grey eyes were surrounded by generous laughter lines. They looked straight into her.

That evening, Runa sat with him in a corner of the room, describing her work with excitement, until the hall manager asked them to leave.

'How about I become an adviser on your new project?'

Yuji was on the phone to Runa the following morning. She was at a loss for words.

'Let's face it. I'm much more familiar with this game than you are.'

Runa couldn't help smiling at his candour. She pressed the phone tight to her ear.

'I know all the people there are to know,' he went on. 'I know what to expect from these massive projects. With me, your very first project is sure to be a success.'

'It's an extraordinary offer,' she said. 'How can I say no?'

That afternoon she stepped into Yuji's office building with her design tucked under her arm. Sunlight streaked across a vast marble floor. A contrast to her dark office which barely held six people.

Yuji came out to greet her and led her into his private office. Photographs and pictures of his past designs covered the walls, many of them familiar to Runa. One photo stood out from the rest and she walked over to it. She caressed its frame.

'You know, this was the piece that inspired me to carry on.'

'You have interesting taste. How about this one?'

He walked over to another photograph. A fat wedding ring caught her eye as he discussed the design. It was a silver ring, the shine muted. She gazed at it, not hearing his words.

Turning away, she noticed an unfinished work on his desk and leaned down to it.

'Didn't anyone tell you it's bad manners to steal a look at a work in progress?' He laughed as he sat down.

'I'm sorry . . .' She stepped back.

'No, no, it's fine. Actually, I'm keen to hear what you think of it.'

'Oh . . .' She hesitated. 'You said a work in progress?'

He nodded.

'It's a lovely piece . . .' She sat down across from him.

Yuji flashed a sharp look. 'No, I want your honest opinion.'

'Er . . . All right. It looks like something you did a long time ago . . . It's slightly old-fashioned . . . This bit for example . . .'

Yuji sat back, flipped his hand up, and laughed out loud.

'Oh, you young people! You seem to think techniques come and go like buses! Well, let me prove how wrong you are. The style's worked for me all these years, and I don't see how –'

He looked up and Runa turned.

'Excuse me.'

A voice came from the door that had been left open. A man wearing a square-bowed pink tie and a carefully ironed shirt, a man about the same age as Runa, was standing there, a pencil behind one ear. His sleeves were rolled up, his brown shoes shone.

'What's up?' Yuji said.

'I'm sorry to interrupt, Furuya-san. It's just that one of our clients . . . He's on the phone, and he sounds . . . well, quite upset.'

'OK, let me deal with it. Tell him I'll ring him back later . . .'

The man nodded and turned to walk out, but lingered, looking at Runa. He changed his voice and spoke to her in a student-like manner.

'Aren't you the winner of the bid yesterday? I was impressed with your work, Miss . . . ?'

'Of course, let me introduce you,' Yuji said. Runa stood up. 'This is Tanaka, one of our very talented young designers here, Miss Saeki.'

Tanaka held out his hand, just as Yuji had done the previous day. Runa looked at it blankly. It was smooth, with no wrinkles, no blemishes. He stood there casually with his hand out. Instead of taking it, she bowed slightly.

Tanaka raised his eyebrows, bit his lip, and slowly took back his hand.

'Well . . .' he murmured.

'Shall we proceed with our discussion?' Runa turned to Yuji.

Yuji sat back in his chair, hands behind his head, watching her with amusement.

'Yeah, sure, why not? Tanaka, do you mind?'

In a crowded elevator, he touched her.

She looked at her stomach, where he had lightly stroked with the back of his fingers. He smiled down at her, knowingly. She blushed, looked away, and then shifted her body in a different direction. He continued to look at her. Straight into her eyes, with confidence.

'What was that?' she asked later, when they were alone.

'Sorry, I didn't mean to,' he said, but his eyes were unapologetic.

'I can't allow it,' she said.

'Sorry,' he repeated.

But Yuji did not withdraw. Instead, he stepped over the line, gently.

'I never noticed those houseboats before.'

The apartment Yuji rented for the two of them had a huge window overlooking Tokyo Bay, which was now crowded with wooden boats, wandering here and there like jellyfish. People were out on deck in their summer kimonos, sitting back and fanning themselves.

'Ah, they suddenly appear in July out of nowhere, when the fireworks season begins,' Yuji said, approaching her with glasses of cold *sake* in his hands. 'We can get the best view of the festivals from here. *We* don't have to rent any boats. The room is perfect, don't you think?'

'Yes, you've told me how it's worth the price, many many times!'

She laughed and watched his hands swiftly set down the glasses and reach for her waist. Just months before, these hands had meant nothing to her. Now they were reworking her designs, stroking her hair, pulling her over to the other side when a car passed close by.

With these hands, Yuji drew her to him.

Runa's project was a success.

She watched the customers flow in and out of the newly opened restaurant. Then she gazed up at Yuji adoringly. He looked around in satisfaction. When he spotted the owner of the building he made a beeline for him, holding out his hands in celebration.

The owner shook his hands briefly, but his eyes went by Yuji, and he stepped over to Runa. He had a new assignment for her, an even bigger project. She listened with delight and turned back to Yuji. He studied her with a faint smile.

At dawn when Runa opened her eyes, Yuji was already awake. She reached out for him, and he abruptly let go of her shoulders and got out of bed. He grabbed hold of a towel, a businesslike expression on his face, and walked briskly across the room. His softening stomach and thighs contrasted with his well-built chest and arms. So different from the younger men with their pencil-thin arms and legs swimming helplessly in their shirts and trousers.

Listening to the shower running, Runa lingered in bed and imagined his day. He would enter his office with a look of authority, gather his team of designers to discuss a project, and sit back at his desk while his secretary brought him coffee. In the evening, he would drive home where his wife awaited him.

Yuji bid Runa goodbye, promising he would return in a few days. She wondered to herself whether she would ever see him again.

But that evening he returned.

'I couldn't keep away from you,' he whispered in her ear. He took hold of her hands, and pulled her into the bedroom.

Runa woke up one night to find Yuji leaning over her desk in their bedroom. She went across and reached forward to turn off the desk light. He grabbed her wrist with a force that startled her.

'What's this?' he asked, with shadowed eyes.

'It's . . . my next assignment,' she faltered. 'It's still at its earliest stages.'

His eyes turned soft and he let go of her.

'Let me see it so that we win the bid next time, not you,' he laughed. With a groan he added some lines with a pencil. 'It's too damn good,' he said, 'and thus I regret to say it must be ruined.'

She let out a nervous laugh. He leaned closer to the paper and started drawing on a different corner.

'These are techniques passed on through generations of designers,' Yuji said, rocking gently to and fro. 'You don't know about them, do you?'

Runa shook her head and took a deep breath.

'Teach me,' she said, drawing close.

She watched him, his back bent over like a little boy with a toy. She did not look at the paper.

Runa never asked Yuji about Sawako, his wife. She only knew they never had a child together because he couldn't bear the presence of one. She saw contempt in Yuji's eyes whenever he mentioned Sawako. The woman's eyes were still, her merriness gone. She had become someone who'd forgotten how to apply rouge to her chalky cheek, who changed her voice to conceal her age. No longer was she interested in the creative life Yuji led. That was how Runa took his wife to be.

Runa tried to wipe Sawako out of her mind. Yet soon enough, the eyes of every wife she passed – their desperate gaze at the husband striding two metres ahead and never glancing back, or their over-attentive look at him – were replaced by the imagined eyes of Sawako. She gripped Runa and refused to let go.

'Can't you stay tonight?' Runa asked one August evening. She had pulled Yuji out of the study, where he seemed to be spending more time on his own.

A thousand fireworks dazzled the humid summer night, the whistles and explosions playing a distant symphony beyond their windows.

He remained silent, a cup of *sake* in his hands. He drank it down and walked over to the music system. He flicked through the selection of CDs.

'No,' he said finally.

'Why not?'

'I go home today, as we agreed.'

'Every week has to be the same?'

He pulled out a CD and started reading the box.

'That design you've been slaving over,' she blurted out. 'It needs something fresh. And you know it.'

Yuji turned around, his eyes cold like marble looking down at her.

'You and I can work together, open up a new avenue for you . . .' she offered.

'What new avenue? The road is wide open to me. You think I need your help?'

He turned away.

'You said your wife never understands . . .' Runa said, approaching him. 'We can work together tonight.'

'I'm not staying.'

He pressed a button. The fury of drums filled the room, soon joined by a frenzy of violins, drowning out the fireworks outside.

Runa returned to the apartment humming and tipsy, carrying a half-finished champagne bottle. She had won another competition, this time for a high-street clothing-store commission. It was nearly two years since she'd met Yuji.

He was in his study, poring over his work under a single light. She noticed tension running through his back. The sight frightened her. But then with her cheery confidence she crossed the floor on soft feet.

'Go away,' he said.

She laughed, set down the bottle, and threw her arms around his neck.

'I said . . .' With that he faced her. Runa immediately saw that he was drunk. She spotted a glass of whisky amongst his papers. She shot a look at them, and saw violent lines that made no sense. He had destroyed one of his drafts.

'What's wrong?' she asked.

A line of fatigue showed on his forehead, his hair straggling over it. For the first time, she saw Yuji as a man of the age that he was.

He stared at the champagne bottle.

'Get out,' he said.

A few hours later, she awoke, still alone in their bed. She went into his study but stepped out again as soon as she heard his voice. He was murmuring into the phone, his words continuing like a long piece of unbreakable thread.

'All my ideas are draining out of me . . . The younger ones are catching up . . . they're taking over the industry . . . I don't know if I can do this any more . . . Yes, dear, I promise I'll come home tomorrow . . .'

It was a voice that Runa had never heard him use.

It was the voice of a husband.

Taking a deep breath, she went in and approached him. As she was about to touch him, he turned around, the phone to his ear. He gasped slightly and paused for a second.

She looked down at him, pleading with her eyes for him to stop. He raised his chin, motioning for a second to speak to her. But then he moved the phone back to his mouth and spoke, with flaring eyes fixed on Runa's.

'Well, the young ones, you see, they seem to think they can ignore all we've achieved,' he said. 'They'd be happy to see us go, I'm sure.'

Runa watched him in disbelief. A smirk appeared at the corner of his mouth. The next moment, he brushed his arm across the desk and sent the champagne bottle flying on to the floor. Its cork sprang out and the golden liquid foamed on to the carpet.

Runa fled the room.

She went to the cupboard and grabbed her jacket. It knocked against a box, spilling the contents. Red and blue leapt at her eyes and she covered her mouth with her hands. It was her first project, with Yuji's handwriting all over it. *What's so original about this?* he had scrawled across the pages.

Her eyes blurred, she could not make sense of it. With weak legs she went into the living room. The window where she and Yuji had viewed countless scenes together stretched wide. Now, only two cargo ships stood still in the dark winter night.

Runa leaves the main funeral hall and enters a separate room where Yuji's relatives and friends are quietly sitting around *sushi* and *sake*.

A woman makes a space for her to sit. Runa accepts the offer and the glass of *sake*. The elderly woman starts talking to her in a croaking voice. 'What is it with talented people?' she asks. 'They have so much to offer, and yet they're taken away from us just like that before their time.' Runa nods, half-heartedly. 'His wife was so loyal to him, you know. She must be devastated . . . Ah, there she is.'

Runa looks up. The crowd in the room all stand up. Runa glimpses Yuji's wife moving to the far end of the room. Some start approaching her. Runa freezes. She sits down again and continues to listen to the woman next to her who talks endlessly, aimlessly, as strangers do. 'Did you know,' the old woman whispers, 'they found him hopelessly drunk behind the wheel?'

Runa can't take in the rest of the woman's words. Her ears start to buzz.

In the two months since she'd left Yuji her telephone had rung incessantly but she had ignored it, until it stopped suddenly four days ago.

The surfaces of the squid, tuna and omelette laid on top of the *sushi* rice are beginning to dry up and lose their gloss; the soup and tea have turned cold. The mourners start to leave. The woman next to Runa pats her shoulder and sets off.

There is still a small crowd around the wife. Runa forces herself to stand up. With trembling knees she wades through the group. Gradually, the face in profile comes into view.

Sawako Furuya.

She is a slender woman, meticulously dressed. Her sharp haircut exposes the fine line of neck and jaw. She is sitting behind a table, talking to a man beside her, no longer the motionless doll that she was in the main hall.

The words the wife utters seem fast and too many. If not for the black dress and the artificial flower with her name pinned on her breast, who would know she is the wife in mourning?

She turns.

Runa looks away instinctively, but turns back immediately.

A colour of red has hit her eyes.

The red, a Matisse red, the red of water melons cut in half, covers the woman's lips. For a single moment, Runa stares in awe at how well the colour suits her. It stands out against a skin pale like the moon and hair black as calligraphy.

Sawako looks up with large provocative eyes that pierce straight into Runa. Yes? her eyes ask.

Runa cannot get any words out. She shakes her head, gives a slight bow, and turns to walk away. As she starts to push through the crowd again, a voice calls from behind. It is a clear voice.

Sawako is standing, watching her. Her figure is faultless. After some hesitation, she comes out from behind the table and approaches her. Her red lips open to speak into Runa's ear. That red so inappropriate for the occasion.

'You know.' Sawako holds Runa's arms.

Runa stiffens.

'He could never tolerate talent other than himself.' She lowers her voice. 'I was another talent he despised.'

Runa looks at her in disbelief.

Sawako's eyes are strong. They look into Runa's with constant movement, with curiosity. As if to search for something that she once was. Then, she stands back.

'Thank you for coming,' Sawako says, and bows deeply. The bow is one that only her generation can manage.

Runa stands there helplessly.

Nevertheless, she tries and returns the same bow.

She looks again into the wife's eyes. Only then does she see the anguish in her eyes.

The next moment, Sawako has returned to her conversation with the man beside her. He is Yuji's colleague, another big name in the industry. Whatever the topic, Sawako is handling it beautifully. She knows what she is talking about. Her voice is lively. Young even.

As Runa moves away, the red lips flash before her again and again. A red so becoming. A red so out of place. A red that says Sawako will not be buried with Yuji.

Runa turns back once more to watch the wife from a distance.

She sits with her chin up, her back straight and tall.

WHEN THE FAT MAN SINGS
Neil Baker

Colin lumbered up the path to his house, straining to hear through the night air. He was right. There were people inside. The lights were out in his living room at the front, but he could hear voices towards the back, in the dining room. Laughter. Like a party. A party in his house, when he was supposed to be on a seven-night cruise, discovering Helsingborg and the fjords of Norway.

As his fingers fumbled for the key, the door swung open. Richard, his neighbour, stood on the threshold with his back to Colin, not noticing him.

'There's plenty more in the cellar,' he shouted down the hallway. A woman's voice – young and lively – said something back from the dining room. 'Not at all,' said Richard. 'Open whatever you like.'

And then he turned and saw Colin on the doorstep. 'Shit,' said Richard.

'Richard?' said Colin.

'Colin!' said Richard. He stepped out of the doorway, paused for a moment, and then quietly closed the door behind him. 'Colin, Colin, *Colin*. What are you doing here? You didn't forget your passport?'

'No.'

The two men stood next to each other on the doorstep. Richard: thin, perma-tanned, fortyish, in white linen trousers and pink silk Hawaiian shirt. Grinning inanely. A little drunk. Colin: grey-skinned, in jeans and sweat-damp T-shirt. Grossly overweight. Defeated. Luggage standing dejected at the end of the drive, waiting where the taxi driver dumped it.

'They wouldn't let me on the boat,' said Colin.

'You forgot your ticket?'

'No, I remembered my ticket.'

'What, then?'

Colin raked his fingers through thinning hair. 'They said I was too fat, Richard. Too fat for their boat.'

'How can you be too fat? It's an ocean-going cruise liner. You can't be too fat for an ocean-going cruise liner.'

Colin stood silently, remembering his humiliation.

'Was it the gangplank?' asked Richard. 'Surely they have to have some sort of extra-wide gangplank. There must be a law. For people like you. It's discrimination. It's outrageous.'

'No, it wasn't the gangplank.'

On the train back from Southampton Colin had thought a lot about why they wouldn't let him on the boat. But here, on the doorstep, with Richard waiting for him to explain himself . . . well, he didn't know what to say any more.

Richard, as usual, misread the reason for his friend's silence. 'You're wondering what's going on, aren't you,' he said.

'Richard?' called the girl's voice inside again.

'Look, I'd better go back in,' he said. 'They'll be worrying about me. We can talk later.'

Only now did Colin wonder why his friend was in his house. Richard saw the concern.

'Don't worry, it's not a problem,' he said. 'You can sleep next door, at my place.'

'I want to sleep in my house.'

'Right,' said Richard, wondering how to explain. 'You were supposed to be on holiday, Colin.'

'But I'm not now.'

'No. But you left me a key. To feed Marmaduke. I didn't break in or anything.'

'Well, who were you talking to? Who else have you got in there?'

'OK, OK, OK,' said Richard. 'Look, this will sound odd, I know, but could you do me a favour?'

Colin looked.

'Can you pretend that this is my house?'

'What?'

'Please. OK? They think this is my –'

And at that moment, the door was flung open again. A young woman in a black cocktail dress stood in the open doorway.

'Richard,' she laughed, placing a balancing hand on his elbow. 'And who do we have here?' She paused to survey the glistening bulk of Colin.

Richard shot Colin an apologetic glance. 'Philomena. Darling. This is my surprise guest,' he said. 'From . . . across the seas. Arrived by boat just this afternoon.'

'By boat!' said the girl. 'Marvellous.' She turned to shout at the dining room. 'Stephen!' she called inside. 'There's a man here who came by boat. A fat man.'

A fat man, thought Colin. 'Look, I –'

'Come in, come in, come *in*,' said Richard. 'Let's get you and your bags inside. I'm so glad you could come.'

'Wonderful,' said Philomena, weaving back down the hall towards the dining room.

'We'll be with you in a tick,' said Richard. 'We'll just get Colin's luggage.'

Richard closed the door to Colin's house and the two men scrunched in silence down the short gravel drive to the flickering street light, under which sat Colin's abandoned bags.

'Well, here we are then,' said Richard.

'Richard, why do you want me to pretend that this is your house?' said Colin.

'Because they think it is,' said Richard.

'But why would they think that?'

Richard paused, breathed deeply and adopted a sheepish expression. 'I've got a confession to make,' he said.

And then he began to tell his story, cautiously at first, a little unsure of himself, but clearly warming to his task as he progressed.

'I've started a new business line,' said Richard. 'I've hooked up with this doctor in Shanghai. Doctor Lee, he's called. He's a cosmetic surgeon. Does amazing things. I'm his appointed UK representative. He can't do any marketing here for regulatory reasons. So any business I drum up, I get ten per cent. It's easy money. The margins are great. Even with the cost of the flights, it's much cheaper than getting it done over here, and you get a holiday in China as part of the bargain – three star, all-in, everything paid for. That guy inside, his name's Stephen Wilson. I met him at a networking evening for recently divorced executives. I was doing my motivational talk – Do-It-Yourself Dignity. He's going to be my first customer.'

Colin winced. He'd heard that talk. The memory of it was embarrassing. 'What do you know about cosmetic surgery?'

'Everything I need to,' said Richard. 'Stephen, very sensibly, listened to my talk, put my tips on enhancing your personality into action and landed that airhead Philomena. So I'm his saviour. Then he contacted me to say he's got issues about his . . . performance. When I told him about Dr Lee he was desperate for the procedure. He could get it done here, but he's too tight – and too greedy to turn down a free holiday. I'm ready to close him.'

Richard smiled. Colin grimaced.

'But why my house?'

'I'll put down a deposit on a swanky clinic with the money from this deal. But right now I need to project a degree of professionalism. I needed somewhere classy for Stephen to sign the contract. Not my pokey little office. And as for my house, Colin . . . Well. Sarah took everything. I've got dust-framed rectangles on the walls where our pictures used to hang and the TV is on an upturned milk crate. Your house is so lovely, Colin. And I just thought, well, what you don't know can't hurt you.'

Colin had watched Richard's face as he told his tale. The twinkly-eyed face of an angel; honest in its confession; not pleading for understanding, but awaiting its arrival as a matter of course – an entitlement. This expression had driven Sarah out of the house, but it suckered Colin every time.

'OK,' he said, with a sigh.

'Colin, you are a gent,' said Richard, picking up the smallest of Colin's bags. 'I'll make sure they're gone by midnight.'

Colin sighed again.

'OK,' said Richard, 'eleven at the very latest. I promise. Eleven. But first, Colin, tell me what happened with the boat.'

'Oh . . . it was nothing. You know I really –'

'OK, you're uncomfortable,' interrupted Richard. 'I can see you don't want to talk about it. It'll keep. Tell me later.' And he walked quickly back to the house.

Despite all the noise that Colin had heard from the drive, Richard only had two guests at his party: Philomena and Stephen. The four of them sat around Colin's dining-room table. It was a simple, but expensive, beech table, bought on an impulse from Heal's on Tottenham Court Road. Colin was trying to put together an anecdote about how he came to buy the table so he could work his way into the conversation. Everyone was ignoring him. But whichever way he put the story together, he never came out looking good. The truth was he hadn't been looking to buy a table, but when he slowed his walk to gaze through the window at Heal's he saw one of the shop assistants, and thought he recognized her, thought he knew her, so went in. He was wrong. This happened a lot to Colin. Usually nothing came of it, but on that occasion he ended up having to buy a table. At least it was a nice table. Then he realized it was supposed to be Richard's table, not his.

So instead he shifted his focus to the pictures that hung on his – or Richard's – dining-room walls. The gallery of opera singers. Fat, sweating, red-faced men. In pride of place, his signed photograph of Jussi Björling, the Swede, whose crackling mono 1956 rendition of *La Bohème* was, Colin fervently believed, the greatest operatic recording ever made; a recording Jussi made one night in New York; a recording that Colin found for ten pence on a stall at Camden Market thirty-three years later, when Colin was piling on the pounds and Jussi was twenty-nine years dead. But again, he couldn't think of anything to say.

He turned his attention to Philomena, sitting in her black dress, surrounded by an aura of ease and privilege, glowing like a halo. What a creature. She was always either laughing or poised with her mouth open, nodding rapidly, while waiting to laugh. Waiting for any opportunity to laugh. Making it absolutely clear to everyone present that they were the most delightful company imaginable and that right now this dining room was the most amusing, witty, fascinating place to be anywhere on the planet. Anywhere.

'He says I'll leave him if he doesn't have it done,' she said. 'I tell him that's nonsense and I love him to bits just as he is. I tell him every day. But it's what he wants. What can I do?' She announced this to the three of them, as if she were addressing a public meeting.

'You can't really stop him if it's what he wants. That's the truth,' said Richard.

'It sounds like a very difficult procedure,' said Colin. 'I didn't even know you could have it done.'

'God, no,' said Richard. 'Everyone's having a nip or a tuck these days, aren't they? This is no more complicated. Stephen's procedure is nothing to a man like Dr Lee. He does this sort of thing all the time. All the time.' Richard leant over for a bottle of wine and topped up Stephen's glass. 'I tell you,' he went on, adopting a more confidential tone, 'this time next year all your friends will want this deal. And you can tell them down the golf club that you got there first. They'll be begging you for my phone number – and I will, of course, reward you for any leads you pass my way.'

Richard let that prospect hang in the air. Then he changed gears for his closing finale. 'And anyway,' he said, 'Stephen here wants it!' He swung his arm dangerously towards Stephen. 'And Stephen here can afford it! So who's going to tell him he can't have it? Who?'

Richard looked around the table, as though he expected someone to burst into the room and stop Stephen having it. Everything was silent. 'See!' he said.

Nobody was sure if they should laugh – Philomena was poised to. There was a moment of silence, and then she decided to talk to Colin instead. 'Colin,' she said, with studied earnestness. 'What do you do?'

The question dragged Colin back to the reality of the dining room. Just what did he do, really? He thought a moment. Philomena waited, pendent, lips pursed.

'Opera,' he said. 'I am an opera singer.'

'Really. Opera. Wow. That's really . . . Wow. Opera.' She looked at Colin, smiling. 'Stephen, did you hear? He said opera.'

Stephen said nothing.

'That would explain . . . you know.' She puffed out her cheeks and wobbled from side to side, pretending she was fat.

'Yes, that's right,' said Colin.

'I devour opera,' said Stephen. 'Where have you performed?'

'I'm big in Japan,' said Colin.

'And in London?'

'No, I don't perform here. The market's overcrowded.'

Stephen was going to say something, but Philomena interrupted. 'And Colin . . . is there a Mrs Colin somewhere? Or a girlfriend?'

Everyone stopped talking. Colin could feel them looking at him. 'Well, actually, yes,' he said. 'There is someone. I met her on the boat.'

'A love boat. Lovely. Do tell.'

Richard looked at Colin, concerned. 'Could you help me in the kitchen for a mo?' he said.

'Of course,' he said. 'Do excuse me.'

When they were both in the kitchen Richard closed the door firmly. 'What are you doing?' he whispered. 'You're an accountant, not an opera singer. And you didn't meet anyone on the boat. You told me you didn't even get on the bloody boat.'

'And what about this being your house and you having a genius in China?'

'It's true about China.'

'And?'

'Look, Colin. This is me. It's what I do. Nothing is ever exactly what it seems.'

'I know. I know.'

'But it's not you, Colin.'

'Everyone was ignoring me.'

'Look, Colin. These are vacuous people. They ignore everybody. But I need them and I don't want anything to muck this up. OK?'

'Hurrah!' said Philomena, when they walked back into the dining room. 'Tell me about the girl you met on the love boat.'

'Oh, you don't want to hear about that,' said Colin.

'Yes, we do. Go on.'

Colin wasn't sure how to proceed. This was uncharted territory. Stephen was staring, bored, at the window; Richard had a pleading look on his face; but Philomena – she was almost bouncing in her seat with excitement. 'It happened before we got on the boat,' he said. 'That's when I saw her.'

Richard frowned, Philomena's smile widened, and Colin began to elaborate his lie.

He described how he'd seen a beautiful young woman leaning on the balustrade, high on the side of the ship. She looked at him and caught his eye. He was too slow to look away, but then surprised when she held his gaze. And how confused he was when she waved at him. How he looked around, but there was no one behind him. How he looked at her again and she pointed to her watch, held up seven fingers, and made to drink from an invisible glass.

'And what was it like when you met?' said Philomena.

What would it have been like? Colin wondered. A failure, most likely. He thought of a tragic-opera fantasy in which she would be waiting for him in a bar somewhere on the boat. Then after a while she'd look for him. He would be easy to find, a man of his size. Perhaps worried, she would check with the crew. What cabin was the . . . large man staying in? She'd hoped to meet him. And they would explain: who? Oh, him – he wasn't allowed on the boat . . . By the doctor . . . Too fat.

'It was wonderful,' said Colin. 'You know, we just got on so well. Right from the start.'

'Isn't that sweet,' she said to Stephen. 'Did you hear that?'

'Yes,' he said.

Richard looked at his friend, blankly. 'Colin. Kitchen,' he said.

Again, he closed the door firmly. 'This is getting out of hand,' he whispered through gritted teeth. 'We're supposed to be talking about Stephen's procedure, not your fantasy boat trip.'

'I'm sorry.'

'I'd like you to tell me about the boat now. I need some facts.'

'Now?'

'Yes.'

'Well, I did get on the boat, briefly. I told them on the booking form about my size and they'd made special arrangements to get me on board.

But when I got to my cabin the doctor came and said I had to have a medical check-up. When I booked I said I was obese, but the doctor said I had a heart condition too, which I hadn't disclosed. He asked if I'd been finding myself more out of breath lately and as soon as I said yes he said I had to get off the boat, because I was an insurance risk.'

'You should have lied.'

'But he told me to think carefully before answering, and to answer truthfully.'

'That's just legal talk. Arse covering. And anyway, you don't have any heart condition. You're just a bit heavy.'

'Well, actually, I do have a heart condition.'

'What?'

'It's a recent thing. I found out in the summer. I didn't mention it because you had your own troubles. I'm sorry.'

'Is it serious?'

'Yes.'

'How serious?'

And then Philomena stumbled into the kitchen. 'Darling, don't hog Colin,' she said. 'Stephen's just had a lovely idea. We thought, if Colin would indulge us, that we could end the evening with a song. Would you, Colin? Would you sing for us?'

Richard stepped in front of his friend. 'Well, now, Colin's really tired and needs to get to bed. He's had a very long journey.'

Stephen appeared in the kitchen doorway, a wry smile on his face. 'Come on, Richard, I'm sure we can let Colin decide if he'd like to sing for us. What do you say, Colin? A little something from your repertoire, then I can sign the papers for Richard's man in China.'

'Oh, don't worry about that now,' said Richard. 'I can bring them round to your office tomorrow.'

'But I might change my mind by tomorrow. Let's do it now, after the song. What will you sing, Colin?'

'Well, I –'

'No, Colin, it's all right,' said Richard, ushering them backwards into the hallway. 'You need to rest. Stephen can sign the papers tomorrow. Colin has had a few drinks and that's not good for his voice.'

'But Richard,' laughed Philomena, 'isn't the customer always right? Come on. A song would be lovely. Don't be a prune.'

'We're not expecting a full concert-level performance,' said Stephen. 'You can rein it in a little, Colin, if you need to protect The Voice.'

Colin turned to his friend. 'Richard, really, I –' And then he stopped himself. He looked into Richard's eyes and saw something change there. Nothing more than a flicker, a dilation.

'How about something to do with girls and boats?' sneered Stephen.

Richard shifted his balance. 'Why don't you just shut up,' he said, to Stephen.

'Well, really,' said Philomena, not laughing. 'We just wanted a song.'

'Perhaps big Colin here's not up to it,' said Stephen. 'Got the stomach for it, but not the heart.'

Colin saw his friend's shoulders go tense, and then relax. 'It's time for you to go now,' said Richard. 'We don't want you here any more.'

'You can't ask us to leave,' protested Stephen. 'You need me. Do you think I can't see through you? You need me.'

'No, we don't,' said Richard. He put one hand on Stephen's arm, opened the door with the other and pushed him out into the dark. 'And you can go, too,' he said to Philomena, who was lingering by the stairs. He slammed the door behind her, then opened it again to throw out their coats.

A full bottle of Talisker later, Richard and Colin stood in the kitchen, side by side, washing dishes. 'But what you said about the girl – did that happen?' said Richard.

'On the boat? No. But there was a girl like that, a long time ago.'

'Who was she?'

'I don't know. It was on a train.'

Richard nodded, but for once said nothing.

'We didn't speak. I caught her eye, nothing more. Then it was her stop, and she was gone. But I see her all the time, or it feels like I do. Whenever I ride down an escalator, she is coming up. When I look out the window of a taxi, she is walking along the pavement. I see her everywhere.'

Richard dried a plate and put it in a cupboard. 'I didn't know that,' he said.

'No, you didn't.'

'Why tell that story tonight?'

'I don't know. It seemed like it could have been real.'

Richard took another plate from the draining board and started to dry it. 'About the singing. I'm sorry about that. They were cruel.'

'Sometimes, Richard, lies get out of hand. You know that.'

Richard smiled at his friend. 'Yes, I know,' he said. 'Sometimes I forget what's real and what's not.'

And at that point Colin started to inhale; slowly, deeply, at length; his chest rising and expanding as he took in more air. He stood there for a moment, holding his breath. And then releasing a low and sonorous hum, that retuned into a baritone, he began to sing. His voice filled the kitchen, and it was beautiful.

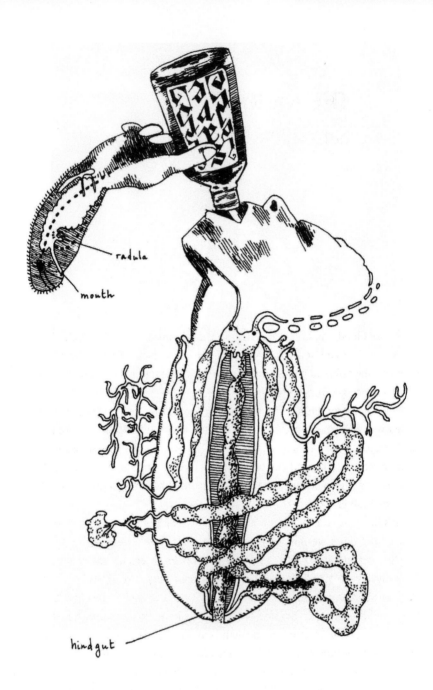

radula

mouth

hindgut

THE NEGOTIATION
Sarah Jane Marshall

'Sixty-six bloody quid.' He scribbled on the bill and handed the top half to the waiter. She said nothing, embarrassed in the wake of the familiar ritual in which she offers to go halves and he refuses. Sometimes she insisted and sometimes he accepted, but not tonight.

The diners were thinning now, the door busy with the shuffling exits of replete and thick-headed customers. They'd sunk fully into their weekends, eased expertly out of their rigid weekday routines by the Brasserie's slick team of waiters. Some of the waiters were clearing tables; others ate at a long bar – a row of white-shirted backs, moored like boats to the brass rail. He folded the bill and put it in his suit pocket.

'It's like you said,' he went on. 'You think this place is cheap but it's not. And I don't think we should see each other any more.'

Her eyes darted upwards, engaging with his for a second. She could feel them displaying 'What? *What?*' but she just said, very slowly, 'OK.'

Immediately, she reached for props – the glass of vodka, the cigarettes. Never mind the cough. She felt her heart swell and push against her ribs, the necklace he'd bought her in Sicily now heavy and cold on her skin. That dark emporium of a shop, bursting with trinkets in the middle of a hot afternoon, on an island somewhere in the Tyrrhenian Sea.

She drained her glass – the ice was clunking about uselessly in the bottom – and half the cigarette was already gone. I forgot to enjoy it, she thought. All that lung damage and I forgot to enjoy it. Grinding the cigarette out in the ashtray before it became a desperate woman's stub, she looked him in the eye.

'When did you decide that?'

'Last week.'

Last week, he was travelling on business. Merging and acquiring. Dinner with a knee surgeon in Izmir – something about a hospital being acquired by another, bigger hospital. Then Amsterdam to visit a cancer research institute – an Irish consortium wanted to buy it. Cancer, he'd said, was a profitable business. So he hadn't missed her, then. A week together, a week apart. She'd missed him – in the desperate and helpless way you miss someone who has begun to slip away.

'*And* they've forgotten the coffee,' he said, refilling his wine glass and looking about for a waiter. She stared at him in disbelief. They watched a waiter scurrying past to attend to a group of four in an adjacent alcove. The men were rowdy, the women searing the end-of-evening atmosphere with occasional peals of laughter. An empty champagne bottle was turned upside down and slammed triumphantly back in the ice bucket.

'What made you change your mind?'

'Oh, no particular incident. I haven't met anyone else – I mean, I'm still *with* you.'

'What, then?'

'Well, the thing is, I'm only about sixty per cent sure, if you know what I mean. And that's not enough, is it?'

'I suppose not.'

He unwrapped a chocolate and popped it in his mouth, rolling the gold foil into a neat little ball between thumb and forefinger. She wondered if he was going to flick it at her.

'I *was* a hundred per cent, you know – in the beginning,' he said.

'So I've lost forty per cent.'

'If you want to put it like that.'

Nearly half his love, gone in a week. But his love had started slipping away before then, peeling off in sheets. It was in Sicily that she'd begun to lose him. It was their first proper holiday together. Each day she'd been unable to prevent another handful of his love escaping through the seams in her desperately cupping hands. They'd said nothing about it, of course. They had separated at Victoria by the Circle Line map, she heading westbound and he east. It had been a quiet, tired parting. She thought her stock might have rallied while he'd been away. Absence, she thought. What a con.

He flagged down a waiter and reminded him about the coffee. 'I have paid for it.' Feigning an elaborate apology, the waiter hurried off.

'The thing is, I can't imagine us married,' he said. 'Can you?'

'Yes.'

'Oh.'

The conversation was beginning to imitate the sketch they'd laughed about in *Vile Bodies* – the Adam and Nina engagement farce. She'd spotted the book on the shelf in his flat and read the passage to him:

> 'We aren't going to be married to-day?'
> 'No.'
> 'I see.'
> 'Well?'
> 'I said, I see.'
> 'Is that all?'
> 'Yes, that's all, Adam.'
> 'I'm sorry.'
> 'I'm sorry, too. Good-bye.'
> 'Good-bye, Nina.'

It seemed like years ago, not months – that quiet November evening, shortly after they'd first met. She remembered the rustling crescendo of the wind in the brittle leaves outside his bay window. Windows of leaves, she'd thought, walking into his flat for the first time. The blue flames of a gas fire flickered weakly in a fireplace of jet marble. She'd headed straight for it, expecting warmth, but it gave out nothing. Instead she'd found herself face to face with a small white bust on the mantelpiece, the blind white eyes. Then there were the books, hundreds of them, arranged on shelves according to height, tall ones at the edges, curving down to shorter ones in the middle; the same curve repeated on each shelf. Shelves of identical smiles.

Her eyes had drifted eagerly from spine to spine, imagining she was plumbing the depths of his mind; but as one unfamiliar title followed another, a panic had begun to rise and she'd started scanning the titles again, methodically sweeping from top left to bottom right, shelf by shelf. *Vile Bodies* had been somewhere in the middle.

'My *favourite!*' she'd said with relief, pulling the book off the shelf.

'Mine too.'

They'd laughed, thrilled by the discovery of something in common. When they'd kissed he'd been almost feverish, clasping her face in his hands, his fingertips gently pressing her temples, forcing her to look at him. The intensity in his eyes had startled her. With the book still open on her lap, he'd told her he loved her. She'd said nothing, watching the blue vapour enveloping the fake coals and listening to the subdued hiss of the gas. But she too had been excited. She'd felt her heart scurrying towards him as she read. They were both guilty of it – this investing of mutual likes and dislikes with a significance they didn't deserve. Marmalade – it had to be thick cut; dogs not cats; the absolute sanctity of Sunday nights; the sea. These were the threads that had shuttled between them, pulling them closer together.

The coffee had arrived. He emptied the little sachet of sugar into the cup, stirring vigorously and for longer than necessary. They focused gratefully on this new activity, painfully aware of the laughter coming from the group in the alcove throwing their own miserable evening into relief. A waiter had appeared with another bottle of champagne. They braced themselves for the sound of the cork. It came, a round muted pop. The cork shot upwards, clipping a frosted-glass lightshade before dropping into the lap of one of the women. She was holding it in front of her, grinning. There was a loud cheer.

'They shouldn't open champagne like that,' he said. 'It's bad form.'

'But you said you loved me.'

And he'd said it to her again and again – over restaurant tables, in the quiet emptiness of his flat, on cold benches in the huddle of his coat. She hadn't responded but he'd known she was listening. He'd known that, in spite of her silence, she would take the words home and suck at their permanence in the darkness of her bedroom.

'You loved me and now you don't. Is that it?'

'That's not what I said.'

'Isn't it?'

He didn't reply, shrugging slightly as if it didn't matter. She stole a sip of wine from his glass, careful not to finish it. He frowned and wrapped his fingers proprietorially around the stem before moving the glass back to where it was.

'You can't love someone one minute and not the next,' she continued. 'That's like giving a present then snatching it back. It just doesn't work like that.'

'Oh? Doesn't it?' He finished his wine and lifted the empty bottle, peering at the glass hillock at the bottle's base. 'My ex-wife told me she loved me. Now she's in New York, married to a man called Bill.' Abruptly, he put the bottle down and a sigh whistled through his teeth. 'Look, is there any point in this?'

No, she thought, it was like shouting in the wind.

Goodbye, Adam.

Goodbye, Nina.

In the absence of a Bakelite telephone receiver to slam down, she knew it was time to stand up and walk away. The great weight of the rest of her life hung on what she did now. Just go. For goodness sake, go! She went through the motions in her head. She could almost hear the chair legs scraping across the tiled restaurant floor as she stood up, the hollow tap of her heels as she strode towards the glass door and out into the weekend. But the thought of what was waiting on the other side of the door pinned her to the chair. Out there, invisible to the thickets of people forming on the street outside the closing bars, waited a monstrous gaping mouth – the unfathomable loneliness of a thousand unshared weekends.

'But I love you,' she said loudly. She remembered the little boat on the mere, where he'd eventually coaxed it out of her. He was rowing when she said it. He'd lain down the oars. She remembered her fingers throbbing in the tight grateful squeeze of his hand.

'I love you,' she repeated, quietly this time.

He shook his head slowly, spreading a hand over his face, his fingers and thumb drawing a white V as he dragged them across his reddened cheeks. For a second, she thought he was going to yawn but he straightened his back and pulled his chair in noisily.

'Look, you'll thank me eventually,' he said cheerfully. 'You'll be much better off without me. I mean, I can be . . . you know, prickly at times.'

Is that how he thought of Dorset? *Prickly*? It was something they never talked about. He'd taken her to a hotel on the coast, all whitewash and seagulls. It was their second weekend away together. The memory of it was severed into two distinct halves. First there'd been the walk along the horseshoe curve of the bay, the firm lock of his arm as her feet slipped on the shifting pebbles. He'd stooped to pick up a large white stone, perfectly oval and smooth like an egg. He'd rubbed it gently against her cheek and then presented it to her, like a gift. They'd embraced, there on the beach, the stone soft and chalky in her hand. And over his shoulder, she'd watched the sea unravelling to a narrow ribbon of indigo out of which rose the shadowy afternoon sky.

Then it happened. Was it on the same day or the following day? The incident had been dislocated, a dismembered chunk of time that she would never be able to reconcile to the same weekend. And no matter how much she'd raked over their conversations since, combing the meaningless chatter, isolating and analysing individual words, she'd never been able to find the trigger. The only warning was a change in tone, like the sudden darkening of the sky before heavy rain. There were angry words – something she'd done or said or not said – but she couldn't remember what they were any more. She remembered only snapshots: the whitened knuckles of his fist, the skin stretched dry between them, the unfamiliar fury in his eyes. Then everything – all memory and order – collapsed to the bar of soap spinning across the room towards her. Only it wasn't a bar of soap, it was the stone from the beach. Fortunately, it had missed her, bouncing off the bed and on to the floor. Maybe he hadn't meant to hit her. But that didn't matter, did it? The possibility should have been enough.

She'd stood on the hotel steps clutching her suitcase in one hand and the train timetable she'd got from the hotel manager in the other.

'Are you coming?' he'd yelled through the car window. It was a simple enough choice but behind it queued other, darker choices. Throwing the timetable into the large urn by the front door, she chose.

'Yes, I'm coming.'

There was a loud clatter from somewhere at the back of the restaurant and the group in the alcove cheered and clapped. One of the waiters at the bar got up and hurried towards the kitchen, disappearing through the swing doors. All evening she'd watched those doors swinging open and shut, open and shut. They were like a valve in the restaurant's heart, each convulsion producing another string of steaming plates. He was watching her now, waiting for her consent, praying for closure. But she said nothing. He shifted in his chair and she felt his leg jogging beneath the table.

'Surely you can see you'd be much better off with someone . . .' – he paused as if he was looking for a particular word – 'nice.'

'Nice?' she spat. 'Who wants nice?'

He glanced first at her and then at the group in the alcove.

'Don't worry,' she said. 'I won't make a *scene.*'

'I think we'd better go.'

'I think you're making a mistake.'

They both reached for the cigarettes at the same time, their hands almost meeting. He withdrew his quickly.

'Don't do this,' he said.

'Do what?' She knew exactly what she was doing. She wasn't the first woman to do it. There were thousands of them: women who break their own hearts.

'You're negotiating yourself into a relationship that isn't going to work.'

'No,' she said, waving a little frantically at a waiter. 'I'm ordering another drink.'

'But we've paid the bill.'

'We'll get another.'

She ordered a double vodka. The waiter turned towards him, raising his eyebrows, pencil poised. He shrugged, ordered a large glass of house red and pulling out the last cigarette, called out to the waiter to bring another packet.

'We're not leaving until you've told me *exactly* why you've changed your mind,' she said.

He lit his cigarette and breathed out a long, measured plume of smoke. She watched it dispersing over the table.

'You want me to be specific?'

'Yes.' She felt like one of those women in variety shows, half naked, her back against a velvet-covered board, waiting for the knives.

'Right. OK, then.' He sounded like he did on the telephone at work, brusque and businesslike. He had an argument to put forward, a deal to close. 'My women friends,' he said defensively. 'I've never slept with them and I never will but I like to see them – regularly.'

The Sirens. She'd wanted to confront him about them before but she'd been too afraid of disturbing the delicate balance of their fledgling love. They all had exotic names, these women friends. She hated them because she'd never met them, because she made up the information he never gave her. They'd formed a tribe in her mind, filling up the years before her. It was Lotus – the cellist – who bothered her most. He cancelled things for Lotus. She knew it was childish, that Lotus was probably an ordinary-looking girl and not the beautiful sylph-like creature with diaphanous dresses that she imagined her to be. But why couldn't she be called Ruth?

'That's fine,' she lied. 'I have friends who are men and –'

'But it's not fine, is it?' he interrupted with sudden vehemence. 'Whenever I mention their names – Lotus, for example – I can feel you bristling with jealousy.'

'Well, what do you expect? You've never introduced me to her. You go off and have dinner with her – and the others – *alone*. If she's such a great friend, why don't you invite me too?'

The waiter returned with the drinks and cigarettes and poured a little of the tonic into her vodka. She poured out the rest, shaking the bottle for every last drop. She always did that – it made the vodka last longer. She was never one to sip. Neither was he.

'Well?' she asked.

He placed his wine glass carefully back on the table and began folding his napkin into a neat rectangle, ironing out the creases with the heel of his hand. It was the slow, deliberate way of moving he adopted when drunk.

'Sicily,' he said confidently. 'That *obviously* didn't work.'

'But you said it was the most amazing holiday you'd ever had.'

'So did you.'

She'd collected the photographs that afternoon and brought them to the restaurant. They were now stacked in a neat column of yellow plastic envelopes on the table between them. Only a few hours earlier, they'd sat on stools at the restaurant bar, flicking through the pictures while their table was being prepared. Elbow to elbow, they'd marvelled at images of this little marina or that little port town, of indistinguishable cobbled streets scruffy with open windows and hanging sheets, of fissured volcanic slopes plunging into a dark glass sea. The appearance of each new photograph had elicited that word. They must have said it a hundred times. So many times that it had now lodged itself like a barb in her brain. Wasn't that hotel in Panarea *amazing*? And Stromboli, now that was *amazing*. All of it – just *amazing*.

'Honeymoon, was it?' the barman had asked. 'Must have been wonderful.' Neither of them had bothered to correct him. They'd both lit cigarettes and waited for the table in silence. The insincerity of it now made her shudder.

What exactly had gone wrong in Sicily? It wasn't like Dorset. She had prepared herself for that but it hadn't happened. She would have preferred anger – it was more tangible, more honest. Instead the passage of the week had been marked by a series of little incidents in which he had slipped a little further from her. Nothing in themselves, together they amounted to a creeping sense of disappointment that had, in the end, been far more shattering than Dorset.

Looking back, she realized the downward turn had begun on day one. Travelling by boat from Palermo, they'd hardly spoken. They'd sat on deck watching the Aeolian Islands emerging first like faint watermarks out of the pale sky before reappearing, quite suddenly, as giant volcanoes out of the twinkling sea. She'd forgiven him his distance, responding with her own withdrawal. He was tired; they'd had an early start. And nerves were only natural at the beginning of their first holiday together. So she'd left him alone staring at the ship's wake from the rear deck, conversing with his own mysterious thoughts. Let him have his space, she'd thought as she made her way up to the foredeck. He'll come back. And leaning over the rail she had let her mind unfurl and stretch itself out over the boundless sea.

But he didn't come back. Was that her mistake, then – walking away, not staying resolutely by his side on that first day? It seemed to her now that the beauty of the islands had illuminated the fragility of their relationship; that the holiday had shown up all that declared love for what it really was: a thin veneer that cracked under the intense Sicilian sun. She could see them now, wandering through endless classical sites on bleached hillsides not as lovers but as what they really were: strangers forced into a familiarity they had not earned. The misery of Stromboli suddenly seemed inevitable.

According to the guidebook, the volcano erupted roughly every fifteen minutes and was best viewed from the sea at night. Nothing could be more romantic, she'd thought. It will put all this nonsense behind us. After dinner, they'd wandered down to the small stone quay and hired a converted fishing boat. As there were no other tourists about that night, they had the boat to themselves. 'Off-season,' the skipper had said with a shrug. They emerged from the protected waters of the harbour into a choppy sea and a strengthening breeze. There were no clouds. It was one of those cavernous night skies prickling with stars. 'Perfect conditions,' the skipper had said. 'The best.' They sat side by side on the foredeck, faces to the wind, while the boat pushed on into the darkness.

Skirting the jagged coast, they slipped past fluted pinnacles of rock that had become severed from the mainland. Eventually the boat slowed and hovered in the lee of a rounded promontory. One or two yachts floated in the fidgeting waters, their mast lights dancing madly in the dark. They were all waiting, looking up at the tapering hulk of the volcano, a vast black shape cut out of the silvered sea. She gasped when the first rocks of fire lit up the rim of the crater. Mesmerized, she watched the molten lava spewing and bubbling over the broken mountain summit, blowing holes of daylight in the dark. Instinctively she reached for his hand but was surprised to find only cold damp deck. She hadn't noticed him move away. Quickly she stood up to look for him. Squinting against the stinging spray, she saw him sitting alone on the other side of the boat, his back to the volcano, his knees drawn up beneath his chin, staring at the black and empty sea. She called out but he didn't move. It was windy but she knew he'd heard her. When she looked back at the volcano, a strip of cloud had occluded the summit. 'Show's over,' the skipper shouted from the cockpit. 'We go back?' She nodded, quickly turning her face away from the deck light so he wouldn't see the tears.

They were distracted by a scuffle of colour and noise in the alcove. The group of four were paying their bill. A tired-looking waiter was trying to co-ordinate a confusion of cards and receipts. She felt quite drunk now.

'Why were you so cruel?' she asked. 'Was the holiday – was I – so disappointing to you?'

He shot her a wounded look. 'I didn't mean to be like that.'

'You *were* disappointed, then?'

'Yes – no. I mean, I don't know what I felt. It was just that everything was different to how I thought it would be. You were different.'

She reached for the cigarettes but thought better of it. Her throat was dry, the taste in her mouth bitter. He was holding the stem of his wine glass between thumb and forefinger and twisting the glass round and round. He seemed to her then like an insect under a magnifying glass, just before the smoke begins to rise. She persisted.

'How could I be different? I was me, *me*. But you hadn't set out on holiday with me, had you? You went on holiday with someone in your head. Your disappointment was the discovery that you were in love with someone you didn't know.'

He said nothing for a while but continued to turn the glass, watching the wine slide up and down the sides. He stopped suddenly and looked at her steadily.

'I'm getting to know you now, it seems.'

She noticed then how puffy his eyes were, the bruising beneath betraying sleepless nights. He looked exhausted, older.

'Yes,' she said quietly. 'We're talking now.'

He opened his mouth as if to speak but said nothing, resorting to a slow nod. It seemed as if something vital to his being had been dislodged and the solid structure to which he had previously adhered was beginning to unravel. Maybe it was just the drink. His hand dropped away from the wine glass, his fingers resting quite still on the tablecloth, close to hers. They were both looking at their hands, at the proximity of their fingertips.

'Everyone falls off their pedestals in the end,' she said softly.

He smiled at her sadly. 'Is that supposed to be a joke?'

'No.'

The conversation slipped into silence again. But it was not the raging silence of before. She had the sensation that something nasty had fallen away and she realized she didn't have anything more to say. Maybe it was the nullifying effect of the alcohol but she almost felt that she could leave now, that she could actually get up and walk alone into the street. She'd be all right, wouldn't she? Her thoughts began to drift away from him, away from their table towards possibilities for tomorrow – for Saturday, for a weekend on her own; but he interrupted her.

'Look. It wasn't easy for me to walk in here and call it all off,' he said. 'I mean, we get on pretty well, don't we? And . . .' He paused and when she looked up she saw that he was waiting for her to prod it out of him.

'And what?'

'I don't want to be alone either.'

The group in the alcove were finally leaving. Glasses were drained, bottles knocked over, coats put on, weekend plans made. She looked around the restaurant and found that they were now sitting amidst a forest of upturned chair legs. The black and white tiles were glistening wet. A waiter was closing in with his mop on a final patch of dry floor in front of the kitchen doors. He backed through them and was gone. A second waiter was managing the departure of the group in the alcove, directing them towards the door with a flourish of charm and smiles. 'Have a nice weekend,' one of the women said as she lurched past their table, throwing a scarf over her shoulder. The man slipped an arm through hers and guided her towards the door. 'Tomorrow, my darling,' she heard him say, 'we can have a lie-in.' She didn't catch the woman's reply but saw her clutch his arm a little more tightly and press her head into his shoulder. Then the door swung shut and the couple were gone. The quiet of the empty restaurant billowed round them. They looked at each other across the debris of empty glasses, chocolate wrappers and crumpled cigarette packets.

'What *are* you doing this weekend?' he asked.

'Oh, you know – this and that.'

He was standing behind her now, pulling out her chair.

'Would you like to go to the cinema?' His voice was soft and warm in the back of her head.

The waiter brought their coats. She did the buttons up slowly, lingering a little over each one, saying nothing. She turned and found both men looking at her expectantly.

'There's a good film on,' he said. 'Will you come and see it with me?'

She pushed the last button through the top hole, her fingers hovering at the collar, adjusting her scarf. The waiter walked off and began noisily closing the restaurant windows. She looked into his face and nodded.

'Yes,' she said. 'I'll come.'

'Great.'

He smiled and turned towards the door. She followed him, listening to the staccato of her heels on the tiles. They sounded like someone else's shoes, not hers. He stopped suddenly and spun round.

'The photographs – we forgot the photographs.'

'Oh, yes.' She hurried back to retrieve them from the table, almost losing her step on the still-slippery floor.

'You take them,' she said.

He took the packets, slipping them into his coat pockets.

'It wasn't such a bad holiday, was it?' he asked.

'No,' she replied. 'It was amazing.'

And they stepped through the open doorway and into the deserted street.

COFFEE GROUNDS
Lenya Samanis

The winter was marked by insomnia. I used to lie awake in bed at night, listening to my father fix himself up to the machine he used whenever he couldn't breathe. It made a noise like the tumble-drier. I'd lie in bed listening: his coughing turning to retching in the bathroom; the cockerel crowing out in the street, stray dogs barking in the valley; his rasping in the hallway. Then the machine, after which a silence stranger than anything else. This is what it will sound like when he's dead, I thought: just the occasional chink of china, cutlery, a drawer closing.

Those hours I spent listening to his labours, my mind ran off in so many directions I found it impossible to sleep myself, and we passed most of the nights awake. Sometimes we'd meet in the cavernous living room, rubbing our eyes, our faces, our arms. We'd both climb on to the two-seater, staring out into the dark, low-slung space together. Our bodies, heavy with sleeplessness, cleaved continually to and from one another. The fire would fill the room with epileptic light and we'd thrust feet out into the warm, gasping and sighing at the chill in our bones.

Sometimes, in those twilight hours, he told me about Greek heroes, old wise men and local fools. Sometimes he asked me for stories, and I'd ransack my brain to find an anecdote he hadn't heard, knowing there were few that weren't of his own devising. And there were so many. We found new words for them. In the same way that my brother was slowly but steadily replacing the parts of his battered old scooter so that what emerged from the wreckage was shiny and bright and beautiful, we tried to spruce up our own little hoard. The stories got bigger, longer, more incredible, and more beloved: our invisible, pored-over collection. We brought them out for visitors. And we took them to bed with us, when we went.

We sat long hours in that small lounge. And it wasn't all talk. At times, long periods of silence stretched out between us and then, out of nowhere, he would smack his hand down hard on my leg; catch the back of my head in his hand, squeeze out some solidarity, let my hair run through his fingers. All in the silence. Then he'd put his foot, bare and shapely, up on to the stocky coffee table. 'You see this foot?' he'd ask me. Then, 'Put your foot here.' I'd place mine, much smaller, alongside his, and he'd tell me about the doctors who'd wanted to take a cast of his foot. 'It's perfect, you see,' he'd say to me, deadpan. 'This foot, it's a model foot. An ideal foot.' Then he'd look at mine, frowning. 'But what happened here? Tell me how a daughter of mine could have such strange feet, now. Tsch, you took your mother's feet. Like your nose.'

'There's nothing wrong with my nose,' I'd tell him.

'OK, OK,' he'd say, as if he were too tired to argue. '*Kyrie eleison*! What was the world going to do with you if you were perfect, anyway? You were going to be too much, now.' We'd sit there in our cold comfort and gaze at the mismatched feet, studying the curves of our insteps, the spaces between our toes. We'd put up a hand each, press them together carefully, palms touching, measuring our difference.

At various moments in those unbroken hours, both of us expressed to the other the feeling we had that something big was about to happen, something that was somehow bad; but for all our anticipation the thing, when it finally came, still packed a punch.

Two years before that insomniac winter, he had been rushed into hospital with a heart attack, and he liked to remember the texture of that week, when there was a deadline on his life. He liked to remember that doctor. 'This doctor,' he'd say, 'he came and stood in front of my bed, and he flicked through the charts at the end of the bed, and he said one word to me. He said, "Change." And he left. He went to leave. And I said, "Wait a minute! What do you mean: change? Change what?" "Your heart," he told me. Anyway, I started laughing. He said to me, "Stop laughing, it's not a joke." "It's not a joke?" I said. "I'm sitting here, you come and take a quick look at my papers, you tell me I need a new heart, and it's not a joke? Where am I supposed to find a new heart? Do they sell them in the kiosk downstairs?" "That's not funny," he said. "Stop laughing.'" He loved that story. 'Anyway, they let me go and they told me I had four days left.' He'd get the sense of grandeur down – the dramatic sweep. 'Nothing changed. I just carried on. I got up; I smoked a few joints; people came round; I drank coffee; I sat; I went to sleep . . . The week was passing smoothly. And then it was Thursday night – the third day – and I had until Friday. And I woke up on Friday, my wife cooked a big meal' – he would smile – 'the Last Supper. And I went to sleep, and Friday passed and I was still here, and I was still here . . . And Saturday came – still here – and Sunday . . . And I called my friend, and I said, "Call that doctor and tell him to fuck off." This was two years ago. Ah, *koumpare*. Four days. That fucking bastard. You know, when I was in the hospital, my nose was frozen, and I mean frozen. And I couldn't work it out and I asked this doctor – and this guy's supposed to be one of the top doctors: they have him on television sometimes, to give his opinion – and he didn't have any idea about my nose. In the end you know what he said to me? "Don't touch it, then." Don't touch it then! *Kyrie eleison!*'

It was sometimes as if he'd carried on living just to tell it, over and over again.

My father's heart threatened to give out with each beat; his lungs had been pronounced poisoned. Yet he kept going, getting paler and thinner and slower. His movements grew more and more gentle. He was fading in front of me. Perhaps that's why I couldn't sleep: I thought I was going to miss something. For him, though, the insomnia was more serious. He started to insist that he'd had no sleep at all for five, six, seven days in sequence. He called the doctors and they said it was impossible, that he should be dead, then. He hung up on them, swore, and told his hospital story again. And me, I went in search.

We tried warm milk, old folk songs sung by men with gravelly voices, and subtitled films. The list of herbal remedies was endless. Just across the road, the botanist, who my father called 'Mr Sage', was busy growing and experimenting with plants of all descriptions. We'd stopped asking for names: we'd never heard of any of them, anyway. When I had tonsillitis, the old man prepared a mixture of herbs for my throat. I saw him crossing the dusty road with them, his tiny, pointy beard supporting his usual serious expression. He gave me strict instructions to boil the plants and gargle with them every hour. 'Tell him you did it,' my father said later, when I returned from the doctor's with antibiotics. We both eyed the bundle of leaves guiltily. For my father's insomnia, the botanist went on a seemingly endless quest. He'd arrive at our door every few days with a new concoction. And my father, I think, felt obliged to behave as guinea pig, compelled to follow the botanist's instructions to the letter by the man's unrelenting dedication. Always knowing the plants would fail him.

Our winter revolved around the problem of sleep. No one else in the family spoke about it, not when they were all getting ten or more hours every day, though the cat, sprawled indolently across every conceivable surface, managed to goad us through example. 'Look at her there,' my father would say, disgusted. 'She has sleep in her pocket.' It was true. She'd wake to bury her head in her food bowl for half an hour, then return to the couch, the window ledge, the nook behind the curtain, and slot herself back into the world of sleep. We'd pull her over, tug on her legs, stick fingers in the spaces between the pads on her feet. She learnt to sleep through it all, surrendered her body to sleep; did what we couldn't.

I was working in a local bingo hall, selling tickets in between the games. The girls took the floor in elegant strides, sweeping round tightly packed tables with a twist, a turn, holding the tickets aloft, the coloured paper fluttering above the taut bodies, under the fluorescent tubes of light. We didn't finish until half three in the morning, for which inconvenience we were making more than the *poutanas* in the strip clubs. I'd get home to find my father already sat on the two-seater. Sometimes the cat was with him. Sometimes he was hooked up to his machine, an oxygen mask strapped to his face, his eyes unreadable.

The girls I worked with were Romanian, or Russian, and hardened from lives spent grafting and scheming, so I found my friends in the kitchen: the fat cook – Anthony – who wanted to go back to Canada, and the kitchen ladies who spent all night with their hands in hot soapy water, talking about their families. I ran for the lowest rung. One night, drinking a coffee out the back, with Anthony, one of the kitchen ladies took my cup from me, turned it on its head.

'She's good,' he said to me.

'I don't really believe in all that stuff,' I told him.

'No, really, she's good. Try. See.'

When the grounds had bled out and dried, she came to sit with us, just outside the back door, and turned the cup in her hand, gazing intently at the patterns laid out across the inside. Anthony threw the remainder of his coffee at two scrawny cats ferreting in the bin bags, and they scuttled off into the night.

'The man you like,' the woman said to me, 'he thinks you're just a friend. He thinks this is what you want. That's why nothing happens with him.' I shrugged, reluctant to admit this could be true; these things could always be true. She went back to the cup. 'Someone near to you will die soon,' she said.

'*What?*' I answered. She ignored me. 'She's meant to say things about long journeys and phone calls and happy news,' I complained to the cook.

'Yes, you will get some good news in three days,' she said, 'or three weeks. But also, someone near to you will die. It will be soon.' She looked up at me as she set the small cup down, brushing off her hands, dusting the magic away. 'Don't worry. It's OK,' she said. Then she left.

'You want some macaronia, *koukla mou*?' Anthony asked.

I had that anxiety in my gut, as I wound my way around the tables. I was a bitch that night. No, I haven't given you my number. No, I'm not going to. No, I don't wanna come sit with you. Buy your fucking tickets from someone else then. Do you seriously think I care?

'Take a break,' my boss said. 'Go have a coffee with Antonis.' The last thing I wanted to see was another coffee cup.

Nikos came and put his arm around me and squeezed before letting go.

'You're OK, *koukla mou*? You don't look good.' His black eyes glittered beyond the swell of his shoulder as he lifted a can of Keanita to his mouth. Did he really think I wanted to be friends?

'I'm OK,' I said, giving him a squeeze as the numbers were called out. My tongue felt out a few coffee grounds on a tooth. I went and stood in my position, ready to work my section of the room as soon as the game finished. Nikos stood up at his section, his eyes on me. I stormed through the rest of the night in a dazed and demented waltz. He caught me at the end of it.

'Come to the park with me, *aggele mou.*'

I wanted to go to the park with him, like a sixteen-year-old; make out among the palm fronds.

'I have to go home,' I said. 'My father's sick.' I left him where the car window had been, leaning in for a kiss, his hair curling into his eyes.

A lot of things went through my head on the drive home.

I used to love the drives home: nothing happening; the mountains swallowed up in the darkness; the illuminated window displays eerie, the mannequins surreal. Music pumping out, insulated against a world in which people ate and worked, laughed and cried. With the window open, the smoke from my cigarette whipped out, along with the tail-ends of my hair. I used to speed through the town, pulling the old car hard round the turns, racing home yet not wanting ever to arrive. 'You know how many years Odysseus was travelling there, darling? How little of that book is about what happened afterwards? It's all about the journey, *mana mou*: that's all there is.'

That night was different. That night the emptied-out landscape was noisy and took ten minutes of for ever. I don't know what I was expecting to find when I got home, exactly, but when I finally stumbled through the front door, the house was shrouded in silence.

The lounge was empty. And the kitchen, the yard, and the bathroom. All the lights were off. There was no rasp, no cough. I listened carefully and could vaguely hear my brother's soft snores in another room. The cat appeared, sycophantic, at my feet and breaking the silence with her loud, strained mews. 'Quiet,' I told her, but she wouldn't, not until I put down cat biscuits too fancy for our budget and some pieces of lamb from the previous night's dinner. If something had happened, wouldn't everyone still be awake? Wouldn't someone have called me? I could go and look in the bedroom for myself, but what if I woke him when he'd finally got to sleep? So I sat up in the living room, watching the walls lighten, hearing the birds come out to do their worst. The cat came to purr and sleep on my lap, leaving a wake of long, white hairs. I ate some of the leftovers, shared more of the lamb with the cat; smoked half a pack of cigarettes, weighing in my mind how it would be when he did finally die.

At around six, my father appeared, ghoulish, in the doorway. I was relieved to see him, but he looked worse than he had for months.

'I slept,' he said, grasping the back of the sofa for support. 'Finally, I slept. And I feel fucking terrible, now. *Kyrie eleison*!' He showed me an expansive shrug and I moved over for him. 'You didn't sleep?' he asked.

I shook my head. He tut-tutted at me, his head semi-inclined to the floor. He looked stoned, but I knew that wasn't the case.

'Never mind,' he said, bringing his hand down hard on my leg with a wry smile. 'The first forty years are difficult. After that it's OK.' He laughed, like he always did at those lines. And I was happy my thigh stung so sharply, that he had enough strength left for that.

My sister appeared, bleary-eyed, shuffling across the stone floor in her pyjamas.

'Did you tell her what happened?' she asked my father, as she slumped into the couch.

Sudden recollection flashed on my father's face and a small smile dawned there. The botanist, across the road, had died suddenly, the previous day, he told me. 'Dead, boom, just like that.' It seemed so outlandish. 'Yes,' he said, 'he woke up, he asked his wife to cut his ear, then he died. Boom.'

'Just like that?' I said.

'Exactly,' he told me, leaning back into the sofa. 'Exactly like that.'

'Why did he ask his wife to cut his ear?' I asked, curling towards him, ready for the details.

'To release the pressure,' he said, as if I was being idiotic. 'They told me you were clever, you know.'

'Oh, I am,' I said. 'I am.'

'Of course you are. You're my daughter.'

My sister shook the conversation out of her curls and disappeared into the bathroom.

'That's terrible for the botanist, though.'

'Yes. Mr Sage.'

'His wife must be devastated.'

He shrugged. He wasn't given to speculating about women and their feelings at the best of times. 'OK, it's bad. It's unexpected. But this is how life goes. And it was sudden. Probably it didn't hurt so much.'

He told me what he'd heard from the old woman who ran the village shop. It had been getting on for dusk; they'd been held up. Maybe it was this, he said, because it was so dark, or perhaps it was something else entirely, but they had the botanist in his coffin and, when they went to move it, it had slipped as they were sliding it on to the table. It had slipped and the lid had swung open. Bang down on the stone floor. My father started to laugh, and when he leaned back to cough up the phlegm brought on by this good humour, there was a genuine delight in his eyes. 'The botanist, he fell out! Sitting up, with his hands in his lap! Imagine him sitting there, looking at them all!' He dissolved into loud laughter, clapping his hands, appealing to the room. 'Oh my God, oh my God! Imagine it, now!' The laughter brought on a small fit.

'His poor wife. It's so undignified,' I said. I looked at him bent double. 'D'you think he would've laughed?'

My father paused for a second – recovering, considering – then waved his hand at me. 'Of course he would've laughed. What, you think dying makes you serious? It's funny. He's up there now. He's laughing. What else is he gonna do?' His arms swung out from the elbow, palms turned to the gods, the right almost smacking me in the face. He stopped appealing to the empty room and turned to face me. He looked like he might be coming back to life again; he'd put indignation into his eye.

'Shall I make us some coffee?' I asked.

'Now this is a good idea,' he said. 'You see, this is how I know you're my daughter.'

'And there's more,' I told him, moving over to the kitchen to fill the *briki*.

He shook his head at me, not understanding.

'I have a new story for you,' I said.

OUT OF THE COUNTRY
Robert Royston

Johnny and Karl arrived on a South African Airways flight from Jan Smuts Airport which touched down at Heathrow at 10:55 a.m. It was October 18th, 1978, sunny, and, as the captain cheerfully told the passengers, an unusual sixty-two degrees Fahrenheit. Johnny, who'd never flown before, had seen on the initial approach amazing boxed fields like an eiderdown, an expanse of water, threads of road, astonishing car parks with what looked like a million glittering hulls. Then the plane had been put in a queue and the pilot told them he'd circle London a few times. Johnny saw other sights he'd never dreamed of. A stunning park with ponds and a pagoda. The Thames, which wound around itself like the human gut. Never-ending houses.

His wonder ended with the juddering landing, the engines screaming in reverse thrust, his body straining forwards against his seat belt.

He thought he might die after that, after the journey in the bus to the forbidding buildings, when they faced the women at Foreign Arrivals. He assumed a relaxed posture and tried to look happy.

The woman stared, grim. What money did they have?

Karl, who had got ahead of Johnny, pulled out of his pocket a fistful of coins, five-rand notes and used tissues, and looked slowly from his fist to the woman's face. Johnny pushed in front of him and kicked backwards with his heel, hitting Karl on the shin.

Karl cried, '*Ow*, man!'

Johnny ignored him and displayed before the increasingly suspicious woman a wad of sterling travellers' cheques and bank statements showing the transfer of money from Standard Bank in Commissioner Street, Johannesburg, to Barclays Bank in Hampstead Village. Mollified, she stamped their passports with six-month visas.

Proceeding through customs was sweaty. Johnny looked as casual as he could. He carried on his back a rucksack from which cardboard tubes protruded. All contained his artwork, but one also contained a slim inner tube packed with two different varieties of Southern African marijuana. Their big rucksacks were on a trolley pushed lugubriously by Karl.

It was only after they passed through the exit unmolested that Johnny again felt human. They walked through cool halls with high windows and majestic potted trees, travelled on humming conveyor belts and escalators and, after buying tickets, stood on Heathrow Central tube platform, which looked stunningly new when Johnny expected England to be decayed with age.

People stood around with their luggage, bored. Johnny couldn't wait for the train and at the same time dreaded it. He looked at the rails set in a concrete channel. One of them was live, he'd been told. Touch it and that was the end of you. You'd be a cinder.

Looking into the hole the train would burst from, Johnny knew a big thing was waiting to happen to him. The rails vibrated and the train came. Shouldering their small rucksacks, dragging the big ones, they clambered on board.

For a long time, outside was darkness, the longest tunnel he'd ever been through. Then *pow*, they were spat out in the open and it was fields, grassy banks, mysterious buildings and here and there snatches of what looked like dense forest.

He wanted to break himself in half and look out both sides at the same time, but without warning a tunnel occurred and with it a deflated explosion that seemed to change the shape of his brain. Everything vanished and the rattle-rattle of the wheels was again mysterious in the dark. Occasional lights showed tunnel walls coated black and hung with coils and cables. This made him feel deep, as though he was injected into

England down a vein. He thought of books he'd read. Sherlock Holmes. Dixon Hawke – Dixon on the cover wearing a hat, holding a gun. And Winnie the Pooh, but that was another England, of lawns and beautiful mothers, or nurses with kids in the park: the kids play, but nurse calls them, reads from the Winnie book how Piglet got wet, then out come the honey sandwiches.

Wap: they were blasted out into light, into dreaming fields, into amazing order. Then they were in a station where train doors banged, and people got on with baggage, one guy with a bike.

Later, more tunnels, other stations, and gradually Johnny understood they had entered London, a low place, mainly brown.

Agitation from the up-to-now silent Karl. Earls Court. They'd arrived. 'Hurry, man.'

Lugging the rucksacks out of the train was a nightmare – the doors about to close, a crowd waiting to get on, red lights behind Johnny's eyes because of not enough sleep. Then he noticed a uniformed guy watching him. He thought, No problem, guy's black, but remembered this was Britain: no apartheid. In South Africa black cops didn't hassle you. During the Second World War they were allowed to be soldiers but not carry guns, had to drill with broomsticks not rifles. Then Johnny saw it wasn't a cop. The guy, a short man with a face that shone, worked for the station, a porter or something, and when he'd seen that the bags were safely on the platform he said something incomprehensible but friendly sounding and waved to the driver. The train doors closed with a rustle and a thump. The whole contraption picked up speed, and as it did so Johnny felt tears come into his eyes. In South Africa if you didn't get your stuff off it was someone yelling at you in Afrikaans. Panic. Nastiness. '*Vat jou goed en trek, Ferriera*. Don't keep us all waiting.'

'Did you see that?' he said.

Big rucksacks up on backs, small rucksacks slung on shoulders, they were making for the exit.

'See what?'

'Guy, he actually waits for us to get our stuff off before sending the train on its way.'

'You think you've come to paradise where everyone loves each other? What nonsense.'

They climbed up stairs on to street level. They showed their tickets and lumbered through a little gate out on to Earls Court Road.

Karl said, looking around, 'What's this bloody place you've brought me to? I thought you said it's the capital city of the world, so where are the buildings? Can you tell me that? As we came in on the train, hey, I was looking up in the sky: clouds. I look down: little houses. Man, it's like Ventersdorp.'

'It's busy, things happening here all the time,' Johnny defended.

'You want to be in a busy place try Joey's, corner Eloff and Joubert Street, rush hour. Hey, we've got to find the Visitors Club. How we going to do that? *Ag, sis* . . . will you look over there? *That* you do not see in Jo'burg, I can tell you.'

'It's nothing. This is a big city. It's just waiting for the truck to take it away,' said Johnny. They were staring at a pile of what Johnny guessed was about fifty black plastic sacks, shiny, bulging, somehow tempting, like presents. A dog had ripped the side of one of the lower bags and rice and what looked like a dead bird had been dragged across the pavement.

'*Ja*,' said Karl, 'but in SA we'd just get a bunch of boys, say "Clean that up." Be done in no time. What did I tell you before we left? They don't work here. No one does the slightest bit of work. *Jy weet*? Marie van Graan told me she was a secretary here in London. Boss gives her a pile of work on Monday. She thinks, this is bloody terrible, this pile of work every day. Man, it was for the whole week.'

Johnny asked a scruffy newspaper vendor the way to the Visitors Club. The guy must have suffered at some time in his life from a malnutrition disease, Johnny thought – sunken face, beaky nose. He was standing on a corner shouting a big load of crap that no one could possibly understand.

But the man, eager to please, made it his mission to see that 'you boys' found the place. Johnny nodded repeatedly, went '*Ja, ja*' and then said, mainly guessing, 'So it's right and then left.'

The man's good will was inexhaustible – he actually left a crony to look after the stand and led them to the address. A big old house. Two guys came out and put rucksacks on the top step, went back, came out with a load more to add to the pile.

Johnny and Karl were exhausted after only fitful sleep on the plane. Karl wanted to slump into one of the beds, then be 'fit as a fiddle to go see Gary'. Johnny said it was a damn good idea, but he himself was OK and would go out and look around.

'What you want to leave me here for,' protested Karl. 'Man, I could use a couple of bottles of Castle lager same as you.'

But Johnny knew Karl was too *skrik* to stay on his own. Something was wrong with him, always had been. He clung to Johnny unless he was feeling strong – was in Johannesburg working at something or other, and everything going well.

They went into a pub called the Digger, with a picture on the sign of a man panning for gold or diamonds – most definitely, they thought, on the Reef near what was now Johannesburg, but maybe in the Cape.

It was unlike Johnny's idea of a pub. This place was modern with a low ceiling and angled lights, tables in new wood. There was no faded red upholstery, no fox-hunting scenes, or photos of dog races, instead pictures of rugby players, mostly in yellow shirts, one of a koala bear and a drawing of a winking crocodile with a can of beer on its head. The place was busy, most people young, and there was a lot of noise. A jukebox was playing: guy with a squeezed voice going on about not wanting to go to Chelsea. Then don't, thought Johnny. A group of youths had their feet in hiking boots up on chairs.

Johnny and Karl sat at the only vacant table, Karl looking sheepish, Johnny worried about it, knowing his friend from childhood.

'Who do these people think they are?' said Karl. 'I'm a South African, I don't take that sort of behaviour.'

'Cool down. What's the matter with you?'

They waited for service.

The noisy group got louder, one guy yelling, 'I bet you, Rory. I bet you, mate. You're wrong, you know you're wrong and you should own up that you're wrong.'

One of the girls emitted meaningless whoops and another banged her bottle on the table several times and then threw her head back, gobbled down beer, and Johnny had to admit he'd never seen anything like it, it was terrible.

In Johannesburg there were no pubs, only bars or, more often, lounges in hotels, or drinking on the hotel veranda. People behaved themselves. Black barmen in white coats balancing silver trays cruised around the veranda in places like the Rosebank Hotel, taking orders, getting people ciggies, maybe a plate of curry and rice.

Johnny was alarmed. Karl was moving his huge hands quickly all over the table. 'Christ, man', he said, 'that *lytie*'s coming over to *sukkle* with me. I'm telling you, I'm going to teach him to tie his own shoelaces if he says one word.'

He half rose.

The approaching character wore a friendly face. He was dressed in shorts, a long purple shirt and desert boots. Johnny said, 'Karl, we got *dagga* in the Visitors Club to stone the British army. No trouble, hey?'

But the man, tanned a darker shade than Johnny or Karl, was smiling, said, 'G'day. Won't you boys come sit with us? Let me get you something to drink in the meantime. Couple of Heineken?'

'Hell, man, that's damn nice of you,' said Johnny. 'Heineken would be *lekker* . . . er . . . nice.'

Karl was sulky. The friendly guy led them over to his table and called out the names of his friends.

Johnny and Karl sat down on chairs pulled up for them.

'What part of Oz you boys from?'

'We're South Africans,' said Johnny.

'Half the people around here are, mate. Welcome home. You don't want to be mixing with the poms, and you don't have to.'

'What's so bad about them?' asked Karl.

'Bad?' a girl said. 'You should ask what's good about them. Shorter answer.'

Laughter roared up around the table.

A girl next to Karl – pigtails tight-plaited and beaded, black bandana – said, 'You better believe it, codger. They don't say what they mean, don't mean what they say. And they're mean, too.'

The guy who'd invited them over came back with tankards of beer.

'How much we got to pay you for this?' said Karl.

'On me. We colonials stick together. There you go, don't spill a drop. What Rhona's saying is spot on. There's more humanity in the thumb of a

South African or an Oz than in the whole of the British Isles. They're cold, mate, they're a cold-blooded people.'

'Just what I thought,' Karl shouted, and drank half his pint in one go, gasping like a surfacing diver and banging the tankard down. 'Didn't I say that, Jannie? They're stone cold?'

'Since when you met an Englishman?'

The woman next to Johnny, who introduced herself as Shirley, seemed to want to talk to him and he was only vaguely able to listen to the rest of the general conversation, which was about how only colonials knew how to have a good time. He heard someone warn Karl that London was full of liberals who would blame him personally for apartheid and the imprisonment of Nelson Mandela.

Shirley wanted to know personal stuff about Johnny – where he'd grown up, what his work was. She was looking at him with interest. 'Are they all as cute as you in Johannesburg?' she said. He couldn't go along with it. She had the right things in the right places, but it was a case of what you saw was what you got. No internal organs, in a way; great teeth but she cast no shadows. Britain on the other hand *was* shadows and in the shadows were more shadows, which was what interested him.

The guy who'd bought their drinks was saying Britain was at the point of collapse. Strikes everywhere. The trains would stop running – 'Come back, Mussolini, all is forgiven' – and the streets would fill with diseased rubbish. Epidemics would occur. The NHS would be the next to go.

'It's a dying civilization, mate.'

Karl, who'd finished his beer, shouted, 'Man, this bloody place. It's like living in a bag. I could choke. What you bring me here for, Jannie, you shit?' he told Johnny.

There was a moment of silence.

'Be friends, you two,' Shirley chastised.

'We are friends,' Johnny said, pushing his beer away and getting up. 'But I got a few things to do.'

He told Karl to stay, he'd go fix things with Gary on his own. But Karl was noisily on his feet right away, promising the baffled Australians he'd 'catch up with you boys and girls later'.

Outside they fronted up to a brisk wind sprung out of nowhere. Karl, who suffered from asthma, began to wheeze. 'Why'd you drag us away? You were brassing that doll. Get your end away before supper.'

Johnny didn't reply. He walked into a shop oddly called a 'newsagent', which had the biggest array of sweets he'd ever seen, and bought an A-Z.

Outside, he looked up Roderick Road, Gospel Oak. It was near a railway line and Hampstead Heath, which was like a big piece of veldt with some dams.

The walk from Hampstead underground to Roderick Road was an eye-opener for Johnny. The elegance of the giant houses was hard to believe: four storey, some five, some with skylights in the roof. He was fascinated by glimpses through ground-floor windows – the most amazing sitting rooms, one with a huge banana plant in a fabulous-looking ceramic jar. And there was other amazing stuff too. Bookcases, paintings, shelves with antiques, plates. In his home there were only his father's things – silver cups for boxing, stuffed heads of animals and, in a glass case on a table, a tiger fish his old man had caught in the Limpopo.

'Look at that, man,' he said to Karl. It was a huge sculpture inside a window, hard to say what of.

'It's bollocks. Everything here's bollocks. You're shit.'

'Don't be so *hardegat*. Learn to live.'

'You be lucky you still living the time I finish with you.' Absently Karl punched Johnny on the upper arm. Johnny stumbled, said '*Eina*' and rubbed his bicep.

They walked in silence.

Gary's house was in a less impressive area. The road was opposite a bridge, probably over a railway line, and maybe the trees beyond were Hampstead Heath.

They turned into Roderick Road, found the house and were confronted by a profusion of doorbells, one bust, with wires hanging. There was only one name-tag: Mr and Mrs Beilby. They rang all the bells at the same time and Johnny's heart started to go too fast. He wondered if it was the walk from the tube, Karl stepping out like he had a point to prove. But it was fear, he realized. Gary's was where they wanted to stay the following night, to get the dope out of that busy place in Earls Court, discuss their long-term living arrangements, get contacts. But who *was* Gary? They didn't even have the guy's current phone number.

No one answered.

Karl elbowed Johnny aside and pounded his fists on the newly painted woodwork. The pretty glass panels in the door jiggled. 'Open the fucking door,' he barked.

The door opened almost immediately and Johnny felt faint: there'd been no approaching human outline in the glass. A voice said, 'Come in, I've been expecting you,' and Karl said, '*Here Got*, man, call the funny farm.'

Standing in the doorway, one hand on the side of the door, was a woman of amazing old age, face a network of collapsed wrinkles. She wore a pink dressing gown and furry slippers and when she spoke her broken voice wandered, rode air currents. 'This is my home. Come, come.'

Johnny said, 'Thanks,' and, without knowing what he was doing, went into dimness and a smell of boiled vegetables. He heard Karl laboriously scraping his shoes on the doormat. The woman walked past Johnny, her gown brushing him, Johnny wincing and stepping aside. She went up the stairs.

'Is Gary up there?' Johnny called to her ascending back.

'Come up,' the woman fluted – she was on the half-landing looking down. Johnny could see stick legs through her gown.

Climbing the stairs, he was careful not to touch diseased walls, but a window on the half-landing exploded light and hey: amazing pink wallpaper; a riot, everything clean. New green carpets too. And a little cubicle on the landing with the door half open. He glimpsed a lavatory, and a bare light-bulb at the end of a cord.

Karl brushed past Johnny, elbowed him to catch the woman. On the next landing a door stood open and she vanished into it. Johnny saw Karl's wide back block the entrance. Karl seemed fearful, stooped as though the doorway was low, took a step, peered this way and that, disappeared inside.

Johnny went in, wondered if he should close the door, decided not to. There was a room to his left and he approached. He felt there was a different gravity here, one that hushed all movement. He went into a sitting room: everything old, everything brown. Wallpaper thick. A standing clock – he heard its heavy tick. On a mantelpiece were trinkets: a glass ballerina, a Scottie dog, a ceramic tulip, a silver sporting trophy, rusted around the rim. In South Africa all houses were white-walled with masses of window light. The air was brown here, one's footsteps halted by a force impossible to name.

He heard Karl's voice: 'You got the wrong idea. We're here to see Gary Cramer.'

Johnny walked out silently.

Karl was half inside another room. Approaching, Johnny glimpsed a bedroom. Thin material was pinned across the window and light was hazy, almost dappled. The woman held her hand like a trumpet over her ear.

Karl bellowed, 'Gary. Cramer.'

'I have a fine sherry to offer you.'

Karl stepped into the room and Johnny, going closer, saw the old woman sit down slowly on to her unmade bed as though dismantling herself. She turned to the uncertain Karl.

'We've come to see Gary,' said Karl.

The woman said, 'You must be tired after your journey.'

Karl said, 'Jesus God Almighty. What journey?'

'Through the desert.'

Johnny slipped out of the flat. He saw two other doors, one partly open – a bathroom with what looked like a boiler on the wall. He heard no sound and climbed to the next landing where there was a single door. He rapped, then banged. It opened cautiously. A tousled man looked out.

'Yea?'

'Gary?'

'He's moved. No idea. No, no forwarding address.'

Johnny went down to the little entrance lobby, and out into the street.

Freedom.

Clean air.

He walked up the road and over the bridge he'd seen as they arrived. Ahead was a child's play area, an athletic track and, behind a line of huge distant trees, a hill where people were flying kites.

He wanted to walk, forget his friend, his cross. He took eighteen slow steps, counting, then abruptly walked back on to the bridge and down the concrete steps on the other side, and saw Karl rushing out of the door of the Roderick Road house. He looked around wildly. Unseen as yet Johnny had time to back away behind a supporting wall at the bottom of the bridge.

Alone, hiding. The sweetness that could bring. Maybe then go to the Tate Gallery. Instead he ran on to the pavement, called out, 'Hey, man.'

Karl, seeing him, shouted, 'I'm going to *niek* you.' He shook his fist.

On the way back Karl wouldn't stop. 'She told me she'd bloody operated on the eye of Lord Salisbury on the battlefield. She put her hand out, flipped the eye, did surgery on the back of it with a knife from the officers' mess! Did you smell the place? Filth. Next thing this girl comes in. Lives in the other flat on that floor. Says, poor Miss Williams, she's ninety-two, she's wonderful, so brave, so brave, and says she's going to do some cleaning for her. Man, I was out of the place, otherwise I'd still be there listening when *I'm* ninety-two. Hey, listen to this, Lord Salisbury said' – Karl's voice rose several octaves – '"Nurse Williams, you're the finest woman in the world, may I have the pleasure of fornicating with you?" She replies, "Get on with you, you cheeky monkey." Man, it's madness. It's poverty like you have never seen. A scandal.'

'Soweto,' said Johnny.

'That's different.'

'Worse.'

They strode on.

'I'm going to kill you,' Karl said as they approached the station. 'It's a cock up. Where we going to stay, can you answer me that?'

'I got another contact,' said Johnny.

By the time they reached Earls Court – dope intact under the mattress – a curtain of silence had come down.

They were famished and after Karl had taken a long bath they went out speechlessly to find a pub that sold food.

Finally they found a place called the Merry Fiddler. They had no idea where they were – Karl refused to eat in the pubs along the way because of 'filth'.

The Merry Fiddler, according to Karl, was a really nice place where a man could feel some pride in himself. But Johnny soon noticed that the other customers without exception were male. There were men in singlets; there were men with cropped hair and moustaches. Karl was already tucking into a shepherd's pie. He progressed quickly through his meal and three bottles of a beer called Newcastle Brown, went off to the counter and came back with a bowl of dessert.

'Let's go,' Johnny said as soon as Karl had spooned up the last of it. But, no, Karl said he needed to go to the toilet.

Johnny waited.

Karl came back. Something had happened.

'My friend, we are leaving this city tomorrow. I am not staying here. Not for a minute. Not for a second: *moffies*. Get me out of this place quick.'

For two weeks the friends stayed in provincial guest-houses; walked along English woodland pathways, between hedgerows, and through farmland with menacing bulls; had cream teas; visited shops that smelt of potpourri.

They carried the *dagga* with them at all times.

Then they stayed for four days in East Sussex with Johnny's uncle Hermanus and his English wife Betty. Karl seemed to like having a home, of sorts. He didn't want to go out, and spent a lot of time with Betty in the kitchen. Johnny was optimistic, wanted to prolong their stay until Karl was willing to return to London.

One night a simmering political argument blew up. It was after midnight. Karl stood in the centre of the sitting room and shouted, 'Look, there is only one way to end racial conflict: all white guys fuck black chicks, all black guys fuck white chicks.'

'What!' Hermanus yelled. 'Then you get a mix-race world.'

'No, man,' said Karl, 'I meant up the arse.'

Johnny and Karl slept the rest of the night in a small public park and took a train to London the next morning, spent two nights in bed and breakfast in Victoria and took a train to Wales for some hill walking.

On Snowdon, Karl walked in huge strides but wheezed, asthmatic in the mist-thickened atmosphere. Johnny was entranced. He couldn't believe the beauty, he couldn't believe the cuteness: tiny lakes down there, a ruined stone building, a cobbled wall, rocks, misty sheep. More dramatic than anything they'd seen on their country walks in England. Karl, though, was not happy. He stood on the path some way behind Johnny, leaning on a stick. Undoubtedly a mighty figure, like a Voortrekker in a foreign land, thought Johnny, excited in this wild place. Karl came closer, his asthma worse.

Johnny said, 'It's bloody terrific up here, isn't it?'

They paused as a small party of walkers passed them, nattily kitted in boots, wind-resistant anoraks and woolly hats, smiling and saying hello. When the mist had swallowed the hikers Karl said, 'Why you bring me here, man? To this bloody place? Think I like being cold all the time?'

'What's the matter? It's beautiful . . .'

'I could be on Durban beach now with a bottle Lion lager in one hand, my cherry in the other.'

Johnny said, 'The cherries here're better.'

Karl was panting. 'No cherry in Limeyland'll look at me – they see a ape, think it's me locked Mandela up, think I stink, because I do – I stink because we got nowhere to stay long enough I can get my things washed.'

Johnny thought Karl might be crying.

'Fuck you, man, I gotta have a home,' Karl shouted. After a few difficult breaths, he went on: 'You little shit. You already a limey, going *kaffir* on me – soon you'll be talking "Yaw yaw yaw, oh do come and hev some din dins at my pad."' He waited for a reply, went on: 'And this *kak* about "Johnny" and "Karl". I am Koos Koekemoor. You are Jannie Hannekom. We are Afrikaners. OK, you only half and half, but man, we are not a pair of cockless poms. I'm tired, man.'

Johnny looked up at the sky. Wall-to-wall grey, but with the wind maybe there'd be a shaft of sun – he'd see hidden colours come alive, soft shadows. Half an hour to the summit, maybe, walking fast. He turned his back on his friend, walked. Something clattered behind him. He turned and saw that Karl had run some way off the path towards a point where the land sheared steeply into the valley. In his shapeless coat Karl stood with a hefted rock. He hurled it down the slope. Johnny heard the leaping crack, rattle, crack of the boulder, the churn of its wake of rubble as it plunged into a flock of sheep grazing precariously on the slope midway down.

Karl shouted, 'Guess what we having for supper. Roast lamb.'

Johnny hiked alone to the top. Maybe his friend would evaporate in the mist or go the way of the rock he'd hurled. At the top he sat down for half an hour on a little wall, drinking coffee out of a Thermos, then set off down the track again, head down, walking quickly, not bothering any more to look around him. No Karl waited morosely beside the path. Good. A long trek. Hard. An hour passed. Still no Karl. He rested. He strode on. A few people passed him going up the slope, several down.

At half past three with darkness coming on, near the bottom, with the road in view, and the shelter, Johnny saw Karl. He was sitting on a rock and got to his feet as Johnny approached. He grinned and hit Johnny in the face so hard Johnny sat down and saw lightning and then saw a weightless Karl floating about, out of context somehow, not in space or time, going round and round. Karl then appeared to be coming closer. Johnny felt something. He couldn't identify the sensation but understood Karl was kicking him hard in the chest and ribs. He thought repeatedly, 'Out of this place, out of this place.' He didn't know why he thought this. He loved the place. He loved Snowdon and the mist.

Without knowing how or why he came to be there, Johnny was sitting in a dreary canteen holding a tissue against his nose. Karl sat opposite him drinking from a paper cup.

Karl smiled broadly and said, 'Didn't I tell you?'

'What?'

'You were a little shit.' He paused. 'You don't leave me, *ja*? Childhood friend. Things we've been through, that I've done for you, you wouldn't be alive without me. You run up the mountain. You admire the sheep. You think you get a nice new life here, no hassles, all you got to do is dump your mate? Forget it.' He meshed his fingers into a twisty knot. 'This is us, *jy weet*?'

Time missed a beat and a man had materialized at the table and was gazing with concern at Johnny.

Karl was saying, from a long way away, 'No, he's OK. It's just that I'm the climber but he keeps trying to get away from me and get ahead. But I kept telling him he'd die doing that, sure as eggs. And now look, the guy's gone arse over Christmas, hit his face on a rock.'

Johnny said, 'When do we arrive in Johannesburg?'

The man said, 'He's concussed.'

'Out of the Country' is an extract from the novel of the same name

CITRUS JUICE
Victor Schonfeld

Aaah! Sultry Virginia! A damn sight kinder to this delicate flesh than frigid Vermont had been. I was musing on my current appointment and its sundry advantages. There was the proximity to the nation's capital. There was the small private office I'd snared in the campus tower – an L-shaped space, meaning the people coming in to see me wouldn't catch sight of my desk before I emerged from round the corner. It was the refuge where my transformation into the kind of thinker I could admire would proceed undisturbed. I might be stuck, but I was free, free to stare at page 123 – the one I hadn't got past in two weeks – without fear of discovery.

But I must – *must* – halt this ruminating habit, lest my next move be sideways once more.

The cursor was pulsing by the tentative title of my opus-to-be, *Consuming Life, a study in choices*, and I leaned back in the chair, quietly chanting.

'Amghar savey too bey. Amghar savey too bey.'

It was a struggle to get my thumb and middle finger comfortably rolling the beads while I recited the mantra. And it was giving my mind free rein, the opposite of the cleansing I'd been promised.

The purr of the phone was an interruption I almost welcomed.

'Listen,' Evie said without so much as a hello. 'I know it's your sacred time. So I'm sorry.'

I took the phone to the window and looked down at the turnpike, lines of iridescent bugs inching their way toward the giant mall, drivers slamming car doors and scurrying through the heat. The midsummer sale day was the lure, plus the air-conditioning would be reliably cool inside. My students in the senior seminar had been three or four down on their usual number. Possibly conducting field research right across the road? Summer semester had a logic of its own, and it was not one to my liking.

'It's OK,' I said, before the hesitation became indecent. 'I've put the inspiration on pause. But only for the love of my life. My ears are all yours.'

Evie gave an odd laugh. 'Harold, I need you to listen to this, and you don't need to tell me again there's the stuff you don't like to talk about.'

'Oh, that's just the medical stuff . . . and the money stuff . . . and the emotional stuff . . . and the –'

She gave the odd laugh again, and started telling me about some Mexican woman she'd met at the pool before work. I was wondering how long it would be before one of the other managers found her on the phone in the staff lounge and Evie would blurt in my ear, 'So the doctor can fit me in next week? That's magic!' hanging up and running back to the floor, leaving me wondering why she'd called. But I could hear traffic noises from Evie's end of the line: she was outside, by a road.

'Get out of the heat,' I said, 'or you'll get one doozey of a headache. And why aren't you at work?'

'I really need you to listen through to this, Harold,' she said.

She went on to tell me about Carlita, a young mother, and her little daughter, Julianne, who were living in a cramped apartment in the poor half of Garret Town. Garret Town – the vaguely bohemian suburb where my wife had charmed a community-pool guest pass out of one of my faculty colleagues. Evie began her day now with an outdoor swim, to relieve her stress, while she dreamed the dream. Me, I was content to go along for the dream-ride, let things pan out how they did.

It turned out that Carlita and little Julianne had been to the pool too this morning: for the girl's fourth birthday, her gift was a swimming lesson. Evie recounted how the teacher sang *A Little Teapot* to get the child pivoting into the water.

'You're losing me,' I said.

'I'm a little teapot, short and stout,' Evie sang in a small voice. 'Here's my handle and here's my –' She stopped and I could hear her suck in her breath. 'She was diving in one lesson, Harold. It was magic!'

She went on in this vein, and I imagined her by the pool: her eyes soaking up the spectacle, newborn swimmer squirming through the water to welcoming arms, like a sperm on its heedless wriggle to the womb.

'Was something wrong at the clinic?' I nudged in my concern. 'The doctor kept you there all this time?'

'Will you listen, Harold?'

'I *am* listening. What else could I be doing?'

She failed to take the hint, instead telling me how this Carlita confided she was desperate. Her husband was in Florida for the citrus-picking season, sending money weekly, but Carlita had to find a job too. She was on stand-by for an interview, a good job in a fine Spanish restaurant, but she was worried that turning up in her old and worn clothes might kill her chances.

Now I knew where this thing was heading – and it was the place drawing everybody to it today except me.

'You should have seen the girl, Harold,' said Evie. 'You could *tell* she needed a father around, the kind of father I had – the kind of father you'd –'

Evie stopped; her voice had gone thin on the line. Something was hurting her was my guess, the irritable bowel seizing up probably, after some stress-making incident with an obstreperous shopper. I contemplated her flat on the floor with the cellphone to her ear, her fingers kneading her belly. A truck revved its engine and reminded me – she's outside, by a road. How long could she hang on to this job? Those playful introductions at faculty dinner parties might come to an end soon: 'Meet Harold who teaches the sociology of consumption and his charming wife Evie who manages the same thing for Lord and Taylor. Call ahead on sales days and she'll put something aside for you!'

It had been after Christmas when Evie turned to me with an innocent smile and asked me why I thought we were compatible. I told her we were like two different species of fruit growing on the same tree, drinking the same water, watching each other ripen slowly under the same sun. Then she asked me if I really loved her. We'd been together eight years, I pointed out, and I said: 'The I being the I that I am, and you being you, yes I do.' This seemed to satisfy her, along with the fact I mentioned that I'd married her, and it wasn't my fault the pregnancies had failed. Evie then told me that she had found the money for the treatments. And thus commenced the monthly cycles of injections and the mad dashes up the throughway to the clinic for the strictly timed procedures. Evie refused to tell me where the money came from. Certainly not from her assistant manager's salary at Lord and Taylor. It must have been Daddy, the building contractor, dispatching the big sums to his baby, no questions asked.

'Where are your hands now, Harold?' she asked me suddenly on the phone. 'Are your hands on the keyboard, Harold? Just this one time – this really needs your undivided attention.'

'I've got hold of that string of beads,' I told her, and indeed it was true as I said it.

How had I got sucked into this? It was the Green Fest Evie dragged me to at the weekend with her instinct for the instant solution. She'd shunted me into the meditation tent and told the first person she saw, 'Give him a lesson,' and then turned to me: 'Harold, you need to relax and connect to your humanness.' The starry-eyed youths in their retro hippie garb, rings of tents with eastern spiritual enticements – it was a mystical extravaganza planted for the afternoon, just two minutes walk from the shopping world, visible through the trees around the park. Repressive tolerance, Herbert Marcuse called it, a system's capacity to accommodate all expressions of resistance. But still, I'd longed for a remedy to revive the inspiration buried under mountainous research. And if a talisman could hoist me out of the All-But-Dissertation mud it would be well worth swallowing pride for. Two years with ABD status and the trifling salary of an adjunct professor was two years too many.

So this afternoon I'd whiled away my dissertation time twiddling with beads and intoning gibberish while my mind drifted back to the injection into Evie's buttock I'd given her at lunchtime and the fuck that came right after on schedule. The injections had grown strangely satisfying, hand relishing the quick stab into pert muscle, like a meditative ritual before the accelerated act to follow. I'd rejected the clinic's offer to make use of their special room, thoughtfully provided with the well-thumbed magazines, and

Evie had undertaken without complaint the routine – the high-speed drive to my fecundity and the even swifter drive to the high-tech office park, plastic vialful of my seed strapped under her arm for the required temperature, to keep the delicate demons alive and contented. Not that the routine I insisted on was so easy for me. I had to summon up all reserves of willpower, think all sorts of alarming thoughts, to motivate the pull-out at the moment I wanted more than anything to plunge in deeper. Withdraw to avoid pregnancy, withdraw to achieve it – either way it was unnatural and unnerving. Be that as it may, Evie would have delivered the little devils in their plastic cage, and should have been back in women's designer wear a couple of hours ago.

'Ev, tell me now.' I pushed in the question. 'Why the call from outside by the road?'

But she carried on as if I hadn't spoken.

It now emerged that Carlita had leapt at the suggestion from Evie, and got herself to Lord and Taylor at opening time – just as I'd guessed. Evie directed mother and child swiftly to the racks with the double-sticker items, marked down twice for the day. There was a good choice of readywear there, and Evie was certain they'd find the woman a steal. Carlita was jubilant. Her interview had been confirmed for today.

Naturally before long the little girl began to moan and complain. But Evie stepped in, and her instinct delivered. She vanished into the storage area, and reappeared with a batch of silver and gold stickers, the big ones with the crests they put on the gift boxes. The girl went quiet, and her mom slipped off to the fitting room with a promising outfit. Evie then unpeeled a sticker and pressed the crest to the girl's arm. She was the perfect gift, Evie told the girl, and gifts don't moan and complain. She pressed a second sticker to the girl's shoulder, and a matching set to her other arm, and Julianne proudly displayed the 'tattoos' to her mom when she came out of the fitting room.

'The gold and silver on that beautiful skin, Harold – it was magic! Her clothes were mended every which way, but you couldn't imagine a more gorgeous girl!'

The mother then reached down, Evie explained, and tried to lift away a sticker from her daughter's arm. But it wouldn't budge. None of the stickers would budge. These were Lord and Taylor quality product – industrial-strength adhesive. The girl started crying and then shrieking, 'I want you to get them off me! I WANT THEM OFF ME!!'

There was a mad dash behind the dress racks, bawling girl in mom's arms, to the Ladies, to hot water and soap. The girl swiftly drenched by the two women. But the silver and gold stickers – praise Lord and Taylor – held fast.

'So that's given you the stomach ache?' I said.

'Did I say I had a stomach ache, Harold?' In the silence that followed, I could hear the traffic noises very distinctly; and I realized something: the store incident had happened *this morning*, and it was now *late afternoon*. So when Evie and I had our lunchtime rendezvous and she got on top and fucked me in even more than usual haste her tears must have been an aftershock of the morning's trouble in the store. I'd handed her the plastic vial and reminded her to write our details on it three hours ago. So why was the creature whose touch so delighted me now destroying all tranquillity with a bizarre tale that could have waited till tonight?

'How did you get the things off in the end?' I asked her.

She murmured something, and then I could tell she was weeping, the dry heaving sounds cutting into the whoosh of the cars close by.

Mother and daughter had to run out from the store, Evie now explained; Evie had been unable to solve the problem she'd given them. So, in her car after our lunchtime thing, en route to the clinic, she steered into Garret Town, to deliver the dress she'd paid for herself. Carlita had taken ages coming to the door, drawn-faced, throwing a sideways glance at the old lady asleep in the living room doubling as a bedroom. And she led Evie to the bathroom, to Julianne in the tub, the little girl inconsolable, begging to get out of the water, a strange pink pulp floating in the bath all around her. The girl's skin was marked with red crests where two stickers had been eased free. Carlita resumed rubbing the joins of sticker and skin with a wedge of pink grapefruit. Her mother-in-law had suggested that citrus juice, an old-fashioned remedy, would do the job best, then she'd lain down for her second nap of the day. The dress Evie had brought was no use, Carlita said. The old lady couldn't look after the little girl in hysterics. Carlita had missed her interview. The job had been filled.

In the silence on the phone this time, I heard myself insisting quietly that Evie tell me where she was right now.

It was a place I'd never really noticed much, though we passed it every day in our cars. A narrow strip of parkland with two or three benches, between the turnpike and another huge mall, where a few days before I'd seen a black guy holding a sign, 'I'll work for food'. It was right by the turning to the throughway, and the route to the clinic. Evie had pulled over there some time ago. This was nowhere for her to be, really – it was hardly a place at all. She'd called in sick to the store, and then perched on the edge of a bench and phoned my number. The plastic vial was just sitting in her lap, she told me. I could visualize the scene clearly now – the line of shrubs and little saplings shielding the weeping woman from the eyes of the shoppers whizzing by in their sealed cars.

Evie now said to me: 'Harold, do you understand this?' I was thinking I did in a way, something about a slow unpredictable path, like a manuscript in the works – it didn't happen until it did. And Evie then told me that in the turmoil of the day she'd forgotten to label the plastic vial, she'd forgotten to write our details on the sticker. 'What should I write on it now, Harold?' She hesitated. 'Sale over?'

The silence was much longer this time. I could hear in the distance something faintly going by. An ambulance maybe, or a squad car. And it occurred to me that with the extraordinary heat out of doors today the delicate demons might still be swimming their heedless swim.

* * *

My faculty colleague had popped the turkey in the oven early, so there'd be time to grab some more Thanksgiving Day bargains after we ate. But I'd got back to my desk quickly – in the top of the L now, fearless in plain sight – where I could tilt my head and look down on it all: the slow crawl of glistening bugs into the lots, shoppers popping out into the cold, scuttling to the warmth. It was five months since Evie had moved her stuff out and flown back to Chicago, and at this moment it hit me: she'd left me the one thing I really needed. With my opus now progressing page after inspired page toward completion, the thing was there at the top of the screen, the title I'd been tearing my hair out for: *SALE OVER* – by Harold Mann. Picturing the dust-jacket on the shelves at Borders lit up the cash register in my mind. I could see the award announcement, speaking engagements across the country, the six-figure advance for the next book, and I saw a little girl looking up to her daddy, the boldly incisive thinker. And abruptly I could see the little girl's eyes, soulful and generous – Evie's eyes, long before they'd met me. I tugged open the desk drawer and grasped the string of beads, fingertips obstinately atremble, like a lonely old man's, until the wiggling motion of thumb and middle finger worked to calm me, and the sonorous recitation of the mantra began slowly to empty my head and heart of all corrosive desire.

HIGHER GROUND
Grahame Gladin

The worst thing was knowing what Mum had done before he did. If it'd been news to me too, I could've at least joined him in his shock. She'd given me time to get used to the idea; time to see what *had* to be done.

'Oh,' she said, 'I forgot to mention,' gently placing her mug on the tablecloth. 'I spoke with Tony the other day.'

Dad stopped chewing. He put his palms on the table and stared at his dinner.

'Funny really,' she said, 'him calling like that, out of the blue 'n' all.'

I watched his big fingers tense up and scratch at the cloth, as she went on.

'He asked for you – asked how you were. I told him that you were down at the doctor's. He said that they needed another apprentice, said that they've just landed a big contract in the city. Said that now Shandy's turned eighteen, he could offer him a job.' She looked at him as if she was about to announce a win on the lottery. 'Says that he can start tomorrow if he wants. Says that –'

Dad launched his plate at the wall behind her. Mum jumped up and let out a horrible shriek, before smothering it with both hands. I sat bolt upright in my chair, like someone had just tightened a noose around my neck.

'Dad! *Please!*'

He turned his eyes on me. 'Shandy. Leave us will yer.'

'But *Dad* . . .'

Then Mum cut in. 'Shandy. Do as yer dad says.'

He looked back at me. 'Get out.'

I looked back at my mum.

'FUCKING GET OUT!'

I knocked my chair over in the process of getting up, marched to the door, and slammed it behind me. I almost ran out into the street. Instead I made for the stairs.

'WHO THE FUCKIN' HELL DO YOU THINK YOU ARE, WOMAN?' His rage in the kitchen chased me up to my room.

'Jack, I –'

'You must take me for the biggest *cunt* that ever walked this earth!'

'Jack!'

'Ain't it good enough for you that I've been reduced to this state?'

'Jack, *please*!'

I heard him struggling to get up from the table. A china mug shattered on the cold tile floor. Then he followed it. I pictured him lying there, big arms flailing around, trying to compensate for those buckled legs. She was crying out. 'Oh, God!'

'Get the fuck away from me, woman!'

She began to sob. 'Jack! I was only trying to help . . . There's not enough money coming into this house. You *know* that. We just can't . . .'

'So you thought you'd pick up the phone and sweet-talk my *brother* into giving us a hand-out, eh?'

'No! It wasn't like that . . .'

'How was it then, Danni?' He started mocking her voice. 'Oh, hi Tony, it's Danni here – you know, your sister-in-law? Yeah, that's right, the one who's married to that crippled brother of yours?'

'Jack, *please*.'

'Yeah, *Jack* . . . You remember – the one you haven't spoken with for the last two years? Ever since he half killed himself working for *you*?'

'Jack, stop.'

'Well, I was wondering . . . Our boy Shandy? I know he's a bit quiet an' all – a bit *weird* – but I was wondering if you might give *him* a job? Cos as you know, Jack's all washed up now! Good for fuck all, I'd say!'

'Jack!' she wailed at him.

'Who knows, maybe he'll get hurt, too! THEN YOU'LL HAVE ANOTHER COMPENSATION CASE TO WALK AWAY FROM!'

I swung around and shut the door. I hit the 'play' button on my stereo. Twisted it up loud. Fell on to my bed and buried my face.

After a while I got up from the bed and sat at my desk in the half-light. The walls of my room were covered in drawings that I'd made. People, animals, birds. They all came from my head. I'd sit for hours drawing and looking at them; knowing that they couldn't look back at me. Real life was too difficult. Especially people. I never knew what they were thinking.

I opened my drawer and took out an old sketchbook I'd saved from when I was a kid. On the front cover I'd written 'DAD. WORKIN.' There must have been twenty felt-pen pictures of skyscrapers in that book. They'd always taken me ages. Floors and floors of rectangle windows. They were all topped off with a brightly coloured matchstick Dad, almost as big as the buildings that he stood on. Like King Kong with a drill in his hand. I turned a page and saw how I'd put his name above his head in bold letters: 'JACK WRIGHT'. I stared at it hard before turning another: 'JACK WRIGHT'. I turned another: same again. Then another, and another. The last page was blank. So I picked up a pencil and started scribbling. He became deformed under my hand; twisted and bent double, over thick wooden sticks. It was grotesque. My fist began to move in sharp, agitated swipes at the paper. The pencil bearing down more and more, until it eventually tore through.

He never spoke about the accident. The only sense I had of it was from being woken by his screams in the middle of the night. And what Mum had tried to explain to me. He'd been working from the top of a suspended platform, twelve floors up in a lift shaft. He went to drive it down, heard a strange noise, and the next thing he knew the brakes had failed. The platform plummeted down the hole, smashing into the floor below. Both of his legs were shattered. The steel ropes snapped up above, and came whipping down to carve him up. He almost lost his left arm. A few inches over, and it would've been his head. He'd lain there, in the darkness, for almost two hours, while they tried to get him out. Losing pint after pint of blood.

*

'Shandy.' She was calling me from the other side of my bedroom door. I opened my eyes. 'Shandy . . .' She'd lowered her voice to a sharp hiss, so it wouldn't carry through the house. 'Shandy. Are you gonna get up?' I opened an eye and looked at the clock. 6:20. I groaned. I heard the creak of the boards as she turned and made her way back down the stairs. I heard the click of the kettle as she entered the kitchen; the release of the toaster; the opening and closing of cupboard doors; the clanking of cutlery. Then it all got drowned out by the TV being turned up in the living room. Dad was making out like he was interested in the morning news. He'd be sitting there in his chair, curtains closed, staring at the walls through the still blue light. He would've been there all night. I rolled over to look out of the window. It was pissing down. I buried my face in the pillow.

The wind blew in a barrage against the glass, rattling it in its frame. I tried to picture where I had to go. I pulled the quilt up over my head. All those new faces. All that expectation: I was 'Jack Wright's son'. How the hell was I going to carry that off? I was no lover of heights for a start. How the fuck was I going to hang off of the top of a forty-floor building? Then it came again: I was Jack Wright's son. My mind got out of bed before I could change it. My body followed.

I sat alone having my breakfast, sipping from a mug of tea and picking at a lump of toast. I avoided the living room on the way to the front porch, treading the boards like a burglar as I passed the door. I sat down on the step, and started lacing up a new pair of work boots. They hurt my feet. I hadn't even stood up in them. Then Mum came into the hallway. She stopped behind me. I felt her stare through the back of my head. I stood up and pulled my hood on. She walked up to the porch doorway and leant against the frame. She wrapped her long cardigan about her and folded her arms. She handed me my backpack.

'You OK, son?'

'Yeah, I'm all right, Mum . . . You?'

She closed her eyes, and gave me a nod. Then her bottom lip gave way.

She began to cry. She couldn't stop. I dropped my pack and put my arms around her.

'I'm *so* sorry, Shandy. I never meant for . . .'

'It's OK, Mum. It's OK. Everything's gonna be all right.'

She looked up from my chest, her eyes swollen with tears. 'I'm afraid, Shandy . . . I don't know . . .'

I took her head, and kissed it. All of a sudden she felt smaller. All of a sudden I felt bigger.

'Don't worry,' I said. 'This is for the best.' I wished I meant it.

By the time I got to the station I was soaked. A couple of girls I'd known from school stood at the end of the platform. They were dressed well in suits and macs. They were trying to control their wind-swept hair. As I passed them, the blond one said something and gave me a look. I stared at the puddles. They giggled after me.

The train pulled in and I went for the last carriage. I looked around, and went and sat at the back. I took my iPod from my bag, and switched it on. The battery died on cue, leaving me to make do with the squawking of commuters. '*EastEnders*', 'make-overs', and 'he said, she said' began to drill into my ears. I looked towards the window for something else. But all I got was glimpses of the looming cityscape through rushing streams of water across the glass.

In my mind Dad had built half of London. I could never go up town without seeing and feeling his influence. From the West End, down to the Isle of Dogs, the evidence was everywhere. There wasn't a thing he didn't know about tall buildings and the way they were built. He could talk about every inch of the process. Start to finish. From their piles, driven deep into a thousand-year layer of city earth, to their rooftops, sitting way up above the skyline. He loved it. He used to tell me how a man could feel *proud* about standing up on those rooftops – on higher ground . . . Where he could look down on the city, with all its history, and all its future, and *know* that he was playing his part.

The train was easing to a halt, and I heard the Tannoy announce my stop. I left the station to join the rush of the city. Ten minutes later I turned out of Houndsditch and stopped. I saw the cranes. There were six of them. Two hundred feet high, I'd say, with booms almost as long. Like big red iron gallows. And rising up amongst them stood a fucking great skeleton of rust-coloured steel hexagons. Distant figures dressed in fluorescent green appeared to be hanging off each level. I rubbed both palms across the top of my head, and down over my face. I shivered. All of a sudden it was real.

The site was circled by high black wooden hoardings, cutting it off from the surrounding streets. I had ten minutes to find security gate 'C', and make it to the induction room. A horn sounded as I stepped off the kerb, and I jumped back as a huge tipper truck rolled up in front of me, muddy tyres skidding to a shrieking halt upon the wet asphalt. The driver in his cab signalled to me that I was a 'wanker'. The truck began to bleep like an alarm, as it swung round to reverse through the gates. I marched up behind one of the men who were guiding it through, like I knew what I was doing.

''Scuse me, mate, can you tell me the way to gate 'C', please?'

He ignored me.

I tried again. ''Scuse me, mate . . .'

He turned around and glared at me from inside a big rain-soaked mac, a walkie-talkie held in his fist. I heard the crackled sound of distant voices. He looked me up and down. He had an unkempt red beard that was dripping wet, and a shitty look in his eye.

'Can't cha see I'm fuckin' busy?' he growled.

'Sorry,' I said. 'My first day. I've gotta make the induction.'

He rolled his eyes, before motioning a direction with his head. He had 'Big Mick' written on his hard hat in black marker pen. 'Down there,' he said, 'third gate on the left.'

Gate 'C' opened on to three flights of scaffolded wooden steps. They were slippery. I made my way up until I reached the third. Around a dozen men stood on the landing. They were waiting outside the door of a Portakabin. On the door were the words 'INDUCTION ROOM – SAFETY FIRST'. They all seemed preoccupied with the damp, shuffling from side to side on their feet. They were smoking cigarettes, drinking from steaming polystyrene cups, and quietly mumbling amongst themselves. I found a space on my own, leant my back against the handrail, pushed my hands deep into my coat pockets, and stared down at my feet. The boots were killing me.

I took in the sounds around. The pull of diesel engines, pneumatic drills pounding at concrete, metal colliding with metal. I blinked instinctively, like I was about to be smacked in the face. Then my head was turned by a man bounding up the stairs in a knee-length high-visibility jacket. He was cleaner than everyone else. He had black boots, with his trousers tucked inside. His hard hat was shiny white, and covered in stickers. He carried a red folder. The men let him through. He unlocked the door, and went inside. We all followed him.

Inside the room were several rows of brown plastic chairs. I took one at the back. A layer of fine concrete dust covered everything. It was hot, and smelt of sweat. At one end of the room stood a paper-strewn desk. Behind it hung a projector screen. The other walls were windowless. They were plastered with big graphic posters of severed limbs, burnt faces, and cartoon-character workers. Men were pictured falling down holes, and having things dropped on their heads. The words 'THINK!' and 'SAFETY!' appeared everywhere.

I got up to leave.

The clean one shouted out from the other end of the room. 'Shut the door, son! There's a good lad!'

I stopped, pushed the door shut, turned around, and sat back down.

'Right, then!' he said. 'Good morning, gentlemen. My name's –'

Just then the door flew back open. A big man, with a blue woolly hat, and straw-like hair spilling out from beneath, came through it. Others stood outside behind him, playfully jostling for position, laughing like a bunch of overgrown kids. He turned towards the official, and produced a grin like the Cheshire Cat.

'All right, Pat?' he said. 'Hope we're not late?'

Some of the other men in the room turned around in their seats to look at him.

'Mr Stark,' said Pat. 'You just made it. I was just about to begin.'

As soon as I heard the name Stark, I instinctively sat up rigid, hands gripping the underside of my chair like it was going to take off. I laid my eyes on him like he was the devil. It was Gabe Stark; my new foreman; Dad's replacement.

'Thank fuck for that,' said Stark, 'I wouldn't wanna miss this for the fuckin' world!'

With that, I watched him walk over to the row in front of me. He pulled back a chair to sit down. Then he must have noticed my stare. He paused, turned around, fixed me with ice-blue eyes. He nodded at me as he spoke.

'You Shandy?'

I nodded back. He held out his hand. It was large, grimy, and covered in scars.

'How you doin', Shandy? I'm Gabriel.'

'All right,' I croaked.

'Good. Soon as this is over, I'll take you outside an' show you the ropes.'

'Sure.'

I let go of his hand. He turned his back on me, and sat down.

The rest of his crew followed him along the line, throwing me the odd glance in the process. The last one stood out from the others. He was younger, more my age. He was glaring at me, like I was sitting in his chair or something. His hair had been shaven into a skinhead to display a raw scar that ran from his temple to his neck. He shoved his chair back, and it pushed into my knees.

'Sorreee,' he said with a mean little grin on his face.

I looked towards the front.

'OK,' said Pat. 'Let's get started, shall we?'

One of the five late entries farted loudly. They all fell about laughing.

'OK,' said Pat, 'very funny, ha ha . . . When you're finished, please . . .' He carried on: 'Now, for those of you who *don't* know me, my name's Pat McCormack. I'm your head of safety.' He took off his hat to reveal a balding ginger head. 'And for those of you whom *I* don't know, not to worry, because you lot are already known to me as *scum*.' Roars of laughter burst out from the row in front of me, whilst one of the men up the front turned and spat on the floor. McCormack backed himself up. 'The reason I say that is not because I want to get a lynching. No. The reason I say that is because every year on UK construction sites hundreds of you lot either get killed, or maimed for life.' The laughing eased up. 'Why does that make you scum? Well, think about it. When do you ever pick up a newspaper and read about these casualties? You don't. Why? Because no one's interested, that's why. Joe public couldn't give a flying fuck about you lot. You're just here to build these things, so that they can look at them, and work in them. They don't care what happens in the process. So, gentlemen, that's why I'm here: to remind you how to look after yourselves.'

For the next hour McCormack spoke about fire drills, regulation protective clothing, signage, evacuation routes, accident procedures, and welfare facilities. Then we watched a film, depicting the victims and their distraught loved ones. I felt ill. I needed to get out. Then, just as my guts started to creep into my mouth, he called time.

'OK, gents, that'll be all today. If you want to make your way to the main security office at lunchtime, you'll be able to pick up your access passes. And remember, lads: safety first.'

With that, Stark stood up, let out a big yawn, and stretched his arms above his head. 'All right, boys, let's get changed, then we can go up top.' He turned to me. 'Shandy, if you wanna come with me, I'll take you down the stores and get you kitted out.' He turned to the others. 'Me an' Shandy'll meet you by the hoist in about twenty minutes.'

I looked at him like he'd just asked me to shoot myself.

'Don't panic,' he said with a grin, 'we're only going up to have a look at the job. We'll be back down in an hour or so. Then we're out of here.' He turned back to the others. They were all staring at me. 'Come on then, lads, chop chop. We'll see you by the hoist.'

We stepped outside. It'd stopped raining, and the sun kept trying to burst through the clouds. The stores were around the other side of the site, which meant that we had to trudge through what the previous night's storm had left of the perimeter pathway. A smell rose up from the mud, like people had been pissing in it. I saw a rat dart out in front of us before scampering off into a stack of pipework along the way. Stark didn't seem to notice it. He looked at me instead.

'Tony ain't gonna be on site today,' he said.

I said nothing.

'He's gone to look at another job. Told me that you're new to this game.'

'Yeah,' I said.

'Hmmm. You seemed a bit edgy back there.'

'I'm all right.'

'Don't let Nipper bovver ya.'

'Nipper?'

'The other lad.'

'Oh.'

'Don't worry about him. He's just *paranoid*. Takes too many drugs. Thinks you've come to replace him. You know . . . being Tony's nephew an' all.'

'Oh . . . right . . . it's OK.'

'So what is it, then?'

I looked into the mud.

'Not scared of heights, are ya?'

"Course not,' I said.

'Nah, 'course not. Couldn't be – not *Jack Wright*'s boy.'

I stopped walking. Lifted my head, and stuck out my chin. 'I'm not my dad,' I snapped. 'I'd prefer it if you didn't talk about him.'

He frowned at me. I couldn't tell if he was going to punch me or hug me. He took off his hat and scratched his head for a moment.

'Look,' he said softly, 'no offence meant. It's just that I knew your dad. He was *my* foreman when I was your age. He taught me this game.'

I was fixed on his face, looking for the slightest hint of insincerity.

He went on. 'Let me tell you this, Shandy. The first day I worked with your dad, my arsehole was pouting so much at the prospect of going up top that I thought I was gonna stick to the induction-room chair. But he saw it.'

When we got round to the hoist entrance, the others were already waiting. They all looked pretty bored, except for Nipper, who started acting up as soon as he saw us coming. But I didn't have time to worry about that. I bent back my neck and looked up. I had to shield my eyes from the sun. The hoist was parked at the top of the building. It looked about the size of a matchbox. For a moment I heard nothing apart from the distant clapping of its tracks as it started coming down towards us. Some of the others started laughing. I turned and looked. Nipper was standing on the loading ramp, looking up at the sky and shaking about wildly, like he was having a fit. He had 'MILLWALL' written down the side of his hard hat in blue marker pen, and on the back of his hi-viz, it said 'NUMBER ONE APPRENTICE'.

'All right, Nipper,' said Stark. 'You wanna lay off the charlie, fella – that stuff's startin' to mess with your nut.'

Then they were laughing *at* him. He looked at me like he wanted to cut my throat.

My heart was pounding as the hoist drew nearer. I looked over at Stark. He gave me a nod. The noise had grown to a loud snapping clatter. I looked up and saw a red meshed cage, the size of a hut, as it came in to ground in front of us. It hissed out a release of air from its brakes.

The gates swung open, and around thirty workers spilled out from inside. They all looked dirty and hardened to the job. Then another load jostled themselves into a bottleneck before me. I stood back. Gabriel went in last, before turning around to hold the gate open. He gestured at me with a flip of his head.

'Room for one more,' he said.

'Come on!' came a voice from inside. Then another. 'Wot's the fuckin' 'old up?' Then another. 'Some of us 'ave got work to do.'

I couldn't move.

Gabriel gestured to me again. 'Come on, Shandy, we've gotta go.' He held out his arm, and beckoned with his fingers.

I slowly walked up the ramp, and got in next to him. He closed the gate, pulled down a heavy mesh shutter, and a loud smack of machinery sent us skywards. I closed my eyes. My legs started trembling. I wanted desperately to hold on to something. But no one was going to take too kindly to me grabbing at them. I felt like I might throw up.

Then suddenly the hoist came to a stop. My knees jolted, and I opened my eyes for balance. The gates opened on to one of the floors, and some of the men were off-loading. I didn't think I could stay in that thing any longer, so I started to follow them. Nipper and the others stayed put. I felt their amusement as I made for the landing. Then a hand on my shoulder held me back. It was Gabriel. I wanted to fall down and cling on to his legs.

'Not so fast,' he said with a smile. 'Here, come and have a look at what you're missing.'

The hoist started up again. He gave me a little tug on my sleeve, and moved over to the edge. My feet couldn't move, but my head turned round to follow him. He stepped up to the mesh and raised his hands against it, his fingers poking through it prisoner style. The wind blew his blond hair about his neck. He had 'Gabe' written across the back of his jacket in large black marker. Below that, he'd drawn a smiley face. I looked at his hard hat. It was old and battered. It had '4MAN' marked on it. Then I looked beyond him. We were rising up above the neighbouring office blocks. Solid walls of glass and steel in every direction. I'd never seen so many windows. The higher we went, the brighter it became. The space grew. Beams of sunlight began to bounce off the glass around us. Soon the other buildings sank below, leaving only rooftops. I turned and slowly stepped up beside Gabe. He looked at me with a huge white grin, and we both turned back to the view.

It became almost balmy with the heat of the sun. The breeze carried the smell of coffee and cooking from the city streets. I heard the occasional horn through the hum of the traffic, reminding me of the chaos we were leaving behind. I put my hands against the mesh like Gabe. Then I put my face against it like a toyshop window. I took in the labyrinth of old city lanes that stretched out in every direction. Buildings of every shape and size seemed to grow out of the rows, like they'd been planted to do so. But we were going higher. Even the churches of white sandstone, which stood out in the sunshine, their huge gold crosses glistening on their spires, were left below. Then I saw a horizon. Distant hills against a cool blue winter sky. I'd never seen something so . . . real. I wanted to capture it in my head for ever.

The hoist came to a halt on the forty-second floor. Another tug on my arm.

'Come on, Shandy, can't stay in here all day. Let's go and see what we're up against.'

I turned around and watched him walk towards the gate. The rest of the crew followed him out on to the landing. Except for Nipper. He hung back inside the hoist. He walked towards me as if he had a bag of cement under each of his arms. Hands twitching by his side like we were going to have a gunfight. He then levelled up to me and nodded inches from my face. His dark eyes fixed beneath his brow.

'So who the fuck are *you*, then?' he barked.

I looked over his shoulder at what was to come. The wind felt good. I turned back and met his stare.

'I'm Shandy Wright. Who the fuck are *you?*'

'Higher Ground' is an extract from the novel of the same name

BLACK VELVET
Franca Torrano

We would do it vigorously at least two or three times a night, usually in the early hours of the morning while Bob and Marian slept. We had a little ritual: I would sneak up on her from behind and proceed to take her with gusto; she would carry on nibbling a remnant of carrot or a dry kernel of corn, pretending all the while to be unaware.

Afterwards, dazed and dizzy with the excitement of our lovemaking, we would nuzzle each other until we felt revived. Then, we would race round and round and up and down the cage, squeaking loudly the whole time and eventually, exhausted but happy, we would flop down, our hearts beating wildly. We would curl up head to paw, her soft fur overlapping mine. I would swell with love and wrap myself more closely around her until I could feel her fluttering heart calm and our breathing start to move as one. With my nose resting under her bushy little tail, inhaling her sweet smell, I was the happiest chinchilla in the world. I, Chin, would drift into the sweetest sleep of deep contentment with Cilla's black eyes on me. Cilla and Chin. Chin and Cilla.

Cilla and I met at Joe's Pet Stores three years ago. I was six weeks old when she arrived. I remember the thrill of anticipation as we watched Joe and his assistant gently ease her out from under one of the older chinchillas. She was fast asleep. They were rather surprised when they held her up and turned her round, the short-tailed *Chinchilla brevicaudata* being almost extinct. Maybe she's a throwback, they said, and then forgot all about her, more interested in the new delivery of parakeets that day.

When Bob came to the pet shop he spent some time looking at the rabbits before he wandered over and spotted Cilla.

'What a beauty,' I heard him whisper as he put his finger into the cage to stroke her.

He took us both away that same day: Cilla, a beautiful black velvet and me, a common standard grey – long-tailed, of course.

'Marian – come and see what I've got!' he shouted as he went carefully up the stairs into their flat.

She stepped out of the kitchen with an oven glove on one hand and a cigarette in the other.

'Rabbits? Are you mad?'

'Chinchillas, Marian. Aren't they beautiful?'

We were tiny then and he held us both in the crook of one arm. Fear and panic wired us to each other and we moved closer together. I didn't see Marian's grimace but Cilla told me much later that she had looked disgusted, as though Bob had brought rats into the house.

We had been perfectly happy at the pet shop, especially when we were allowed to sleep pressed up against one of the older chinchillas or stay up to listen to the stories they told each other. We would lie awake in the dark, listening to tales of our ancestors and our real home high up in the snowy mountains of Peru. We would hear stories of battles against trappers and how we travelled further into the mountains to avoid famine. We heard tales about brave chinchillas avoiding capture or fighting off hawks and foxes. I would listen, transported to this far-away place, and long to go there some day.

I still do. Sometimes, even now, when the moonlight streams into my cage on a cold crisp winter night, I feel a twitching in my nostrils and a prickling under my fur. I inhale deeply and try to breathe in something far out there. I fill my lungs with it but a yearning restlessness stays with me until dawn.

Bob was studying for his Ph.D. so we watched a lot of daytime television together: children's programmes in the morning and cookery followed by *Countdown* in the afternoon. Then in the evening, when Marian stayed out drinking with her work colleagues, Bob would let me out to watch my favourite – wildlife programmes. I would sit up close to the television, not moving a whisker until the end. Bob would rub my ears before putting me back in the cage and going to his study. Cilla was never very interested but when Marian was at work Bob would let her sit at the window and watch the birds in the garden.

The night before it happened we had just floated into the honeyed sleep of the innocent when the sound of Marian's flip-flops jerked us horribly and instantly from safety. She appeared in front of the cage and stared at us as she pulled hard on a cigarette.

'So . . .'

She brought her face up close and blew a cloud of smoke over us.

'. . . you two have finished *fucking* . . .'

Her long red nails poked through the wires of the cage.

'. . . and decided to settle down for the night, I suppose. How sweet.'

She straightened up.

'I have to get up at six tomorrow, you little . . .'

I heard the hiss of her cigarette being stubbed out somewhere above me.

I could still feel Cilla trembling as Marian flip-flopped to the bathroom. We lay stiff and unmoving, straining to hear the noises of water and then the creak of the bed that meant Marian had done with us. Our tense bodies relaxed a little but after that we slept fitfully.

The next morning Bob, who usually emerged at a leisurely pace wearing only his boxer shorts, hopped into the living room half dressed, pulling on socks and shoes as he refilled the water bowl and topped up the dried food. He was going out somewhere. He scratched the soft fur on the back of Cilla's neck and pulled gently on my ears.

'Sorry, my lovelies. Got to rush – make up for it later.'

That evening Marian came home late. The door banged shut so loudly that Bob came rushing out, tea towel in his hand.

'What's wrong?'

She pushed past him and threw her bag, then herself, on to the sofa.

'You're what's wrong! Why can't you be like other men and get a proper job?'

'Darling, that's not fair. I went for that interview today like you asked me to.' He stood in front of her. 'And you know that once my Ph.D. is finished my job prospects will be great.'

She jabbed viciously at the remote control. 'It'll all be too late by then.'

Bob threw down the tea towel and stormed out. The door banged even more loudly. Marian started crying. Her mouth gaped open. She sounded like the seal we had seen on the wildlife programme the previous evening. Suddenly, the noise stopped and she stood up and strode towards us. In horror we both scurried to the little house that Bob had built for us at the back of the cage. I made it to the doorway but stopped and turned to see Cilla frozen with fear. Before I could do anything, Marian's hand flew in and grabbed Cilla by the ears. She pulled her close to her neck and crooned as she walked over to the sofa.

'Poor Marian. Give Marian a little love. That's a good girl.'

Cilla struggled a little but Marian's tight grip kept her close. I saw the red nails drag furrows through Cilla's glossy black fur as she stroked her. I pressed myself up against the cage, straining to see Cilla, but Marian had burrowed deep into the sofa and only the top of her head was visible.

The television came on. 'A number of people were injured after riot police charged the crowd.'

'Serves them right,' Marian growled.

She got up and paced around the room, moving in and out of sight. A car door slammed somewhere outside.

'Oh, nice. Thinks he can come crawling back here after that display, does he?'

I couldn't see them but I heard Cilla squeal and Marian curse.

The door opened and Bob walked into the living room with his head down. He picked up a book without saying a word and walked out again. Marian stamped after him, thrusting Cilla roughly into the cage. Their voices were loud but I wasn't listening. Cilla was lying on her side. She looked strange.

I nudged at her with my head to get up but she didn't move. I nuzzled her ears and rubbed her cheek with my own. I pressed my nose against her neck, pushing at her, wanting her to play and push me back but she wouldn't. I walked round and round her. She had her eyes fixed on mine but I could see that the effort was too much and I lay down, resting my head on her. I could feel only the faintest pat of her heart against her chest. I held myself still, hardly breathing. I looked up and saw the light in Cilla's eyes go dull. A faint sound came from her throat and I felt her body twitching.

Some time later, Marian led Bob through by his tie and, without putting down the almost-empty wine bottle, she pulled him on top of her as she fell on to the sofa. He started thrusting at her, not waiting for her to shout, 'If you're a real man, prove it!' This time she made sounds unlike anything I had heard on any wildlife programme. The noise got louder and louder until Bob stopped and got up awkwardly. He stumbled out of the room and I watched her eyes follow him. They were filled with hunger, the hunger of the huntress.

A few minutes later he tiptoed past clutching a full bottle of wine.

'Cheeky Chin. Silly Cilla.'

The next morning he cried like a baby as he knelt on the floor, rocking Cilla's cold stiff body back and forth. Marian wrapped her arms around him.

'Don't worry, darling – she was only a pet. We'll soon have the real thing.'

She looked at me, releasing a snake that slithered towards me and grabbed me by the throat.

'The real thing, darling.'

She kissed the back of his neck and he howled even more loudly than before.

For the next few weeks Bob was inconsolable and barely left the flat. Marian stormed out most mornings.

'Oh, for Christ's sake. It was only a bloody rabbit!'

And another morning, before she slammed the door: 'They're pests in Australia. They use myxomatosis to get rid of them!'

Bob grew paler and paler. Marian seemed to blossom and bloom. My fur grew dull and matted.

Bob stopped shaving and washing. Marian's skin and hair glowed. My fur fell out in clumps.

Bob and I stopped eating. Marian's face swelled like a cherub's.

One day, Marian started screaming in the bedroom and I could hear the thud of things being thrown against the wall. Bob emerged, dressed in an old tracksuit.

'It's like you've dug your claws into me. I'm trapped.' He started pulling CDs off the shelf into a large bag. 'I'm leaving. You can stay as long as you like.'

Marian appeared in the doorway.

'No!' She hurled a book at him.

Bob picked the book up off the floor and put it in the bag with the CDs.

'I have to sort my life out. This just isn't working any more.'

Marian punched him on the chest. Bob looked sad. He grabbed her wrist. Her other hand swiped at him and spots of blood appeared in a dotted line across his cheek. He let go of her and slung the bag over his shoulder.

'I'll call you in a few weeks.'

This was lost amidst her screams and the sound of her running after him. I imagined him sprinting to the car and locking the door quickly. I imagined her laid across the bonnet clinging to his windscreen wipers. But with a bang that made the building shudder from top to bottom she had slammed the door on him as he left.

I stayed in my dark corner listening to Marian shouting and banging in the kitchen. She appeared after some time clutching two bottles of wine and lay down on the floor, propping her bare feet up on the coffee table. She spent the next few hours making phone calls. I watched her as she worked her way through her address book. It grew dark outside. She dialled another number and lit a cigarette and waited. I could see the slight tremor in her hand as she brought the cigarette to her lips and dragged her life up through it.

'Nora, it's Marian.'

Nora is Bob's mother.

'I know Bob's there and I really need to speak to him.' Her voice was high. 'He's being such a silly. It was all nothing and I forgive him. He gets into such a temper . . . It's the drink, Nora. If only he could give up the drink we might make something together . . . You appreciate what I've done for him, don't you? If it hadn't been for me – well, he'd still be in that gutter I found him in . . . You'll tell him I love him, won't you? And that I'll have him back if he apologizes.'

Marian had been drinking and smoking continuously and now sat under a heavy cloud of smoke, staring at the silent handset. She raised her eyebrows at it and put it down slowly. She reached for her cigarettes and took out another. She tapped it on the packet, once, twice, three times before replacing it carefully. Slowly she stood up and turned her eyes towards me. A harpoon of vibrating hatred shot me through and pinned me to the spot in my dark refuge.

I watched, immobilized, as a smile spread from her wine-red lips and her flashing teeth to the roots of her jet-black hair. It missed her glistening emerald eyes and I shuddered. She came alive and grew before me. A line of sheer force snapped taut between us and then she moved. I reeled, ensnared. She seemed to glide towards me.

'Come to Mummy.'

I took a clumsy step back.

'Little Chin.'

I pressed myself against the wall.

'By the hair of my chinny chin chin.'

I flattened myself into the darkness.

'COME TO MUMMY!'

Her hand shot into the cage but by the skin of my skinny skin skin something awoke in me and I shot forward in a badly judged leap and landed in her lap. Some judicious scrabbling and ripping propelled me away from her and I found myself cowering and quivering beneath the sofa. She was there before I could even think 'Jack Rabbit', lying on the floor looking straight at me.

'Poor scabby Chin. We upset cos of Cilla?'

She wriggled closer.

'How was I to know the little old lady had a heart murmur? Come on, Chin.'

Her hand slipped towards me.

'I didn't mean it.'

My own heart murmured, then shrieked, and I rocketed headlong, ears flat, behind the television. I could hear her stumble and trip behind me.

'You overgrown BUNNY! We eat the likes of you *à l'orange*!'

I knew that to be untrue and I have nothing against rabbits so I took heart at her ignorance and looked around me. I had made it to the recess in the wall behind the television. I had been in here once before (a little escapade in the spring) and knew immediately why I was here now. A tiny red glow was enough to show me what I needed to see. They had never noticed a split in the main cable and I could see the live wire exposed. I inched closer to it until my nose was a hair's breadth from the precise spot where I must bite when she grabbed me. Her body blocked out the light as she knelt cursing on the tangle of wires and cables that should have been neatly tucked away in the recess.

I thought of Cilla and I knew that this was the only way out. I could hear talons scratch behind me. I could smell Marian's fermenting breath. I braced myself. In the darkness I closed my eyes. The air was cold and a shiver ran up and down my spine. I inhaled deeply. And again. I could smell freshly falling snow. I could feel it on my back.

I could feel it on my back. Cold on my back. Cold hand on my back. Bite! BITE!

I was frozen. Her hand was like ice fused to me. I was dragged out in a wrenching birthing. I scrabbled and clawed at the wires trying to pull myself back in. Desperately I flailed as her strong grip squeezed my ribs. I twisted and turned to loosen her hold but I was raised in the air and my stomach lurched. I was oblivious to pain and I thrashed wildly. I continued to thrash and twist until I realized that I was struggling alone. Panting and limp, I looked up. Above me Bob held Marian by both wrists. She jerked and yanked silently and I thought I might have gone deaf. Bob's lips didn't move but Marian's opened and closed around a noiseless chasm. Her hands clenched and unclenched.

In the bedroom Bob had held me gently against his shoulder as he pushed more things into his bulging bag. Now, as we stood in the living room, he held me tight.

'Goodbye, Marian.'

Marian was sitting staring straight ahead of her. Her hands clutched the remote control in her lap.

Bob turned to leave and I looked back. On the television a black panther was prowling around a cage. It came close and opened its mouth wide. Its green eyes filled the screen.

GWENDOLEN'S FLIGHT
Lisa Appignanesi

The pale earth was crusty with pebbles. The path rose, a little steep for her heeled shoes. Their passage grated in the silence. But each forced step seemed to give her more substance. She rearranged her cloak to mask the image she had cut from the panel. She didn't want to seem *exceptional*. Out of place. And she was determined. She had already come so far. The picture was for no one but George.

'Exceptional'. That was the word *she* had used to trap her in. *She rejoiced to feel herself exceptional.* It was a tease. An Olympian barb. Intended to smite her. To convey its opposite.

The sun shone despite her mood. Clear and bright above the park on the hill and its neighbouring cemetery. The glossy vegetation danced with light. Green, like her dress, which shimmered. Green, like those emeralds, once pawned, for ever returned.

Bramble and ivy and vines crept everywhere. Dropping from inordinate heights on to unkempt stone. Lichen-mottled. Crumbling. Returning to earth. The names on the tombs had grown faint, become hieroglyphs in search of interpreters. Inscriptions could only murmur a feeble chant to the passage of time. But the vegetation was securely rooted. A wet forest smell exuded from it. She breathed it in and saw the wall of dappled leaf ahead. A bird thrashed from its midst. She was coming close.

The air was cold here. Three monuments rose one after another from the incline. She peered and read. Not the first substantial square of roseate stone which housed a family, but the second. It climbed and climbed, a sheer, smooth expanse of spire, an Egyptian obelisk, stark and godless against the greenery. Its high polish made the reading easier, despite the coil of vine and the sudden colour of pink primulas erupting from its base. Primulas. Like a genteel romance planted by some admirer. Or a stray wind.

George had damned her with that 'genteel romance', had granted her 'exceptional' stature only to snatch it away. No good, it seemed, was ever wholly to be allowed her. *She rejoiced to feel herself exceptional; but her horizon was that of the genteel romance.* That's what she had written about her, condemning her to a perpetuity of bluestocking snickers.

No more. She had torn herself away from the sentence and got here. Torn herself out of all their imaginings. Finally. She allowed herself to smile at the irony of the pale, fluttering primulas on her oh-so-serious maker's tomb. Smiled still, as she placed the picture of the upturned dead face next to them.

The smile was secret. Her attention was all on the stone, not on the man half hidden behind it who had, until her appearance, himself been engaged in urging stone to speak.

Was she beautiful or not beautiful? he wondered as he looked. *And what was the secret of form or expression which gave the dynamic quality to her glance?*

She was cleaning away scraps of earth with a tapering finger, delicately gloved, so that the writing came clear.

HERE LIES THE BODY

OF

'GEORGE ELIOT'

MARY ANN CROSS

George was the name she knew her by. The name the world knew. Not that latter-day acquisition of Cross which made a respectable woman of her. Had she asked to have that name on her grave? Or was it his idea, the late suitor, so young he had set the gossips' tongues wagging? She had donned a frivolity of headgear for him, though it sat badly with her solemnity of face, let alone her age. Which it was that had prompted his plunge into the Venice canal was fodder for speculation. But at least and at last, she was officially married, not merely partnered. That respectability had come late for George, just a year before her death. Too late, perhaps. Though evidently she had wanted it.

Why was it that in her own case, even marriage had failed to confer respectability? *Poor Gwendolen.* That's what she called her. Not that she could have meant it with any sympathy. After all, George had made her 'poor', lorded it over her creation and loaded the dice from the very beginning. *Les jeux sont faits.* And Gwendolen was doomed. Doomed by her maker.

Doomed but not dead. Instead, it was George who lay here, 'dead in body'. While Gwendolen went round and round, eternally young, a sylph, a *Nereid in sea-green robes and silver ornaments, with a pale sea-green feather fastened in silver falling backward over her green hat and light-brown hair.* Gwendolen Harleth.

Gwendolen Harlot, George might as well have written, given the way she had treated her. A harlot with *both too much and too little mental power and dignity to make herself exceptional.*

Oh, how the readers had argued across the course of the years, more than a century of them. Argued and written and prodded and analysed and distilled her essence, kept her going round and round in a maze of meanings – good and evil, narcissist, Lamia, dangerous, desiring, cold, unfeeling, selfish – round and round and always, in comparison to her creator, just 'poor Gwendolen'. But Gwendolen had been kept alive by their contention, ever beautiful and alive. While George . . . George just lay there, her body extinguished. It was right to return the panel to her. Now that Gwendolen had escaped, the ghoulish painted face no longer had the power to haunt.

The sound of a voice reading the words inscribed on the tomb made her jump back.

Of those immortal dead who live again
In minds made better by their presence

'So sorry. Did I startle you?' The hand was quick to settle on her arm to steady her. She was quick to shake it off.

'Are you an admirer?'

She didn't respond, simply gave him her cool gaze.

'Silly question. Obviously you are. You've left her a tribute.' He looked down at the dead painted face, his own evidence of its uncertain taste.

'It comes from a house of hers,' Gwendolen offered, quite calm.

'I see.'

'Do you?'

The man had one of those thin, bony faces which should have been pale from library life, but instead wore a bronzed sheen.

'I'm writing a thesis on James. Henry James . . .' he said, as if it were an answer. As he pronounced the writer's name and met her eyes, embarrassment overcame him, mingled with a touch of scepticism. 'You've heard of him, perhaps? He was an admirer of George Eliot's.'

Gwendolen hadn't been party to countless classes and tutorials for nothing. 'A borrower, I'd say. Even if he did judge her ugly. "Equine" was the word he used, wasn't it? But we know what he meant . . . He tempered it, a little. Equine with "a delightful expression". He was a guest, after all. And she the great Victorian saint.'

The man grinned. 'Well, no one ever called her beautiful. James, at least, approved. Even approved of her "partner", as we'd now say, approved of his "gay cosmopolitanism". He was one of the few. Lewes is buried just behind here. Did you know?'

Only now did she notice his accent. American. Yes, she knew, though she had never visited before. Knew so much now. About them both. George and George. About all the books. All the friends and enemies. She had come to suspect that Lewes, the old rake, would have given 'poor Gwendolen' a different destiny, if he'd had half a chance. But he never interfered when Marian was George.

Had Gwendolen had the choice, she would have changed her name, too, and not to her husband's. Grandcourt. But only popes and priests and authors could change their names, apart from wives, without anyone batting an eye. And criminals, perhaps. George had made her into half a criminal. Stacked the cards, so some even suspected she had helped

Grandcourt to his watery end, rather than simply standing by. Bad enough in George's book, whatever her one-time husband's indolent cruelty.

'Why did her maker so want to punish her?' The American had misread her silence. Thick eyebrows gathered in a peak. 'I didn't mean "gay" in our sense. James might have been, of course. Though I suspect he was one of those who'd repressed his sexuality for so long, he couldn't remember his orientation.'

He was waiting for her to laugh. Instead, she gave him the languid smile that had tantalized Deronda all those years ago and made him want to look again, despite himself. Yes, look again.

Over the maze of interpretation the years had brought, she had begun to suspect that it was for that second look she had been punished. A look that George, when she was all-too-plain Marian, would have coveted.

'Do you know the source of the quotation on her tomb?' Her fellow visitor began to read once more. '"Of those immortal dead –"'

'It's from a poem she wrote. She wanted to join the choir of the invisible dead, the immortals.' Gwendolen quoted:

Oh, may I join the choir invisible
Of those immortal dead who live again
In minds made better by their presence; live
In pulses stirred to generosity,
In deeds of daring rectitude, in scorn
For miserable aims that end with self,
In thoughts sublime that pierce the night like stars,
And with their mild persistence urge men's search
To vaster issues. So to live is heaven:
To make undying music in the world . . .

Gwendolen stopped. George had never allowed her to make undying music. That was the rub. What might have saved her, had been taken away from her. Nothing transcendent was to be permitted her. Because of that childhood incident, perhaps. The canary-bird. Yes, yes, she had strangled its voice. But everything had been so mixed up back then, with her sisters screaming and her father dying and the ghastly stepfather.

The thought of it, even now, made her freeze. A paralysis of cold.

Around them, the day had grown suddenly dark. Thick black cloud filled the sky. Leaves and ferns rustled with savage gusts. Ivy heaved.

'Uh oh. We'd better run. Would you like a coffee? There's a place in the park. Not far.'

Gwendolen couldn't move. It was too late, in any event. The sky released a torrent of hail. It battered the ground, flailed the tombs. The world turned white. Had George willed it? Was she still there, her mind so strong that it could force Gwendolen back to the sentence from which she thought she had escaped?

George had been able to make everyone do her bidding, even the composer, Klesmer. He had put Gwendolen roundly in her place. What was it he had said to her, when she had wanted to support the family with her voice and escape Grandcourt? The words had once been indelibly printed in her mind, an ultimate humiliation. *Too old . . . you will not, at best, achieve more than mediocrity – hard, incessant work, uncertain praise – bread coming slowly, scantily, perhaps not at all – mortifications, people no longer feigning not to see your blunders – glaring insignificance . . .* The indignity of it. No, art was not for the likes of Gwendolen. 'Poor thing.'

Why wouldn't George allow it? Gwendolen would have worked given half a chance. Worked hard. Instead she was only allowed to look beautiful on the various stages George provided. In tableaux where dead faces reared up at her, in mirrors, in men's eyes. She was allowed to move beautifully on horseback or as she aimed her arrows. Allowed to provide a beautiful object for Grandcourt to desecrate. Or Deronda to judge. That was almost the worst. Because she relished the quality of his attention.

Yes, George had so made her that imagination of the sterner kind seemed beyond her, self-reflection an impossibility. So she deserved nothing but appearance and the dross of romance. Singing . . . well, that was art, that was reserved for Mirah, or for Deronda's mother. For George herself.

And why? Unless it was that George wanted to hoard the talents to herself, certainly not allow them to any woman endowed with youth and beauty. That was it. That was it. She was jealous of her own creation. Jealous of what she had never herself possessed. She had to punish

Gwendolen for the very favours she had bestowed on her. George, too, had her vanity. Hadn't she lied about her age, like any ordinary woman? Taken a year off from the figures etched on her tombstone?

'Come over here. Under the tree. You'll get drenched. Quickly.'

Gwendolen at last heard the young man's voice above the storm. She moved to where he gestured her. The tall oak provided a sort of canopy from the pelting hail. The noise was all round them.

'I'm John, by the way. John Hudson. And you?'

'Gwendolen.'

'Gwendolen?'

'Yes.'

'As in *Daniel Deronda*?' The American chuckled, then stopped abruptly. 'Yes, I can see. You . . . you look like her. You're beautiful.'

'No longer.'

He misunderstood her and rushed to reassure.

But she wasn't paying attention. She was thinking of Deronda. He had wanted her. Yes, he had. They were kindred souls in so many respects. But George had intervened. She had forced her to Grandcourt. And she had given Deronda the soulful Mirah, that girlish, suffering echo of his own mother, but one he could tame. That old virago, Alcharisi, wasn't tameable. She would have nothing of him, even if she was his mother. Had sent him clear away. For the sake of her talent.

And for all her boldness, George hadn't allowed the more challenging match, the one which didn't force like to like, the match between herself and Deronda. She had to learn through renunciation. Hadn't she learned enough by then? But youth and beauty were not to be rewarded. She was allowed life, not love . . . while George went off with her John Cross, a youthful poultice to her wounded vanity.

The hail had turned to rain, thick and pounding. Enough. Enough. She had come to say goodbye to George. She had torn herself out and away and made the journey to her maker's tomb. The dead face she had cut from the panel at Offendene glowed like some Baptist or Holofernes.

She felt free now. Free to live, as she had so long ago promised Deronda she would do. Even free to change her name.

A sodden sheet of paper flew past her and came to rest on the upturned head. It clung to it, as if to cover its painted horror. Gwendolen moved to pick it up and saw an image of a vast butterfly. Its velvety eye rimmed with gold looked out at her. With a shiver, she left the creature in its place. Had George called it here?

Beneath the butterfly, a list of names emerged. An exhibition. Artists. Yes, perhaps George had.

'I'm thinking of changing my name,' Gwendolen announced to this John, who had taken off streaming glasses, so that his face looked bare, exposed.

'No longer Gwendolen, then. What now?'

She looked down at the flier. The names were running into each other. 'I don't know. Maybe Brigitte or Annika or Sara. Or Roxy. Or better still, one of those men's names. Tony or Paul. Maybe even George.'

'Gwendolen's Flight' first appeared in *Infallible, In Search of the Real George Eliot* edited by Roxy Walsh, ARTicle Press, 2005

SUNDAYS ARE BEST FOR PEOPLE-WATCHING
Amy Popovich

Robert is standing, binoculars in hand, at the windowed wall of the swank Upper West Side apartment he shares with Ernesto, parting the thick velvet curtains just enough so he can see out but no one can see in. It's Sunday morning; he's wearing his maroon smoking-jacket with the gold family crest. On a small, ornately carved table beside him is a round white mug filled with coffee and rum, an open bag of wheat-free bread, an ashtray, a pad of paper and a digital SLR with 600mm zoom lens. He watches the joggers trek endlessly by in the park fifteen storeys below.

Ernesto should be there with him, but is in his bedroom, trying to sleep off a hangover. A sudden wind snaps against the curtains and Ernie's sure the morning sun creeping through the bedroom window like a cat burglar is someone sneaking around his room. He's a bit paranoid, didn't have much privacy growing up. Even though he'll be thirty this year, Ernesto Cavallo only just moved out of his dad's fortress into his own place. Well, he's not completely on his own; Bert's there. Living alone was awesome at first – so unexpectedly liberating. Even through his twenties he had been woken every morning by Lupe coming into his room; he'd lie there embarrassed in his underwear as she walked around, hunched over, putting away his clean laundry, collecting used glasses and muttering in Portuguese; or by his father's voice barking down the intercom: 'Rise and shine, Son. We'll have breakfast by 0800 hours, so we can get out to the range by 0900.' But after the first few days alone in his new place he started acting like an in-patient, paralysed by his solitude. Hours would pass and he'd just sit in his plush Lay-Z-Boy, staring blankly at the flat-panel widescreen whether it was on or not.

Bert answered his ad, and Ernesto is grateful for his contribution of constant noise to their life. Now he can hear the pounding techno beat from Bert's stereo in the next room; notices that it is making the golfing trophies on his dresser vibrate. He reaches for his bedside walkie-talkie as he climbs to his knees, parts the curtains and reaches for the monocular that hangs from the cord.

'Red Eagle to Blue Panther. Red Eagle to Blue Panther.' He drops the radio amongst his pillows.

Is she there yet? Has he overslept? Desperation gallops across his face as he nervously scans the park for the object of his obsession. His crush, the love of his life, the woman about whom he keeps a detailed log of sightings and activities, is nowhere to be seen. She jogs on a strict schedule. He searches his room in vain for the time – a watch, a clock. Does he own either of these? It looks as if it's rained all night, but the warm autumn sun, muddy jogging paths and glorious smell of wet asphalt never fail to pack the park with leisuresuits and take-away coffee cups. When he doesn't immediately see her he panics and rushes into the den where he knows Bert will already be in position, binoculars in hand, taking notes.

'Hey, Bert.'

'Hey, Ernie.'

'What time is it?' Ernie says urgently. His hands go through his dark bed-ruffled hair. How will he maintain authority with this behaviour? he scolds himself in his father's voice.

'Time for you to get a watch!' Bert, as expected, is already immersed in surveillance, his hand scribbling madly at a notebook on the table as his gaze remains glued to the park. Doesn't this guy ever sleep? Ernie scowls at the jacket with the gold crest of that fake pretentious family Bert does not belong to.

'Why are you so chipper this morning?' Ernie grunts, sarcastic. 'You been up all night, junkie?'

'Nah, nah. Stayed at one of the Jennifers' last night. You know, the one with the ass? Rrrruff! That's one nasty little girl! She wanted to do it all night, man. Couldn't get a wink in. I was gonna try and go back to bed but on my way home I saw your girl Raquel go into the park and then she was talking to one of the Pretty Boy Blues. So I couldn't let it go. You're missin' all the action, man.'

'What? When? Is she still there?' Ernie quickly selects his favourite pair of SuperVision goggles from the stainless-steel briefcase open on the coffee table, straps them to his head and joins Bert at the windows. His gaze pauses on his own balcony, as he remembers the Real Estate Barbie who showed him the apartment. How her hair and skirt were blowing around in the wind as she had stood at the rail, telling him how much chicks loved a place with a view. That its proximity to Central Park made it 'priceless'. But they never went out there any more; the Super looked after the plants and they had decided it was better, safer, to stay behind the thick velvet curtains that separated their den of deception from the street, the park, the city.

'So, out with it, what'd I miss? You been logging it all?'

'Of course, baby. I got your back! So, this morning, I'm on my way home, right? Minding my own business and then suddenly, bam! There's your girl, Raquel Welch, coming out of the Parkside Manor! I almost said hi to her – you know, wasn't expecting to see her there so just thought, There's someone I know.'

'What was she doing at the Parkside? She lives on the other side of the museum.'

'I know! I think she's getting some on the side. But when I look on the spreadsheet we got no one who lives at the Parkside. So, Ernie: you, my man, have a new mission.'

Bert pokes a finger at Ernie's shoulder and he flinches. Raquel is Ernie's mark, exclusively; he feels a sharp pang of jealousy at the thought that Bert has seen her doing something so personal, so dangerous.

'All right, I'll find out who she visits there.' Ernie tries hard not to show his annoyance. He is supposed to be the leader of The Project, give the orders.

The Project: a title that validates their unconventional pastime. At first

Ernie could not imagine a more perfect room-mate. From the first day it was so easy. He had the lush apartment, invited people round to see it, to rent out a room. Such a professional, businesslike thing to do. Ernie felt very grown up having gained authority over his own space. The buzzer rang and he opened the door, full of his own bravado. Bert. Ernie. They'd found the joke amusing in their email correspondence. But they both swore the sweaters were not planned. There was Robert in a new blue and green striped number from the Gap, eighty per cent cashmere, dry clean only. Before meeting eyes they had stared at the sweaters. Ernesto was wearing the exact same one, but in red and orange. Then they laughed.

'Good look,' Robert said, giving Ernesto a playful fake upper-jab, undercut punch.

'Hey, Bert.'

'Hey, Ernie.' He charged into the room. 'Hey, you mind if we put on the end of the Knicks game? I've got five Franklins on it.' He grinned, grabbed the remote from the marble coffee table and moved in a week later.

It only took about a week for them to settle in, and realize that neither had much to do, they were both homebodies during the days. They had the same taste in everything, from women (yes) to drugs (please) to attitude (whatever), career (yes, Father, I understand), hobbies (all of the above). They even had similar trust funds. Imagine that! So a month later they were stoned and hung over, slumped on the couch, when the infomercial for the radio headsets came on television: **Call Now! Just $49.99 when you buy a pair of limited-edition SpyTech v2.0 Professional Binoculars. Call within the next hour and receive FREE shipping!**

Bert and Ernie simultaneously reached for their cellphones.

Once the binoculars arrived things escalated quickly. Really getting to know their neighbours was far more addictive then either had anticipated. The obvious thing to watch from their window was the park. It was like a real-life soap opera playing out before them, just for them. And it was a well-rounded cast, complete with couples arguing and making up, artists loitering on the lawns and health-nuts doing tai chi. Plenty of transgressive behaviour with the drug deals and occasional night-time violence, the intermittent conspiracy-based meeting of smart-suited gentlemen, searching for a place to talk away from the threat of wire-taps.

The logs had started casually, they thought they might start a blog, and The Project was born. For the first time Ernie felt like he had something to get out of bed for in the morning. With Bert beside him he developed a new self-confidence. The structure of it, the careful recording, the occasional embellishment; his hours were filled, and fulfilling.

After the binoculars came the Soviet Spy Monocular that Ernie hung by his bed, the SuperEar Sound Enhancer System systematically deposited in trees within range, the Tele Monitor 2000 (why they decided to tap their own phone is still unclear), and the 007 Wristwatch Cameras with 10x digital zoom, every spoiled boy's wet dream. Inspired by their new props they let their innocent hobby evolve into a full-blown obsession.

So here they are now, watching, recording everything.

'The Parkside, huh?' Ernie looks at a street map taped to the curtain before them. 'And did she spend the night?' He inserts a pushpin.

'She had to've. Sun wasn't even up when I was coming home, and she was rushing out of there like she didn't want no one to see her, you know?'

'What were *you* doing there again?'

'Wait, it gets better.' Bert ignores Ernie's suspicion. 'So I rush home, right, grab my eyes and run up to the lookout to get a better view. I lie down in position and guess who comes out of the Parkside Manor not five minutes later?'

'Who?' asks Ernie.

'Mussolini!' Bert jumps a little into the air, causing his spiked hair to wobble back and forth before the sculpting gel reaffirms its authority.

'Well, that must just be a coincidence. No way she stayed there with him.' Ernie shoves an entire piece of bread into his mouth, hands one to Bert.

'Yeah, I know, but now we know where he lives, too.'

'Man, that guy gives me the creeps. You want to go diggin' in his life, that's your job. I'm keeping my hands clean of that one.'

'Whatever. He's harmless, just some crazy old guy. I wouldn't have expected him to be at the Parkside, though. Always imagined him living in some project with like twenty women and babies wrapped in wool blankets 'n' shit.'

'You're an asshole, Bert.'

'C'mon! That creepy Hitler moustache!' Bert raises his index finger below his nose and purses his lips together. 'The dirty trench coat. The fur hat! You can't tell me he's Fifth Avenue material.'

'You never know. Maybe he's in the Mafia or some shit. There's something about him. He's no run-of-the-mill immigrant. Not like *your* shady German ass.'

'Ah, piss off, Ernie. My parents came here like for ever ago. So did yours.' Bert pauses and stares out at the park. His eyes are following a middle-aged Middle Eastern woman power-walking a pit bull. 'At least I've been up and recorded it all in the log. If I had been sleeping all day like *some* people we would have missed it.'

'I'm gonna get some coffee.' Ernie slides the goggles up on to his forehead and stretches his arms above his head. He doubts Bert has recorded it all in the log, as he glances back into the room and notices the Project computer is not powered on.

'Wait, wait! There she is!' Bert pulls at his arm. 'And she's with that Pretty Boy Blue I told you about!'

Ernie snaps the goggles back into position and re-parts the curtains. Sure enough, there she is. He hasn't missed her after all. Raquel Welch is jogging, as she does every morning, past their luxury apartment. But it is not every morning that one of the Pretty Boy Blues has the courage to talk to her, let alone jog with her.

About the joggers: they're the most consistent presence in the park, the easiest for the boys to keep tabs on because they tend to have regular schedules. The dog walkers will be there most days, but their intrigue gauge is much lower, as they're usually just on their cellphones or throwing balls and following their mutts around with plastic bags on their hands. But the joggers, sweating, determined, desperate: they are worth watching. Worth following.

So there are the Jen Jenny Jennifers, groups of college-aged girls who come to the park together around noon, barely work up a sweat in their assorted university hoodies before sitting down to gossip. Then there are the Juicy Girls, their sworn rivals, mostly Puerto Ricans down from Harlem, all made up and decked out in velour sweatsuits, trying to meet some Wall Streeters. Of course there are the John Johnsons and the Steve Stevensons, the beer-bellied middle-aged men who leave their poor wives in Queens with the kids on the pretence of going jogging, but once in the park will find any excuse to not actually exercise.

But Ernie doesn't really care about any of them. He only has eyes for Raquel Welch, an obsessive jogger who pushes herself hard, sometimes runs until she staggers. She runs every morning, sometimes in the evenings, too. She has an endless catwalk of tracksuits, Puma and Prada mostly, and when it's cold she wears a sexy headband of white fur around her forehead, her dark-brown hair swaying from a tight, impossibly high pony-tail. She has long legs and an ample bosom that bounces as she runs, as she apparently hasn't caught on to the sports-bra trend. He wonders if this gives her back problems. He's bought her numerous support bras, but never worked up the courage to give one to her. She has thin tanned fingers and high cheek-bones. He's sure she's European.

Sometimes during the day at his father's office Ernie catches himself doodling, fantasizing about her. His dad's in politics, and runs a CCTV monopoly in mid-town. Ernie only makes it in once or twice a week, but even then he can't concentrate: the army of sensuous, overly friendly women who work for his father all remind him of her. And the way they all listen to, obey, his father; the Senator seems to have control over all of them.

One such fantasy involves going around to Raquel's apartment during the day when her rich old husband isn't at home and being invited in, ostensibly to help her fix something, then ravishing her on the kitchen table, or in the laundry room, or some other vortex of domesticity.

With his eyes closed he pictures her when he is screwing the ditzy Jimmy Choo girls he and Bert bring home from the bars every weekend. They giggle and bat their eyelashes, thinking it will make up for the fact that they have no idea what to do with a cock. But Raquel Welch, she is a sex goddess. She would do anything asked of her, with precision and skill, could get him off without a tedious tutorial. He owns all her films on DVD, and usually puts on *Le Fate*, his favourite, before he goes to sleep, whether he is alone or not.

As he watches her in the park now, Ernie tries to imagine what she would have been doing at the Parkside Manor that morning. Most likely, she is having an affair. This sort of woman is not likely to be sincerely in love with the seventy-plus man she lives with. At least it will go into the log that way. Ernie has followed her enough times to know that the man she lives with is not her father, although he is certainly old enough. Once a week the old fart puts on a suit and is chauffeured to Madison Ave and East 62nd: board meeting. But here is a new piece of the puzzle: Raquel Welch seen leaving Parkside Manor, 5 a.m. Sunday.

Ernie pulls an orange corduroy beanbag up to the windows and sits down, crossing his legs. He makes some notes in a sketchpad. Bert brings him another mug of rum and pulls up next to him in an electric-blue bag of the same sort. Raquel looks like she's been at it for hours, and he wonders if she has been doing the full six-mile loop and, if so, how many times. In the evenings she tends to take the short cuts, but it's almost always full laps in the mornings. It's good exercise for Ernie, trying to keep up with her.

Now Ernie looks over at Bert, whose face is magnified five times by his goggles. He sees Bert's pale pink lips, his unshaven chin. He is sucking on a joint, passing it to Ernie.

''Ere, hold this, man. I'll be right back.' Bert hands the thin paper to Ernie, rolls out of his seat and monkey-crawls, then trots off down the hall towards his bedroom. Ernie waits, holding the joint, smokes some, waits some more. Bert doesn't come back.

Ernie shrugs it off, goes over to the table and boots up the computer, begins surfing through the logs. In the beginning they had divvied up the 'joggers', basically everyone who frequented the park, thus making it into their story, and each was given their own marks to watch. It made it easier. But as Ernie skims through Bert's logs, he notices, as he had begun to suspect, that Bert is watching and following only women, all the women, and following them too closely. He hadn't bought Bert's story about how he just happened to be passing the Parkside that morning. Now he reads about date after date that Bert has been on with nearly every woman they have a record of setting foot in the park. Sure, they both date the Jennies, but that's different. They're college girls, young and single, and they want to go out with hot rich faux-European guys. They love it.

But Bert is going after the elderly women with dogs, the multi-tasking moms with strollers, the female halves of the arguing couples. He has followed them all.

They started out on the same page. At least Ernie thought they had. They know what they are doing is wrong on some level, but they don't feel they are really breaking any of the important laws. It's just for fun. Anyone who chooses to leave their curtains open cannot possibly fool themselves that no one can see in from the surrounding towers. And the park is fair game, plain sight, public domain. They are just people-watching, after all. Everyone does it.

He reads on, file after file. How much of it can possibly be true? Could Bert really have slept with the power lesbians who play tennis on their lunch break? Would he actually steal a collection of antique Fabergé eggs from the sweet old granny with the Scottie? Does he have it in him to chase down and bludgeon a teenaged mugger? The more Ernie reads the more he becomes convinced it is all fiction. It has to be. Where could Bert even have found the time to do all these things? He would have to be sat in the apartment all day. He would need to have disguises if he was going into the park that often.

Ernie can hear Bert in his room working out, screaming out with each bench press or bicep curl. Wasn't he supposed to 'be right back'? What's he getting pumped up for? Ernie knows the entries are most likely the result of a few nights of cocaine and whisky dinners, but can't help feeling suspicious. At the very least Bert has undermined The Project by filling the logs with fantastic adventures of deceit and deliverance. At worst, he is a psychotic lunatic with delusions of grandeur who has taken it upon himself to single-handedly make an impression on the entire neighbourhood.

Ernie gets up from the desk and paces the room. Running his fingers through his hair he thinks about what he should do. He won't have The Project made a mockery of. His suspicions have been right. He will have to confront Bert. But it won't be pretty. Bert is bound to get defensive. If it comes to blows now, Bert will win for sure: he's been working out, his muscles warmed. No, now is not the time. Give the information some time to sink in; form a plan of attack. Yes, Ernie will watch him a bit, see if he really is doing the things he says; in that way regain control.

He creeps into the top of the hall, stopping opposite the bathroom, just feet away from Bert's door. From this position, Ernie knows from experience, he can quickly duck into the bathroom if he hears Bert coming. He presses his ear to the wall, holding up between them a palm-sized flat metal disc. An Invisible Walls sound amplifier, $19.99 on spy.com. Ernie ruffles his eyebrows. Bert is no longer working out, but smashing about; sounds like he's throwing things against the walls. What is that maniac up to? Ernie takes his notepad and pencil from his robe pocket and scribbles a few words.

Returning to the den he tiptoes over to the leftmost window and pulls back the curtains. Quietly he cracks open the door and extends a small mirror on a hinged metal arm towards Bert's window. Damn, the paranoid bastard has drawn the curtains. The mirror goes back into his pocket. He hears Bert's door fly open abruptly, footsteps in the hall. Ernie turns around expecting to face him, but there is no one there. He waits. Silence. Cautiously he slippers across the room, just far enough that he can see into the kitchen, grab a reflection off the black glass oven. He thinks he sees a movement, a flash of gold. The crested jacket? Then nothing.

Ernie backs across the room and resumes a position at the farthest window from the hall. There is no way Bert can cross the entire room without him hearing it. Raquel has finished her run, is stretching by the small pond over towards the Met. Lunges, squats, calisthenics. In his notepad he records it all and returns to the computer to log the morning's events, keeping one eye on the hallway. But when he opens the Raquel folder he finds there has been a new entry since he last wrote. And since Raquel is *his* mark this is uncalled for.

Double-click: open file. It is not in his style of writing at all. The font is different; the typeface tiny; it begins with sprawling run-on sentences populated with 'dude', 'man', 'you know', and other such unprofessional colloquialisms that Ernie keeps out of his own writing. The Raquel File has been polluted. And when he reads the report his temper flies out of control. His nostrils flare, his face grows hot and swollen with anger. When he has finally had enough he stands up so violently the chair goes flying backwards across the polished hardwood floor.

Ernie charges down the hall, ready to confront him. But Bert meets him at the door to his bedroom, as if he knows Ernie is coming.

'Did you take my knife?' Bert asks as Ernie runs right into him in the doorway.

'What? No, why would I take your knife?' Ernie steps back.

'It's not where I left it. I keep it in a specific spot, always, I always put it there.' Bert turns and points vaguely back into the stuffy room. 'And now I can't find it. It's not anywhere in my room. It's not where I put it.' He's ranting, sweating.

'Oh, it's not where you put it after you used it to attack Raquel on Thursday?' Ernie throws it out there. It's now or never.

Bert is taken aback. For a moment he forgets about The Maniacal Rage of the Lost Knife and looks up to the right, searching for words with which to defend himself.

'What are you talking about? I didn't attack anyone! What the fuck . . . ?'

'Give it up, Bert! I read the logs. What, you thought I wouldn't see it? You know she's mine. That's *my* project! How could you? You know, you've really gone over the line this time.' Ernie pushes him back into the room.

'Hey! Get off me!' Bert stumbles back. 'You don't know what you're talking about!'

'Oh, don't I? I read what you did, you sick freak! Aren't there enough bitches in the park? Why'd you have to go after mine?' Ernie pushes him again. Bert retaliates with a strong shove that sends Ernie flying back against the wall.

'I didn't do anything! She wanted me there. And half the stuff you read in that stupid log didn't even happen. I made it up, you dick!'

'Oh, she wanted you there? Yeah, I don't doubt that when you showed up and started sweet-talking her she let your sleazy ass in. But that's no excuse for what you did!'

'What? What is it you think I did?'

'Oh, you don't remember now? So you didn't push her down on the couch and cut her dress off when she tried to throw you out?'

'She didn't try to throw me out! That bitch was begging me to stay, stripping off all her clothes. She wanted me, man!'

'Fuck you! I saw what you wrote! How she asked you to leave and what she said to you and you went mental and pulled your knife on her! You fucking prick! Are you trying to get us both arrested! You're way out of control!'

'*I'm* out of control?! *You* are the one going mental now! You're in my room all screaming and shit, accusing me of all sorts! This whole thing was your fucking idea, remember?'

'You wrote it down! You might have been fucked up, but you wrote it down, you miserable shit. You can't lie about it now. That is not what The Project is about!'

'Oh and what is *The Project* about then?' Bert mocks him, waves both hands in the air next to his face. 'Huh, Ernie? You're so obsessed with just watching everyone and recording. For what? I'm sorry but I can't watch someone's behaviour and get to know them and follow them and then hide in the bushes like a coward and not talk to them. They're a part of my life, too, you know!' Bert's voice quivers, and Ernie thinks he sees a tear well up in Bert's eye.

'That does not mean you can take advantage of them and use them!'

'Oh, you don't take advantage of them?! You don't follow the Jennies to school and pretend to be in their classes? I've seen their notebooks in your room, I know you follow them to acting or dance or whatever-the-fuck. Don't you dare act like you are all Mr Perfect and you haven't ever gotten into one of those bitches' bedrooms under false pretences!'

Now Ernie is taken aback. How does Bert know all that? He's been so careful.

'That's different and you know it! I've never pulled a knife on anyone! I've never forced myself on them if they ask me to leave. You're a fucking psychopath if you've done half the things you wrote in that journal! And if you haven't you're going to end up paying for it anyway when the cops come round and haul us both in for the shit you wrote!'

Ernie shoves Bert's left shoulder back with his right hand.

'I told you to stay the fuck off me, man.'

Bert shoves him back, opposite shoulder, opposite hand. Ernie returns it; back and forth they push each other until Bert takes a swing at his chin.

This sets it off and they wrestle each other to the floor. Over and around they roll, knocking into bookshelves and emptying Bert's mini-bar of its assorted bottles, until Bert gets Ernie into a headlock and holds his forearm flexed tight against Ernie's throat. Ernie claws at him and kicks his legs out on the floor. He flails and fights, and tries to wriggle out of the hold.

Finally he gets his elbow back into Bert's side, and Bert lets go. Ernie coughs and pants and crawls across the room to slump against the wall that is now dripping with liquor. He catches his breath as Bert climbs to his feet and slowly crosses the room towards him.

'What the fuck, man?' Ernie breathes. 'You could have fucking killed me!'

'Oh, and you weren't trying to kill *me* just now?'

'No, Bert. I wasn't.'

They stare at each other for what seems like ages. Finally Bert moves towards the door.

'I'm going for a walk. Somewhere *other* than the park.'

He leaves Ernie in the room and storms out. Ernie hears ceramic smashing on the kitchen tiles, what sounds like a book hitting the wall, the slamming of the hardwood door. He hears the elevator ding, the heavy doors squeak open and close, then silence.

Ernie drags himself to his feet, into the bathroom where he sticks his head in the sink and drinks the stale tap water, spitting it back mixed with his own warm blood. Wiping his face with his bathrobe sleeve he walks wearily into the den and back to the windows. He picks up Bert's binoculars from the beanbag where they were abandoned and parts the curtains. Bert is crossing the road, jogging through the gate, into the park.

'There you go, that's right,' Ernie says aloud as he watches his room-mate through the binoculars. He picks up his schedule book from the floor next to the beanbag, checks the clock. Nearly noon. Mussolini will be out for his morning walk any time now. Yes, there he is, right on cue. Walking towards Bert. But what's that he has in his hand? Shiny, silver. Is that . . . ? Ernie turns the focus wheel on the front of the binoculars to zoom in closer. Yes, he'd recognize it anywhere. It is Bert's knife. But how did he . . . ?

'Ooh, this is gonna be good,' Ernie says as his grin widens and he reaches for his notepad.

AH-GONG IS COMING
Christine Hsu

Ah-gong is coming. Grandpa is coming all the way from Taipei to visit us in Illinois. Ma-mah has been vacuuming all day, and Ba-bah has been searching for an hour in the attic for the cheap, bronze spray-painted sailboat Ah-gong bought for us at Sam's Club the last time he came. Little Kimmie keeps crying, and my older sister Wendy just reads her Nancy Drew book upstairs with the door shut. I dangle my ratty little teddy bear in front of Kimmie, and she grabs it. She starts chewing on its ear. That's the last time I give her my Mr BoBo stuffed animal to play with. But Kimmie's quiet so I can go back and play with my Barbies.

I'm kinda scared of seeing Ah-gong again. He's not the grandpa my friends at school have with a soft, big belly you can hug and a shiny bald head that glimmers in the sun. He has lots of greying hair, tiny square glasses so he can lower his eyes at you with a frown, and is thin but not fragile.

I remember my ah-gong screaming at me in Taiwanese. I put my chopsticks sticking into the rice bowl instead of laying them on top of the bowl's rim like two parallel balancing bridges. Ah-gong got super-mad at me and said I had no manners because poking the chopsticks into the rice and leaving them there means go to hell. Ba-bah told Ah-gong that I didn't know any better. Tears gushed out of my eyes. Wendy gave me an evil grin, while Ma-mah fed baby Kimmie more banana mush. I thought Ah-gong would be proud that I could use chopsticks. A lot of my classmates could only use knives and forks.

I was always scared to enter Ah-gong's room. It would be dark with only a desk lamp on while he would do his calculations with an abacus. He would move the wooden beads swiftly up and down the contraption's tiny poles and make marks in his accounting book with a black fountain pen. My dad told me not to disturb him when he was working on his accounts.

Ah-gong was always giving my sister Wendy presents. He made flash cards a few years ago, before Kimmie was born, to help Wendy learn. I got the hand-me-down cards with the number '5' on one side and then five delicately painted flamingos all standing on one leg on the other side. I never got my own set of flash cards.

Every year I try really hard to speak Taiwanese and Mandarin and English all at the same time. I was going to preschool and English seemed so much easier to speak to everyone there. My ah-gong confused me with all the languages he knew. He didn't like English much.

Last time Ah-gong was here he and Ba-bah fought over the bill at Wok and Roll, the best Chinese restaurant in Morton Grove. Ba-bah stole the receipt right as the plate of orange slices and fortune cookies would land on the table.

'It's my turn to pay, Dad. You're come from so far away! Relax. I've got it!' Ba-bah said in Chinese while he glanced at the total of the bill.

Before reaching into his wallet, Ah-gong ripped the receipt out of his hand and said, 'No, no, no! You're my family. I would be more than happy to take care of the bill. Anyways, the last time I came you paid for the bill already.'

'No! You're a guest in my house, and it would be a treat for me to pay,' Dad said back to Ah-gong.

This went on for five minutes and Kimmie laughed along and clapped her hands thinking they were playing a fun game of verbal tag. Ba-bah won that round of who was going to treat the family with a joking, reluctant smile from Ah-gong, but the next time we went out to dinner Ah-gong made Ba-bah promise not to pay. Yet they never kept their promise and always fought over the bill.

The dishes were spicy and sweet. We could never finish all the food but we would always go through two pots of jasmine tea during the meal. I drank ice water, but Wendy could already drink a small portion of tea. Sometimes Kimmie would knock over the teapot or glasses of water if we weren't careful to watch her.

I told my friends at school that my grandpa was coming. They asked if I was excited. I said I guess so. I wish my ah-gong would talk to me more instead of paying attention to Wendy so much. Sometimes I think he wishes he had little boys instead of girls.

Ma-mah keeps telling me I have to be on my best behaviour when Ah-gong is here. All three of us grandchildren have to show respect to him. Last time Ah-gong came he told Ma-mah that the house wasn't clean enough. Maybe that's why she's vacuuming so much. I think Ba-bah is saying bad words upstairs because he still can't find the ugly sailboat we never put out unless Ah-gong is around. Whenever Ah-gong is here my Ba-bah gets goose bumps on his arms when Ah-gong talks harshly to him. I get nervous for Ba-bah.

My favourite thing about my ah-gong is the gardening he does. Every year when he visits, he sweeps up and cleans out all the dead leaves in the front yard in big black trash bags. Then he plants the most beautiful flowers. Last year were pink roses and the year before were camellias. He usually leaves at the end of spring when all the fragrances of the flowers waft in the air and all the pretty butterflies come to our garden. We have the best garden in the block because Ah-gong tends to it.

Maybe Ah-gong will like me better this year. I'm trying to get good at math with the flash cards. I don't read as much as Wendy, but I try to help around the house with Kimmie. I have to remember never to stick my chopsticks into my rice bowl. I don't like getting screamed at by my ah-gong.

I wake up extra early today because we are picking Ah-gong up at the airport. Ma-mah nags at me all morning.

'Sarah, get up! *Liah – liah!*'

'Five more minutes.'

'Don't make me come up the stairs! Wendy is already dressed.'

Wendy was *always* already dressed.

'Fine.'

I plop on to the floor and push myself up.

Whenever we go driving I sit behind Dad on the left side. He always drives and Mom sits to the right side of him, shotgun. Me and Wendy beg to ride shotgun, but Dad says only when we get older. Wendy sits behind Mom and Kimmie is sandwiched between us in the back seat of our grey, rusty stationwagon.

I love going to Chicago O'Hare Airport. The planes keep going in and out to exotic places. I want to jump on one of those planes and go to cities like Timbuktu or Luxemburg just because they have weird names and I saw them on the globe at home. I've never been on a plane before, but Ba-bah says that one day we're all going to Taiwan to see Ah-gong. It would be weird to go there. I imagine everyone looking like me. When I go to school most everyone is white.

The last time we went to the airport was to pick up my uncle Wai-bing. He was on business and had a man with a neat black hat holding a sign with his name on it at the gate. I thought it was exciting and special to have someone waiting with a big poster with your name. Wai-bing politely told the chauffeur that he was coming home with us instead of using the company's town car. I think secretly my dad was embarrassed by our old stationwagon but Wai-bing didn't seem to mind. In the morning eating my Captain Crunch I told Mom that I wanted to write a big sign for Ah-gong like the uniformed man did for Wai-bing. She told me not to be silly, but I still think it would be a cool idea.

When Ah-gong gets off of the plane, there is no jumping up and down and hugging right away like there is for some people I see around us. No, Ba-bah waves for him to come over, and they do a little reserved pat on the back. Ma-mah and I cower to the side but Kimmie is already trying to hug and hold Ah-gong, practically leaping out of Ba-bah's arms. Ah-gong just ruffles her hair and smiles at Wendy, who gives a huge grin just for Ah-gong. Left out, Kimmie pouts and turns red like a tomato when Ah-gong turns his attentions towards Wendy. Ma-mah tickles Kimmie and takes her off of Ba-bah's hands. Kimmie giggles and forgets about Ah-gong for a while. I feel like I need to say something or let Ah-gong know I'm excited he's around, but Ba-bah is already guiding Ah-gong to the parking garage and Ma-mah is dragging me along by the hand so I keep up.

In the car I look jealously at Ah-gong. He sits shotgun in front of Wendy, as my mom scoots in between Ah-gong and Ba-bah. Wendy practically glows because she's closest to Ah-gong in the back seat. I listen quietly as Ba-bah and Ah-gong catch up, while we speed along the highway.

Ma-mah spent all day yesterday shopping for all the ingredients to Ah-gong's favourite dishes. Bitter melon for a soup, pig's feet and peanuts to eat with the steamed rice, and cans of lychees for dessert. I hate bitter melon. It looks like a cucumber with icky warts. Pig's feet are yummy but people at school think I'm weird because I eat them. I love lychees. They are my favourite and I wish I could have them for all of my meals.

At dinner Ah-gong sits where Dad regularly sits. We usually have the evening news on in the living room, and Dad flips through *Newsweek* or comments on the latest reports to Mom. But today with Ah-gong here everything changes. The TV is shut off and all the magazines are tidily hidden under the coffee table. It's weird not to have background noise – news anchor and page turns.

I nibble on a pig's foot and delicately lay my chopsticks over my rice bowl and turn to Ah-gong sitting across the table from me diagonally. Wendy and Dad sit at the best seats next to Ah-gong.

'I have a question, Ah-gong,' I state to him, waiting to see if anyone else in my family is listening.

Ah-gong swallows his rice and turns to me slowly.

With his attention, I proceed. 'In school someone said I was Chinese. He said that Taiwan was part of China. His parents come from China. Is that true?'

'You are not Chinese. You are Taiwanese. Taiwan *not* part of China!' Ah-gong yells and bashes his fist down on the dinner table.

Ah-gong's eyes turn into Atomic Fireballs when you get him mad.

'We are not communist! We have own government. You must remember!' Ah-gong continues.

Ma-mah and Ba-bah start agreeing with him and vigorously nod their heads up and down like bobbing-head toys. Kimmie starts crying because Ah-gong's voice sounds so angry. I am not sure, but I'm almost sure that Wendy rolled her eyes at me before sipping some of her bitter melon soup.

I go back to eating my rice in silence and wonder if Ah-gong ever makes mistakes.

When I got back from school today Ma-mah was nervous. I could tell by the way she rubbed her hands against her coffee mug. Usually she has some Ritz crackers for me to chow down with my apple Juicy-Juice straw-box, but nothing was on the table.

'I was waiting for you,' my mom says anxiously.

'Is anything wrong?' I ask hesitantly as I pick a grape off from the fruit bowl on the kitchen counter-top to pop in my mouth.

'Ah-gong is in the hospital.'

While Mom was out shopping with Kimmie at the grocery store, Dad was at work, and Wendy and I were at school, Ah-gong had an accident.

The soil was still hard from a harsh winter even in mid March, so Ah-gong decided to take a break from the gardening and started a new hobby. My dad has a habit of buying lots of stuff to start a new hobby but never actually doing it. He has camping gear, oil-painting guides and hardware equipment. We have never gone camping, and there are paintings in my house that were never painted by my dad but were bought by Ah-gong or my mom, and the scary cutting saw has never seen a speck of wood in its life. All of the stuff is new like the first day it was bought. Ah-gong had given up on trying to fertilize and sow the garden and ventured into the garage for some ideas of other things to do to fix up the house. He was a city man and never went camping, paintings were for old ladies he thought, so he was left with unopened hardware equipment to use at last.

Each year hummingbirds, blue jays and cardinals flock to our backyard, but they never stay too long. They are social creatures and like to visit other backyards and see their friends. This year Ah-gong thought it would be nice to make a bird-house next to the garage to have a little family of birds to stay for a while.

Over the weekend Ah-gong dragged Ba-bah out to Home Depot to buy some lumber. Every day Ah-gong would use his wrinkled tan hands to treat the wood. Sandpapering, measuring, and eventually cutting.

When the entire family was gone, Ah-gong had finally started to cut the wood with the scary electric cutting saw that goes around in circles.

Outside there are still a few small carefully cut pieces of wood lying next to the machine. In the far corner there is a crooked piece of wood splattered with blood I hadn't noticed when I walked by it this afternoon.

'Is he all right?' I ask, worried.

'Wendy and Ba-bah are already at the hospital and Kimmie is sleeping but we can go when I wake her up.'

'How did it happen?'

'Ah-gong just slipped when he was holding the wood plank. Luckily our neighbours rushed him to the hospital. You know how Ah-gong's English isn't very good, but they drove him to the emergency room after they saw him ring on the doorbell and that he was bleeding with a towel over his hand.'

I am scared to ask how bad it is.

Hospitals have a funny smell and weird people come in and out because bad things have happened to them. This is my first time at the hospital besides being born, but I don't remember that. Ah-gong's room is far away from the parking lot so Ma-mah, Kimmie and me have to walk a long time before we reach it.

When I get there Wendy is sitting next to Ah-gong's hospital bed and Ba-bah is out getting a quick cup of coffee.

'*Ni hao ma?*' I ask in my bad Chinese whether or not Ah-gong is doing OK.

Ah-gong is pale and not moving much. Before he can answer, Wendy jumps in. 'He almost chopped his index and thumb fingers in half, but only got part of the nails whacked off on each finger.'

Ma-mah breathes a sigh of relief and bounces Kimmie up and down, to her delight.

I try and think of ways to make Ah-gong feel better.

'I bruised my knee today because I fell off the jungle gym. I bet it doesn't hurt as much as your fingers. At least you get to keep your fingers!'

'Sarah!' my mom gasps.

Ah-gong gives me a wary smile and says to Mom calmly that I was right. He did get to keep his fingers.

Wendy adds, 'Well, I hurt myself pretty bad last year trying to learn how to ride my bike.'

'Kimmie bumps her head a lot on the coffee table when she's trying to walk if we don't look after her, too,' I say.

Ma-mah looks exasperated – that's a super-big word I learned in school from my teacher when we were all annoying her.

'*Bai tou*! Ah-gong made a mistake, but the doctors here are going to fix him up,' Ma-mah states simply.

When I was really little I always thought Ah-gong was a god-like kinda grandfather. Not happy and joyful like the Buddha statue of the fat man next to the fireplace, but serious and wise like the God from the Bible that I see my friends read sometimes with pretty pictures. Today he doesn't look like God or Buddha, but just an old man.

Even through all the pain, Ah-gong tells us in Chinese that he is still going to finish making the bird-house so that a little family of cardinals can make baby birds in the spring. He may be hurt and getting old but he still cares about us. Ah-gong doesn't look so scary any more in the hospital bed.

It has been a week now and Ah-gong is recovering. The sun is finally shining and the kids in my block are playing kick-ball again. Wendy joins in the game, but I stick around and hand Ah-gong a cold glass of lemonade. He says thank you in English and takes a huge sip before placing the glass on the ground. The bird-house is almost finished, all except painting on a gooey varnish to make it shiny. I ask if I can paint, too, and Ma-mah makes me wear one of Dad's old shirts to make sure I don't get all messy. Ah-gong gives me a smile as we dip our paintbrushes into the tin of smelly varnish. We glide our brushes up and down at the same time and finish the bird-house together.

THERE WAS A TURTLE
Kavita Jindal

'I live a charmed life,' Anil said with a little self-deprecating laugh. It was his stock response to any comment on the pendant that hung around his neck. Although in the beginning he had only half meant it, it was a good line, and it was true, because his life seemed to glide over ruts on the path, his wheels never got bogged down, and like all things half truth and half superstition, the sentence had turned into belief. He had lived with his charms for thirty years.

He was saying this now, modestly, to his new neighbour, who had recently moved in to the house next door. She came round to deliver a parcel she had taken for him from the postman that morning, when he was out doing his twenty-five lengths of the pool. She remarked on the turtle charm at his neck, its sea sheen contrasting vividly with his dark skin. He could tell she was longing to ask him why he didn't go to work every morning, why he seemed so much at ease with time. He had noticed her husband leave at seven thirty in the morning and return at seven thirty in the evening. It made him appreciate his freedom even more. How good it was to have made your money and taken the decision to sit back and enjoy your life. Anil spent the afternoons in his study making his money work for him, but he wasn't going to tell her that.

He carried in the small parcel, checking that it really was for him. It seemed to have been professionally gift-wrapped in glossy paper the colour

197

of cornflowers. He noticed that the address label was blue grey, co-ordinating with the paper. The distinctive black handwriting was Scarlett's. This was unexpected. It had been a long time since she had sent him anything. Anil had begun to believe that, finally, Scarlett didn't remember him much any more. He counted the years. The last parcel was twelve years ago. And what a domestic drama that had created.

Scarlett was his first long-term girlfriend. He was just nudging twenty on that first day of his art course when he was introduced to her. He didn't even properly register his other classmates the whole first week. He recalled looking into Scarlett's eyes as they shook hands. A chemical reaction kicking into their fingers. It was difficult to release his grasp and he didn't want to shake hands with anyone else for fear of losing that mad dislocated feeling.

It was Scarlett who had carved the mother-of-pearl turtle, strung it on to brown leather and garlanded him with it. 'For wisdom,' she said, 'or longevity. For the beginning of the world. Depends which culture you pick your meaning from. But I'm giving it to you for good luck. Keep it here' – she patted the skin at the top of his chest – 'and you'll have my luck-wish always with you.' A new light was shining in her eyes as if she had just discovered something magical. Back then, they were each deciding what kind of artist they wanted to be. Anil wondered if big sculptural works were his thing, although that involved a steep learning curve and the idea didn't thrill him as it should. He was inspired by a visit to his aunt's home in Belsize Park; she had collected cow-pats on her trip to India and encased them in a Perspex box. He could do a big display on a theme like that. It was more conceptual, a statement of old worlds embraced by the new, much more suited to his mind.

On carving that first turtle, Scarlett had found her métier. 'Small is beautiful,' she would croon, adding disturbingly, 'Small is powerful.' She seemed to have discovered an intense pleasure in carving small animal charms, each with a personality, an emotion she had embedded in it. She took a long time creating them, painstakingly learning the techniques, spending birthday money from her grandmother on micro carving tools ordered from Germany and setting up a studio time-share with a sculptor of busts. She spent hours sourcing the right materials – chunks of marble, alabaster, turquoise or onyx – and kept them under her pillow while she decided which animal it was to be and how much spirit she would give it.

Anil had laughingly called it her fetish phase, for this is where her sudden inspiration had come from, the Native American traditions, but he had stopped winking and laughing soon enough, the night he had gone late to her shared flat for a promised visit and found her engrossed in viewing the video *The Complete Guide to Sharpening Your Tools*.

At first she crafted three pieces, which she gave away as gifts, having sworn the recipients, the first being Anil, to wearing them constantly. The finely engraved amulets were widely admired in the college and soon Scarlett was making and selling charms on commission, first for her peers and then for friends of friends of friends. Her obsessive fetish phase was turning into a livelihood – albeit a meagre one.

Anil didn't know if the other recipients of the first three charms had kept their promise to wear the pendants constantly, or if they had removed them after a suitably loyal period. He himself had not intended to wear the turtle for ever, but her luck-wish for him seemed to work so well, bringing him jolts of good fortune and better health, with his asthma almost disappearing, that he felt his life was now tied to it. The turtle had become something of a signature piece.

Anil wore a carved wolf, too, in taut-muscled onyx, which lived round his wrist on a slender plait of leather. Scarlett had given it to him on what would have been their third anniversary together, had they not broken up a couple of months before. It had been left in a small box with a card in her neat hand spelling out its meaning. The wolf had a curiously far-away expression, which at first unsettled Anil. But then he read the card: Pathfinder. Teacher. He put on the bracelet and immediately felt its power synchronizing with his skin, working for him. He warmed to the wolf; a pathfinder was just what he needed. He had not taken it off since then, except to replace the frayed leather.

From Anil's perspective their break-up had been amicable, or as amicable as a splintering of lovers can be. He told their friends that for their age they had done well to sustain such an intense relationship for almost three years. He instigated their parting; he and Scarlett seemed to be aiming for different things, disparate lives. Anil wanted a sense of grandeur in everything and his take on life was to say: 'I'll dive into the mêlée and emerge with gems.' Living on the fringes was losing its appeal, however intense or enfolding the company may be. Scarlett had agreed that they were now different people from when they first met. 'At least one of us has changed,' she said drily.

On his traverse through life, Anil had left Art and Scarlett behind, but occasionally he caught glimpses of her existence on the edges of the gallery world. He had seen a review of a show in the *Independent*; his eye had been drawn to the colourful photograph and he had been surprised to see her name in the caption, credited as the artist. It was a show of paintings, large canvases, so big that they were made to take up one wall of a room entirely; to fit a dining room, possibly, or a client reception area. He wasn't surprised that they weren't particularly saleable. She wasn't letting you choose whether to rest your eye on splashy pink and peach peonies in three feet by two feet; no, she was compelling you to look at – or look away from – a wall covered with them, waving at you, shouting out their none-too-subliminal messages. *Such a contrast to the exquisite charms, weighty with intent. A release from them?*

Anil often wondered what he would paint, if he tried again. Would anything inspire him to pick up a brush? He never did, although he hoarded his old work, his notebooks, his materials. 'I'm a sentimental fool,' he chided himself, when he came across letters, lists, even budgets, in the recesses of drawers, at the back of his cupboards, in shoeboxes.

Scarlett had not told him that she would be sending him occasional gifts when they had gone their separate ways. A package had arrived the day before his twenty-sixth birthday. It was an alabaster dog on a long leather cord. Under the magnifying glass Anil looked for her nuanced touches. He decided from the sleek ears hanging down and the long snout that it was a German pointer or similar breed. The dog's mouth was part open in a smile. Scarlett had enclosed a note: 'For loyalty and friendship. Wear it to give you whatever you want at the moment.' *Wealth.* Unable to resist he had slung it on. It lay above his navel, hidden for the most part. It had provoked a rush of confidence and ideas and he could swear the charm worked, for he was making headway and money was being earned and earned.

He didn't list his expenses any more. As a fund manager, he had turned out to have an appetite for risk. The bigger the risk, the bigger the gain. Anil figured he had nothing to lose and no responsibilities; he didn't worry about staking his name, or losing his game. This innate confidence in his decisions led to early successes, which multiplied into successes in the big stakes. Anil worked hard, he had to, but knowing his market was one thing. Combining this with an impeccable sense of timing, and further combining it with favourable luck, was another.

Some months later he wrote to thank Scarlett for the alabaster dog, and told her that he genuinely thought of his charms as his stairway to the moon. He wrote he was doing well, asked after her and signed off with 'Keep in touch'. That last was a sentence he didn't mean. He knew she would realize that from the sign-off itself – she knew him well enough.

It was just as well she hadn't called 'to chat' or wanted to meet for a 'catch-up'. He didn't have the stomach for that sort of thing. It would be an awkward and graceless meeting, he knew. What's past is past. Even if the powerful resonance of the past, her crafted good-will tokens, lived with him as talismans on his body, a part of his persona.

Scarlett herself seemed remote to him now; he didn't think of her often. If he saw someone wearing an animal pendant, or he heard the Peter Frampton song, *I'm In You*, which she used to play in her studio, he would see a vision of Scarlett. Her head bent over the table, hair falling forward, her long hands cupping the small shapes, her fingers with knobbly knuckles jutting out as she worked. Her pile of books on ancient wisdoms. She drew from several cultures; this was one reason why the physical act of sculpting these animals so appealed to her: she imbued them with the spirit of their attributes and her own wishes for the wearer.

He remembered teasing her about being animistic in her beliefs. When asked to make Celtic symbols or a laughing Buddha, she had refused, and dismissed those commissions. She would carve just animals. She maintained there was a long enough list to choose from. 'Oh, carve a Buddha,' Anil had urged once, eyeing her as she chiselled and whittled away at a miniature red-brown rooster. 'What's it to you?'

Her reply had been grandiose. In what Anil termed College Language. 'An artist who compromises her integrity is doomed.'

Once, at his firm's annual drinks party, he bumped into Estelle, a classmate from art college, who told him she had just commissioned a pendant from Scarlett. A lizard. Anil had smiled. *So, Scarlett was still carving animals.* He didn't know what else was going on in her life, but sometimes he thought she was standing rooted in the same spot. His life was a lightning-streak climb from the point where he had started to where he was now.

'Scarlett lives in Wales, in an artists' community. Did you know?' asked Estelle.

'Yes, she sent me her address.'

'You don't see her at all?'

'No, not really.'

Estelle was going out with a colleague of Anil's. He guessed she must have heard that he was doing well. But he was careful not to show off to his ex-classmates, especially those who were artists. It was almost embarrassing how much he earned.

'I hear you've bought a house in Highgate.' *Yes, Estelle was up with the gossip.*

'Uh huh.'

'Are you living there now?'

'No, it's being refurbished . . . It'll take a few months. You know how these things drag on . . .' Anil shrugged and fiddled with the wolf at his wrist. Then he excused himself to drift off to another knot of people. If Scarlett saw his new house, he knew she would refer to it as a 'mansion', just as she would tell him that he had become 'another faceless suit'. What she would say about the Porsche, he didn't want to know; he was sure the word 'typical' would be used.

He smiled to himself again. He had never been so happy. He had everything a man could want. Almost. Because just when he thought he had everything, he'd think of something else which would add to his life, make it perfect.

A fragile package from Wales found its way to him in his Highgate home a few years later. Anil was about to get married. He opened the little box and found a green lump inside. Scarlett's note said it was a caterpillar, not that he could discern that. It lacked her usual fine etching. He couldn't tell which ancient culture it derived from, if any; possibly because loneliness was a feature of modern culture. She had written that she was lonely, the past year or two had been difficult; sending a charm to him had dispelled some of her isolation, some of the meaninglessness. 'I know when you receive this I'll begin to feel better. I know your wishes will be with me.'

This intent, the alleviation of her loneliness, came attached to the caterpillar, making it feel heavier than it was. He couldn't bear to put it around his neck. He clipped off the attached cord and for Scarlett's sake he carried the charm in his pocket. He wrote back that it was different and interesting, and he hoped that the caterpillar being with him would nudge the lonely spaces around her to be filled with friendship and love. Anil could talk the talk when needed. He suspected this was the right response, even if Scarlett guessed it was slightly false. After three months or so of being dutifully carried around, the green lump had gone into a small walnut box where he kept disused cufflinks, and there it had stayed.

He had not mentioned the caterpillar to Maya, his wife. He didn't want to add to the displeasure which he imagined existed about his charms. Because it would be natural, normal, although Maya denied any resentment. She had not known him without them and, in her serene way, she seemed generally accepting of their place in his history.

On their honeymoon she asked, just once, if he had constantly to wear all three talismans together. 'It's not really you,' she said. Anil knew what she meant, but he bristled all the same. 'They are a part of me,' he replied. 'Look at everything these charms have brought me.' He gestured expansively at the azure ocean, the pink horizon, the tasteful white hotel. He turned a serious gaze on Maya. 'My luck has brought me you,' he said, 'and you are the most precious thing in my life.'

It was true. Anil believed himself fortunate, in every respect. Even marriage had not let him down. 'Somewhere, inside, I must be clever or wise,' he would say. 'How did I know to choose Maya?' Though truth be told, he thought of Maya as the wise one. The one with the calm personality and deep reserves of affection, which he had slowly uncovered when they first met.

Together they had abandoned their old lifestyles, side-stepped into the slow lane and embraced a life of family and leisure. They had the house, the garden (indeed, it had been featured in *House and Garden* after the last re-vamp) and they had the brilliant child.

Anil was satisfied with how it had all turned out. When he had needed to disentangle himself from the notion of Art and make a success of himself in other ways, he had managed to do that, working hard but being rewarded for it, always, and not demanding too much of life, not demanding everything all at one time. He had achieved the most difficult thing of all: contentment.

When he did think of Scarlett, he wished the same for her. But he was beginning to wonder. Scarlett had surprised him by sending another charm five years after the caterpillar. It was the month of his fifth wedding anniversary and the third birthday of his daughter. Resting in white tissue lay a light-brown bird in profile. He laid the carving on his palm, feeling its weight, its spirit. Skills he had learned from Scarlett. The bird, innocent as it was, made him uneasy. His stomach tightened. He set the little thing down. He emptied the small carton it came in, separating the packaging. There was no note. He would have to investigate the meaning himself to becalm his superstition. He was looking up relevant Web pages when Maya came into the study. He showed her the charm.

'I think it's a hummingbird,' he said. 'Look at the beak.'

Maya's reaction stunned him. 'She can't send you a charm!' was her first exclamation. Then, angrily, 'What is the woman thinking?'

'This might be antler bone,' Anil mused, ignoring her outburst. 'Antler bone is expensive.'

He couldn't deflect Maya's glare from the carved bird. She picked it up. 'What does it mean?'

Anil knew his symbolism fairly well, but the hummingbird was proving difficult to divine. He prevaricated. 'Usually, birds are messengers in some form. It could mean a change in consciousness.'

'Hmmn . . .' Maya glanced over him at the monitor. 'Stopper of time,' she read out.

There was an uncomfortable silence.

'Nothing sounds quite right,' said Anil. He shrugged. 'Anyway, it doesn't matter. I'll just put it away.'

Maya dangled the bird from its cord. 'She wants you to wear this. Like the others you wear. After all this time. How many years? What *is* she playing at?'

Anil regretted not mentioning the caterpillar to Maya, but now was not the moment.

'Send it back,' said Maya. 'At once. Tell Scarlett not to send you any more charms. Ever.'

'I can't do that,' he protested. He watched Maya's darkening brow. 'She'll feel really bad. After all the fantastic luck I've had.'

'Have you seen her lately, been in touch?'

'No. No. It's just . . . I think she sends me things when she's going through a bad patch. If it helps her to send me something, I don't mind.'

'Anil, are you sending this back right now?'

'No.'

'Then I will.' And Maya had picked up the box and was reading the address on the back.

'You will not.'

'I will.'

They struggled with the box. Anil wrested the squeezed cardboard from Maya.

'Please,' he cajoled. 'There's no need to be hasty. Nothing really for you to get worked up about. It's just a bird. Nothing at all.'

'I'm not getting worked up.' Her face had flushed. She'd stomped away and been sullen for days.

Anil had not written to Scarlett. He couldn't find the words to tell her not to send him any more charms. But there was no need for the letter. They had both forgotten. He stuck the bird out of sight at the back of his desk drawer. But when he came across it as he hunted for an old pen or a lost note, his fingers felt singed, as if a current was passing through them, and he would withdraw his hand. Gingerly he would take the bird out, lay it on the skin of his forearm, testing it again. It sent tingles down the length of his arm, and after a few minutes, if he left it there, it would clutch like a hot hand inside his stomach. Eventually, he had wrapped it up in an old tie and shoved it to the very back of the drawer.

Now, twelve years later, he was holding this most recent present from

Scarlett, fancily wrapped in cornflower blue. Anil went up the stairs to his study and shut the door. He placed the parcel on his desk, studying it again before he tore off the wrapping paper.

Inside was a white cardboard box stuffed with tissue which he pulled out and unrolled. A small figurine fell on to the amber leather of his desk. His brow furrowed. This didn't look like Scarlett's work at all. He looked inside the box for a note. Once again, nothing.

Pensively, he picked up the carving. It was unwearable, charmless, unexplainable to Maya. 'Power,' he imagined Scarlett crooning.

He gazed at the trees outside his window, leaves peeling off in the wind. He would be fifty in two months. Young by modern standards and old by the standards of the young. Scarlett's new talisman was bringing on an unnatural sensation. He felt both too young and too old. Too young.

He sighed and laid the new arrival on his palm. It wasn't an animal. It looked like a representation of the human figure. A narrow rectangular block. Wooden or resin? A mixture of both, perhaps. Male? There was a black snake coiled around the brown block. He set it on the table to examine it under a magnifying glass. The snake coiled from an indentation near the bottom of the rectangle, which could be ankle height, to an indentation near the top, which could be the neck.

Him, Anil. He knew about snakes and humans. Powerful mythology – life, death, creation, transmutation. So, she was sending him on his way to enjoy a rebirth? He laughed out loud. Then he found himself standing up, humour draining away. Why had she sent a human figure? She'd broken her own rules. Why?

He sat back down. He would write to Scarlett. He would ask, 'Lettie, is it really what it seems? Have you turned me into a choking doll?' *Ridiculous.* His thoughts were running away with him, running so fast they were making him physically sick. He realized he was sweating and blinking. The charms he was wearing were beginning to make his skin itch. On his jugular, on his pulse, on the solar plexus. His skin was chafing against them. He removed them: the now-clammy turtle which nestled in the hollow of his neck; the far-away wolf which had hugged his wrist; the companionable dog on the long cord.

With trembling fingers Anil brought out the hummingbird from the recesses of his desk and unshrouded it. His stomach lurched. He took down the box of old cufflinks from the shelf and brought out the caterpillar, into the light after all these years. The shapeless green crackled against the skin of his palm.

Anil wiped the sweat off his face, but he wouldn't stop what he was doing now. He could feel his blood surging in strange places inside him: in his joints, at the back of his skull, in his toenails and fingernails. His stomach clasping itself over and over. Methodically, he lined up the carvings on his desk. Made from stones and bones. In the case of the turtle, made from the distress juices of tortured oysters. *Love them, loathe them, burn them.*

Trying to take a deep breath, he brought out writing paper. He could calm his mind if he tried. He could write her a reasonable letter. He could find a way to ask if she was unconsoled. Spleenful. Deep breath, he said to himself, to the blood spurting inside, hot and heavy. He, too, could exercise his will.

'Scarlett,' he wrote on the blue paper. His ankles, feverish and painful, pulled to the floor. His elbows weighed him down. His pen hovered above the paper while he formed the first question carefully. He ignored the pain, to think it through, but his wrists were flushed and swollen and, tiring, his right hand came down to rest on the desk.

His forehead followed, shoulders rounded, and he turned his face so his left cheek was pressed to the paper. He lay quietly.

THE FIRST HIT
Laura Peters

The cab swooshes to a stop. The passenger window winds down as I walk towards it.

'Ms Olson?'

I lean into the window frame. 'Yes. Thanks.'

'White Hart Road was it, love?'

The wipers squeak a slow arc.

'Please.'

I scrunch my eyes against the drizzle, and unclick the back door handle. I dip my head, climb in and flinch as I make the door slam shut. The car smells of forest pine. A green card tree hangs from the rear-view mirror. I watch it jiggle as we move off.

The OUT-PATIENTS sign looms through the water-beaded window. I quickly turn away from it. I sit behind a glass screen dividing the driver and myself. Smoothing down my damp hair I wince as my finger touches my forehead. I catch my reflection in the glass. A translucent version of myself. I scan the figure with the grey-blond hair, the pale face, the hands folded in her lap. I narrow my eyes to check for the graze on her head. I stop looking. I turn back to the window, to the puddles on the pavement, to the orange-yellow piles of soggy shovelled leaves. We pass avenues of bare spiky trees, rain varnished and shining in the headlights. I fix my eyes on a single water droplet on the glass, and rest them there, until the trees all blur into one.

Dad stood beside me on the beach that day. We were watching Tom on his hands and knees frantically scrabbling at the sand. Tom was encouraging Rubus to dig with him.

'Come on, boy! Rubes, whatcha got, whatcha found?'

He starts laughing as Rubus quickly paws at the sand, flicking it up behind his body. We watch them digging head to head. The bright blond hair and the big black muzzle. Rubus bounds back a few steps, and spins round full circle, before diving back down again to Tom. We watch him barking into the hole, pawing at the sand as his tail thuds against his hind legs. Dad's laughing. I'm laughing. Dad turns to the promenade. Luka's skimming stones at the seagulls. He calls him over.

'Luka's coming home with me, so you and Tom be careful. No getting into any mischief.' He adjusts the windbreaker in his right hand. It whips in the breeze.

'Right, Bridie' – he pushes the sleeve of his sweater back and checks his watch – 'home by seven thirty, all right?'

'Yeeeessss Daaad.' I drone the words out.

'I mean it, seven thirty.'

I nod and pass Dad my bucket. He turns towards the sea. The tide's almost in.

'See you later, Tom!' he calls out.

Tom springs up and runs over, Rubus bounding beside him.

'Bye, Mr Olson.'

Dad turns round to us, walking backwards a few steps.

'Don't go too far!'

Rubus follows Dad and Luka to the railing. I give Tom a smile and we both call Rubes back.

We'd spent that whole day at the beach. The sea was like blue-green glass. And the gentle white roll of the waves broke smoothly over the sand. The sea rushed into the bay in layers. There were at least five thin white ridges on the horizon, like the crests of an eyelash, but only the nearest ridge would sweep on to the sand. A pot-bellied child in a Minnie Mouse swimming-costume screamed and ran from a wave as the cool water touched her toes. When the water sucked itself back, she turned and ran towards it again, bucket in hand. By the promenade wall, kids with plastic spades or chalk stones carved their names in giant letters into the sand. Two children carefully tried to bury their father before he woke from a sun-drenched snooze. Only his head was left free. I knew how the sand would crinkle over his body, how they would have to pack a lot of sand on top of him before it stuck to him in a perfect mould.

Up above the promenade, brightly coloured kites wheeled high over the cliff top. Outside the blue and yellow beach huts, sandalled ladies in bikinis adjusted themselves under the sun, and old men with orange-brown skin like tanned leather sat in stripy deckchairs. The seagulls strutted along the prom, occasionally scraping at mushed-up chips on the paving. They were always there, lining the blue railings outside the café, eyeing up the passing food.

Dad took us out in the dinghy that afternoon. We'd lost the oars the summer before. He attached a length of blue plastic cord to the front of the dinghy so he could pull us around in the water. I trailed my hand under the lip of the waves, and watched Dad guiding us through the sea. Tom leaned forward as he called out to Rubus, revealing the sprinkling of freckles on his neck. And I wonder if he ever felt the weight of my eyes on his back, on his neck, on those freckles.

'Rube! Rubus!' He leant to his right, tilting our boat slightly as he splashed his hand in the water. And Rubus, muzzle up, ears back, swam in close, paddling alongside us. We all sat in seawater, even though we'd tried to keep it out. It made my swimming-costume cling to my skin. The rubber squeaked as Luka stretched a leg out from behind me and it made the dinghy wobble on the water. Dad joked around with us out there.

'Ohhh, I'm going to let go! You'd better hold on!'

We watched the rope in his hand.

'No! No!' we squealed.

'Ohhhh, it's going!'

'You're not gonna!'

But he did. He let a few waves rock us away, the blue rope floating on the water, before he laughed and splashed back out to grab it. I liked that feeling – Dad holding the rope, slightly silhouetted in the sun, so that all you could see was the water sparkling on his skin.

Tom joined us at a time of hay fights. We had to wait a few days for a good one. We'd hear the machines chugging outside the front of the house, whipping up the weeds and spitting out the undergrowth. And then we'd wait. You could fight in the cool, earthy, wet grass, but it never had the same effect. We'd wait for the greens to turn to browns and yellows. We'd wait for the perfect itchy-scratchiness of it. The rules were simple. I'd follow Luka outside and we'd start rustling through the field towards the tree at the far corner. Luka kicked clumps of hay to his left with his right foot. A footballer's kick. The hay hissed and scattered. My feet prickled as the blades stuck between the straps of my sandals and jabbed at my skin. We looked towards the tree. We heard the shiver of leaves, a snap, and then the thud. Tom. His white-blond hair flopped in front of his face. He flicked his head to one side and smiled. I never understood how he could climb so high. Luka would walk on towards him, and I'd watch the back of his head, the tight corkscrew curls. I crouched down slowly to the hay, made my fingers rake-like, and quietly clawed the dry grass towards me before standing.

'Luka!'

He half turned towards me. I pelted a clump of hay at his face. The first hit. I felt the fizz of excitement in my belly. I started running. I could hear the quickening swish of his stride behind me. Luka grabbed the back of my shirt, and the material stretched like elastic. He tried to knock my feet out from under me. I slipped forwards but had already learnt how to make cushions of my hands. Luka pushed the bone of his knee into my back. My cheek scratched in the grass. Luka stuffed a load down the back of my neck. I twisted my ear into the ground.

'Ahh ha! Luka! Get off!'

'Eat hay, Bridie!'

I blew the hair from the corner of my mouth. I could smell the earth beneath my face.

'Luka!'

It was Tom. The weight lifted from my back. I heard the whoosh and hiss as a fistful of hay hit Luka's head.

'Can't get me, Luka!'

I looked up at the yellow-brown straw poking scarecrow-like from his head. It always stuck better in Luka's hair.

'Can't get me, Luka-verruca!'

I heard Tom scrabble with the hay at his feet. Then the final, 'Looka-verroo-ca!' before Luka took the bait, pressing down on my shoulders to push himself up and run after Tom.

And the game continued.

The sky would darken to a sugar-paste yellow blue and begin to turn the tree into a silhouette.

'Luka! Bridie!' We'd hear the call. 'Luka! Bridie! Tea's ready!'

I'd turn to look at Luka. He'd catch my eye, then turn and run towards the house, arms swinging at loose right angles. I'd look back towards the tree. I'd turn and wave across the grass and watch Tom watching us go in. In the fading light all you could see clearly was the bright blond of his hair, as he let his handful of hay fall to the ground.

Inside, Harriet would be slouched in Mum's lap, the back of her head resting in the crook of Mum's arm. She was very small back then.

I smile. I have a clear image of her sitting on the floor at home, brushing her hair with an unopened chocolate bar. 'This is your comb, Harriet,' I'd tell her. She'd look up at me with those wide ocean-blue eyes, open-mouthed, as I pulled the soft white bristles through my hair. 'Brush brush, Harriet.' She'd raise an arm towards me and I'd smile as I passed her the comb. 'Brush brush.' And she'd lift both hands to her head to continue brushing her hair. Always back to front. From the back of her head to the fluffy blond swirls by her ears. A shiny purple wrapper scraping one ear, and the soft bristles touching the other. Grinning a half-moon gappy smile at me.

I suppose we knew we'd end up at the marina. We'd stayed out to go there. It was our place. Mine and Tom's. It was the first place I ever took him the summer he arrived. We used to wait until the last of the kids had kicked down their castles, jumping on the sandy remains. We'd walk along the calm, flat still of the beach to the marina. The late-afternoon sun would throw the shadow of the prom rail out on to the sand in huge grey rectangles. And there'd be lime-green lichen, the colour of a moray eel, covering the curve of the promenade wall. I liked looking for the scattered crab shells. Tiny brown cups speckled with blue, emptied by the gulls. I'd always find the white bony crab legs, their pincers inept. I'd hear the seagulls screeching overhead, as they soared over the cliff top, over the promenade. A flock of them, gliding in vague circles, wings outstretched, so that their perfectly smooth shadows would float across the sand. Out in the distance, before the thin slit of the sea, were the rock pools. The white chalk stone covered in seaweed in blacks and bottle greens. We'd throw chalk pebbles for Rubus. Watch his sleek black body tearing after them, before he lolloped back to Tom, dropping the stone at his feet, tail up, ears up, with a thick pink tongue hanging from one side of his jaw.

I knew how the cool sand became a canvas of hard ripples by the marina. How I'd have to tiptoe up to the edge of it to stop the arches of my feet from hurting. We'd stand on the brown rock wall and skim stones across the water. Plink, plink, plink, plink. Then the splash as Rubus jumped in after them. It always made Tom laugh. He'd laugh, look up, and smile that wide, raspberry-lipped smile at me. And I'd catch that smile and pass another one back. It was easy.

'Come on, Rubes!' He'd tap his hand on his leg. 'Come on!' And we'd see the black head gliding towards us. We'd walk to the corner of the marina where the water was deepest, and look down.

'Look, Bride! You see 'em?'

'No, where?'

'There.' He'd point closer to the water. 'Look.'

And I'd see the shoal of tiny grey fish, before Rubus got too close and made them dart. We'd walk the edge of the marina, round to the flight of steps leading down from the prom. We'd hold the cold metal rail that made our fingers feel sticky, to pull us up the first step. And Rubus would swim over, race us to the top, and spray us with a salty shake of his coat.

That evening, we walked towards the promenade steps, patting our legs at Rubus. The tide had already rolled in across most of the bay. We crossed the prom and climbed the steps that led up to the hills on the cliff top. The hills were steep mounds of grass banks that ran along both sides of a winding Tarmac path. They made a gentle gorge of the track. The wind caught us as we came up out of the pathway and reached higher ground. My hair stung my cheeks as it whipped against them. It had already started spitting. We had to walk almost as far as the marina to shelter behind the secluded crescent of a hedgerow. We used to make camps up there. I looked up at the sky, and felt the light patter of water on my face. The clouds looked heavy. I thought of how the sky had sucked up all the stuffy heat of the day, and how it was churning it into thick grey storm clouds. We heard a rumble in the distance. We wouldn't be able to stay out long.

We waited for the rain to ease. My body felt heavy. I'd been cheated out of my time with Tom. I looked at my watch and thought of Dad. We got up quickly to leave. Rubus leapt up with us, excited by the sudden movement. He jumped up at Tom, and bolted off down the path.

'Rubus!' We called him back laughing. 'Come on, Rubes! We're not going back down there.'

But he'd turned the corner of the hedge and we couldn't see him. We started running after him, half laughing at his excitement, half laughing at ourselves chasing a dog in the rain. We turned the end of the hedgerow. Rubus stood at the top of the promenade steps waiting for us.

'Rubus! Here boy!' Tom took a step towards him. Rubus stood for a moment, then turned and ran down the steps.

We heard the waves before we saw them. That crash, boom, slap as they hit the prom wall and spat the salt water over the side. Crash boom slap. Crash boom slap. We ran down after him. I turned the last flight of stone steps to see the rails of the marina in front of us on the promenade. And Rubus standing there. The wet hair hanging from his belly, his face and legs already soaked. I looked at the water, hearing that rush and boom as the waves crashed into the wall, throwing the water up so that it splattered on to the prom.

'Rubus!' Tom slapped his thigh. Hard. 'Rubus!'

The dog looked up at us. Then back to the sea. Tom moved towards him. Rubus turned at the sound, and ran to the rails, ears up, tail up.

'Rubus! NO!'

He ran down into the water.

'Rubus!' We ran to the rails. There were two steps of the marina left above the water. We looked down. We saw the black head. 'Rubus! Come here!'

He looked at us, paddled towards us, but drifted to the right.

'Rubus! Come on!'

Tom ran down the steps. He gripped the rail. I heard him gasp as a wave hit the step and splashed up at him.

'Tom!'

I ran to the edge of the steps. A wave hit Rubus, dragging him out as it sucked back. He started whining.

'RUBUS!' Tom climbed through the rail, holding it tight. He kept one hand on the rail, balancing on the edge of the step, and reached over the water. 'RUBUS!'

The dog's ears were pinned back. He was paddling hard. His muzzle strained up over the lip of the waves. He was getting closer. Whimpering. Tom crouched lower and grabbed out for him.

'Swim, Rubus! Swim!'

Tom stretched out further and made contact with the scruff of his neck.

We didn't see the wave. We were fixed on Rubus. It broke over the black of his body flushing him beneath the murky grey.

'RUBUS!'

'TOM! GET HIM OUT! GET HIM OUT!'

Tom thrashed his hand under the water, reaching, reaching. Something twisted in my stomach like thick wet rope. I could taste the salt on my lips.

'TOM!'

I saw the muzzle, an ear, the black head.

'RUBUS!' Tom yelled, his voice straining over the roar.

And then another wave. CRASH BOOM SLAP. It ripped his hand from the railing.

'TOM!' I grabbed the rail. *I can't let go. Don't let go.* 'TOM!' I screamed.

His arms flailed working hard against the water. Waves smothered him, cocooning him, pushing his head under. He retched and coughed and spat out water. It was sucking him down.

I reached out, reached out. *Please just give me his hand. Please just give me his hand.* I saw a wave swelling on the horizon. *Please. Please. Please.*

My phone rings. I flinch at the shrill tinny ring tone. I'm suddenly aware of the trees, the wet streets, the cars. I take the phone from my pocket. I don't recognize the number. I place the flashing green screen to my ear.

'Hello?'

'Bride? Bridie?'

'Harriet, it's you.'

'My God, Bridie. Where are you? What happened? Are you all right?'

She's speaking quickly. My head starts to pound. I press my forehead.

'I didn't recognize your number.'

'It's a work phone. Are you all right? Where are you? Luka just called me.'

'I'm OK, Harriet. I'm just on my way home.'

'You're not driving? Tell me you're not driving.'

'No, no.' I shake my head. 'I'm in a taxi.'

I clock the driver's eyes in the rear-view mirror. I turn to face the window.

'What's happened to the car?'

'I think Luka said he'll pick it up tomorrow for me.'

'Bloody hell, Bride. Is it a write-off?'

'No, it wasn't that bad. It's got a bit of a dent above the wheel arch, that's all.'

'That's all! Jesus, Bridie, you scared me half to death.'

'I'm fine, Harriet. Just a few scratches. Really.'

'And the other car? Is the woman all right?'

'Yes, she's OK. She came off better than me, I think.' I muster a weak smile.

Harriet blows out a sigh down the phone. 'Why didn't you call me, Bride?'

'I called Luka. I knew he'd be at home. You were working, Harriet. I just called Luka.'

'Well, thank God you're all right. Listen, I'll be over straight after work.'

'Harriet, you don't need to, it's –'

'I want to. I need to see you for myself. No buts. I'll be over at seven. You just get home and get some rest, OK?'

I say nothing. There's nothing to say.

'Bridie? You still there?'

'Yeah, yes, sorry. It just got me thinking, that's all.'

'Well, you've had quite a shock.'

I nod my assent.

'Harriet, do you remember Rubus?'

'Rubus?'

'Tom's old dog,' I prompt her. 'You remember Tom.'

'Vaguely. I didn't know he ever had a dog. Bridie? Listen, where are you now? Are you nearly home?'

I look at the grey streets, the old churchyard, the dripping elm.

'Yeah,' I tell her. 'I'm pretty close.'

I don't know how long we stood there. Soaking wet. Watching the water. From the corner of my eye I saw the white blond of Tom's hair whipping in the wind. I drew my elbows into me, pulling my jumper to my chin. Still we watched the water. We scanned it. Nothing. Another wave. Still nothing. Our silence clung to me like oil on a seabird.

'Tom?' I heard myself mumble.

'Tom?' My voice felt thin. He didn't move. He looked at the water. My stomach lurched. I swallowed down hard. 'Maybe he swam somewhere else.'

He said nothing. I turned to look at him. At his hair, his face, his hands. I wanted to move closer. But I couldn't. I didn't.

'Tom?' I felt the warm smears run down my face. My eyes blurred. I turned away. All I could see was the grey of the waves.

I didn't see Tom the next day, or the one after that, but I heard that Mr Sullivan took him back to the marina, and scoured the beach for Rubus. They never found him.

I sat a week later on the warm sand behind a rainbow windbreaker, and took the sandwiches as Dad passed them out of a blue plastic cool-box. I looked down at my lunch.

'Eat up, Bridie.'

I looked at Dad, then back at the sandwich. I took a bite. Egg. Something grated between my teeth as though the shell had been left in. My tongue slid round the slimy, gritty egg, and I swallowed hard. I heard Luka belch next to me. The sickly sweet smell of orange squash hung in the air for a second, then dissipated into the pungent salty seaweed. Luka stood up.

'Come on, Bride!'

He ran towards the sea. I watched him go. I looked at the sea. I turned my head back. Dad was looking at me. I got up and started walking, my feet sinking in the soft sand, like stepping into a bowl of icing sugar. Luka was already paddling in the waves. I saw him bending over, hands under the water. He turned to look at me as I neared him.

'Bridie! Come on!'

I took a few steps into the water and gasped as it lapped at my ankles. Luka was already up to his waist.

'Come on, Bridie! What's wrong with you?'

I waded out. Slowly. The water rose to my knees. I looked ahead. The hairs tingled along my arms. My mouth felt dry and sticky. I saw the black shadow in the water. My stomach clenched. I couldn't move. 'Luka.' The words were a whispered breath. It floated nearer. It reached my knee. I felt something touch my calf. I jerked my leg back. A tendril of black seaweed reached out from its wavy mass. A dull beat boomed through my body.

'Bridie!'

I looked up.

'Oww!' I squeezed my left eye shut and pressed the palm of my hand to it to stop the salty sting. I heard Luka laughing.

'Gotcha, Bride!'

I slowly lifted my head to see the clear red pistol in his hand. I didn't wait for him to refill and do it again.

The taxi jerks as we lurch into a stream of traffic. I look down at my hands to find them shaking. The phone in my hand is shaking. I think of how I held Mum close to me then. Nuzzling my face into the warm, peach-scented crook of her neck. I pulled her closer, held her tighter. I dug my clammy palms into her soft body, needing the weight of her hand as it soothingly smoothed a slick of sweaty hair to one side of my head. I think of her, take a deep breath, and slowly slide my fingers, then palm, down the back of my head.

Harriet was asleep on the sofa, sprawled out like a starfish. I knelt down beside her, and watched the rise and fall of her tiny chest. I watched her little pink-white fingers curled naturally, peacefully, like tiny shelled prawns. I brushed a few wispy blond hairs carefully behind her ears.

'I don't know how Tom is, Harriet. I don't know where Rubus is.'

I watched the rise and fall. Rise and fall. I rested my elbow beside her on the sofa, and cupped my face in my hand. I looked down at my elbow, and saw a purple graze. I picked at the edge of the purple crust.

'We lost him, Harriet.'

Her eyelids twitched in sleep. I slid my head down my forearm, until my chin rested above the graze.

'I don't think he's coming back.' I mumbled the words into my scab.

I shuffle in my pocket for my purse, count the change, and hand it through a sliding screen in the glass divide. I unclick the door handle, dip my head beneath the doorframe, and breathe in the crisp October air. It is thick with moisture and the sky rolls heavily above me.

'Imagine that, Harriet,' I say, my breath misting. 'Imagine that.' As a black bird wheels into the grey, and disappears behind the clouds.

AT HOME WITH JODIE FOSTER AND GEORGE CLOONEY

Kate Pullinger

I was at home with a sick child when the doorbell rang.

My boy was not the kind of kid who didn't want to go to school; he liked the business of rubbing shoulders with his pals and playing football on the Tarmac during playtime; he liked the food the dinner ladies served at lunch. So when he said he didn't feel well enough to go to school, even though he had no temperature, no cough, no sign of any ill health whatsoever, I had to agree. Ruthie was off at a conference, so it fell to me to stay home. Not such a bad fate really; my boy and I could watch children's telly and lie around, bored and moaning.

But, like I said, the doorbell rang, and when I went to peer out through the glass in the door (we used to have nets hanging there, but they were always filthy, and had a kind of prim but grim feeling to them that my wife and I both rebelled against – 'rebelled', I know, it is sad when your only remaining form of rebellion is removing the net curtains in order to make yourself feel less suburban, but there you go), I was faced with a small army of Mormons. Mormons are unmistakable, especially the men in their suits and short hair. British Mormons have always puzzled me, but lots of people want to be American these days. I, myself, would like to be George Clooney; we are the same age after all, as I remind Ruthie from time to time. Anyway, there they were, the Mormons, ten of them, all men. I don't know that I've ever had a Mormon lady come to my door. They're all at home, I guess, having their polygamous babies.

'We have come to share our news with you and your boy.' The tallest one spoke first.

'You have?' How did they know about the boy?

'Yes, Richard, we have heard you calling us, late at night. We have heard your voice in the blessed ether.'

'You have?' How did they know my name? And calling out, late at night – this was news to me. Or was it? Did I call out at night for a God I did not believe in? The idea felt uncomfortably familiar. What was Ruthie not telling me? There'd been stuff in the papers recently about a man who, late at night, gets up and cooks in his sleep. Maybe at night I become a Mormon preacher without realizing it. But the sleepcooker was actually a chef during the daytime whereas I – well, I'm practically a professional atheist. I work as an orderly in the secure psychiatric wing of a hospital. God abandoned those people a long time ago.

'You know,' I said – I wasn't going to be rude, how could you be rude to the most polite people in the world, no matter how deluded they might be? – 'the boy's not well. We're having a quiet day. You'll have to come back another time.'

'We don't have long here on this earth.' It was the shortest one speaking this time, and he actually was an American. 'Things are happening.'

'Well, nothing is happening in my house. Thank you.'

I closed the door and wished I had some net curtains to peer through. They turned away and, as they turned, a couple of them gave each other stiff masculine hugs. They shook their heads and mumbled to each other, as though expressing the depth of their disappointment in me.

I went back into the sitting room where my boy was watching a bunch of kids sing karaoke. I lay down on the sofa, and my boy came over and got on top of me. I put my arms around him and we turned our full attention to the telly.

Late that evening, I was still lying on the sofa and watching TV when Ruthie got home. The boy had been tucked into his bed hours ago. I heard her key in the lock, then I heard her put her bag down. Without leaving the sofa, I could picture her every movement. She took off her coat and hung it in the closet. She took off her shoes and put on her slippers (we both wear slippers, a true sign of middle age; I know, it's not good, but who in their right mind can resist a nice comfy pair of slippers of an evening?) and then she called out 'Hello' to me. She walked through to the kitchen without entering the sitting room, and I heard her put on the kettle.

'How did it go?' I said, raising my voice above the volume of the TV.

'It was fine,' she called back to me, her voice even louder as the kettle began to boil. 'They seemed happy enough with the presentation. Train was late, though.'

'The boy's OK,' I shouted back at her. 'His cold is a little better.'

Ruthie came into the room now; she had made camomile tea for us both. I've never felt able to tell her that I can't stand camomile tea. It tastes like brewed compost heap (and yes, I have one of those as well, to add to my list of suburban accomplishments).

'What did you do all day?' she asked.

I shook my head. 'Nothing.' I didn't have the heart to tell her that we'd watched TV, and then we'd watched TV. 'Oh,' I said, 'some Mormons came by.'

She sat down and put her feet up on the pouf. Here's a sad but true fact: I gave her that pouf for her birthday. She's the same age as Jodie Foster.

'Did you tell them to go to hell?' she asked.

'Yes.' I looked at my wife. She works hard; she's the reason we can afford slippers and poufs and compost heaps. 'Do I turn into a Mormon preacher late at night?'

She laughed. 'Not that I'm aware of, honey.'

We drank our tea and watched yet more telly. Then we went to bed, happy.

FOR FEAR OF DROWNING
Harriet Fisher

Laura lies, hot and resentful, on the dry summer lawn, forced into a skirt that doesn't suit her and uncomfortable in a shirt buttoned tight against the neck.

Hearing the crunch of gravel she scrambles to her feet.

It's him.

She crams herself into his arms, the crisp cotton of his shirt brushing against her cheek. He kisses the top of her head and pulls himself free.

'Happy birthday, darling.'

He runs his hands quickly over his shirt, smoothing away the wrinkles left by her hug.

Laura tries to take hold of his hand but he slides it into his pocket. She takes him to the table on the lawn where her grandparents sit. Her grandmother raises a hand and her grandfather shouts hello. Laura's stomach tightens and she tries to match her father's speed and confidence as he strides across the grass.

Today is her fifteenth birthday and her father is the guest of honour. Since her last birthday she has seen him only twice. Each time she guards him jealously, counting the time he spends with her against the time he spends with others, wishing privately that he would ignore the others completely.

The party is at her grandparents' house, complete with lawns stretching out towards a small wood, pristine tennis courts and a swimming pool. The house her mother grew up in. The table is set with the finest tea things and plates holding complicated-looking cakes; she starts to worry about dropping the plates, breaking the cups, or eating the wrong thing at the wrong time with the wrong fork. There are too many unspoken rules here designed to catch her out. She is forever treading on croquet lawns, pouring milk straight from the carton and forgetting to take her jam with a small spoon. She is too much like her mother.

Her father, as he strides towards the table, hand out, smile beaming, is so charming and so graceful, so obviously endowed with qualities that Laura does not possess. Her grandparents stand as he arrives at the table and their faces glow with pleasure. He is good-looking, even through a daughter's eyes, and as he greets them she stands with the cuff of his shirt grazing her arm and her head resting on his shoulder.

Her grandmother glances sharply at her. 'Don't stand there staring, Laura, go and help your mother bring out the tea. Give your father room to breathe.'

As she moves reluctantly away from the table she hears her grandmother muttering to her father. 'Her mother is too soft. She needs a firm hand. You should say something, Rob.'

Laura is doing as she is told and misses his reply.

Her mother is in the kitchen putting cups on a tray.

'He's here,' Laura says.

Her mother turns quickly, expecting to see him there beside Laura. Disappointment and relief run across her face.

'He's in the garden.'

Her mother nods and continues arranging the tea things. The cups jangle sharply as she puts them on the tray.

'I'll help.' Laura starts to move towards her.

'No. I'm all right.'

Her mother snatches up the tray and walks out into the garden. Laura watches her as she walks. The sunlight falls on her hair, plainly cut and hanging just above her shoulders, which lean forward as if escaping from the rest of her. Laura has inherited her father's thick, dark hair but her mother's pale features and embarrassing clumsiness.

The voices stop as her mother arrives with the tea, Laura following behind like a smaller, slighter shadow. Her grandmother rises to her feet and takes the cups from her mother's hands, calling out as she does so. 'Milk? . . . Sugar? . . . One or two? . . . Biscuit?'

A plate of dry biscuits is waved under their noses and a cup thrust into their hands. As her grandmother picks up pace her mother falters, giving way to her sheer force of will, and soon she abandons the tray and sits down.

Laura is still standing, barefoot, toes fiddling with the grass, crushing it, letting it spring back up and then crushing it again. Her father catches her eye and winks, a gesture she likes to think he keeps for her alone, and a smile breaks across her face.

'You look almost pretty when you smile,' her grandmother remarks and looks at her husband for encouragement. 'Doesn't she?'

He nods and says, 'She is pretty.'

There is a silence during which her grandmother considers this. She looks as if she is about to reply when her father, taking advantage of the silence, raises his teacup.

'To Laura. Happy birthday.'

His voice is smooth and deep; Laura sometimes thinks he purrs as he speaks. The others follow his lead and Laura mutters a thank you.

He pulls a small, sky-blue paper bag out of his jacket pocket and hands it to her, kissing her forehead quickly as he does so. A deep flush starts in her chest and creeps up her neck. She turns her attention to the present; it is the prettiest bag she has ever seen, with a pink ribbon tie and letters stamped in shiny black. Inside is a box made of navy-blue leather, which puckers when she presses her finger into the soft top. She holds it for a moment, not sure whether to open it, not wanting to look up and catch someone's eye for fear of being told to hurry up.

She snaps open the box and looks inside.

Nestling on a pink velvet cushion is a silver chain and on the end of the chain is a tiny diamond encased in a silver band. Pulling it out of the box she holds it up. The diamond twists on the chain, catching the light as it turns. Laura is certain, looking at it, that it will stay around her neck for as long as she lives.

'Do you like it?'

She says nothing but puts it on and offers herself up for inspection. 'Charming,' her grandmother acknowledges before taking the teapot to the kitchen to refill it. Her grandfather seizes his opportunity to stand up and leave, kissing her and muttering 'Lovely,' as he does so. Laura and her parents are alone in the garden.

Her father is still smiling and her mother is looking at him with an expression that makes Laura stare at her feet.

'It suits her. You're good at this. You always were.'

Her mother attempts a smile but looks as if she is going to cry.

'I'm going to look in the mirror,' Laura says, a little too loudly, and runs into the house and up to her room.

She throws herself on to the bed. Her heart is pounding. She wants to scream at her mother and beg her to see sense. Why doesn't she do something, say something? If she wasn't always so miserable, then maybe they would have a chance, maybe he would come back to them. Laura doubts whether she has even had the guts to ask him. This weekend was the opportunity Laura had been waiting for, hoping that he would see them both and realize how much he missed them, how much he needed them.

She turns over on to her back and gazes at the ceiling. Perhaps her mother was talking to him about it now, less embarrassed without Laura there. Maybe that was it – she was shocked at first, seeing him after so long, and then Laura was there and they couldn't discuss it properly, not really. The thought cheers her and she jumps up and off the bed, hurries downstairs and out through the back door, leaving her parents alone on the patio to talk things over.

She stands by the pool, the water dappled with light sifted through leaves, the sounds of nature obliterated by the gurgle of the filter.

The others are in the house, occupied with the chores that make up the days here. Each moment is spent preparing for the next: the time after breakfast spent preparing lunch, the time after lunch spent preparing tea and then dinner. After dinner there are coffee and drinks and then the day is put away, but not without first laying the table for breakfast.

This is the pool where Laura's small cousin Edward was almost drowned. Her great aunt Susan threw him in and stood by listening to him scream, believing that if he could see that he would not be rescued he would instantly learn to swim for fear of drowning. As it was, her father, hearing the screams from the garden, pulled him from the water and handed him safely back to his parents.

Laura had stood bursting with pride as her father dived into the pool. He had emerged carrying Edward, water streaming down his face, Edward's arms wrapped tightly around his neck. She saw then, with a stab of envy, that Edward was unwilling to leave his side for the rest of the day. On the journey home she had noticed a new, but fleeting, warmth between her parents.

She sits down on the ledge and slips her feet in. It is cold and her skin protests in goose bumps. The water is a clear and artificial blue, made welcoming by the sun burning into the back of her neck.

Pushing off from the side she crashes into the water, eyes squeezed shut. Letting herself fall as far as she can she slowly opens her eyes. Her shorts billow out like clouds and her T-shirt hovers around her neck, the diamond necklace caught in its folds. She looks up and out at the sky, swaying gently with the surface of the water. She lies for a few moments suspended, clothes twisting around her. She tries to pull down to sit on the bottom but is running out of breath and, kicking hard, swims back to the top.

As her head breaks the surface the warm air envelops her. Rubbing her eyes free of chlorine she looks up and sees the tips of her father's shoes lined up against the concrete ledge. He is looking down at her, frowning.

'Laura,' he says, as if reminding himself of her name.

Scraping the straggly bits of hair back off her face she swims towards him. Her fingers fold over the edge, almost touching the sides of his shoes; the watery prints spread, dying the concrete a darker shade of grey.

He clears his throat and she can see him casting about for something to say.

'How's school?'

'Fine.'

'Friends?'

She looks up at him, unsure whether he is asking if she has any or is enquiring after their health.

'You ought to have friends.'

She examines the toes of his shoes. They look expensive, like the box the necklace came in.

'I do.'

It's true but feels like a desperate attempt to appease him. Her voice hangs between them sounding like a lie. He crouches down and smiles at her.

'I know, I know. Of course you do.'

He smoothes back her damp hair with his clean, neat hands. 'You're OK here, though? I mean, there's plenty to do, you don't get bored?'

She wants to shout at him, 'I do, I do get bored here, of course I do.' Why does he think she's here, floating in the pool, alone and fully clothed? But she can't say it. She can't tell him that she wants him to pull her out of this pool, wrap her in a towel, carry her into the house and tell her that he is coming back to them.

He stands up, wiping his wet hands with a crisp handkerchief pulled from his pocket.

'Laura . . .'

She nods, her fingers pressing hard into the concrete ledge. She looks up at him, trying to read his face, waiting, hoping for some sort of announcement. He clears his throat. This is it; he is going to tell her now. He has talked to her mother and he is coming back. She holds her breath and waits.

He smiles, says nothing and pulls her up to stand beside him. They walk back together and she is silent, wanting him desperately to say something, her stomach fluttering between excitement and fear. As they draw near they can hear voices from the kitchen. Laura turns to him; avoiding her gaze he pats her awkwardly on the shoulder and steps ahead of her into the house. She stands for a moment in the hallway, dripping on to the carpet, before running quickly upstairs to change.

Throwing her wet clothes into the bath she puts on dry ones, rearranging her hair and the necklace quickly in front of the mirror. She is in a hurry to be downstairs with the others and fumbles at the catch. She can hear footsteps echoing across hard, stone floors and her father's voice rumbling up towards her, but she can't make out the words. The sounds grow distant before moving out of earshot altogether. A door slams and she hears footsteps on gravel; someone is in the garden.

As she turns her head to take one final look in the mirror she catches sight of her father opening his car door and climbing in. She runs to the window and presses her face against it, willing him to see her. He doesn't look up. She raises her hand to knock on the glass but stops and stands there, fist raised. The door shuts with a thud. Her thoughts come slowly; she should say something, call out to him. She doesn't move. The engine starts. She hears the crunch of gravel as he pulls away and watches as he turns out of the drive. Her arm falls heavily to her side. Her feet are rooted to the ground. Her mouth is dry and there is a dull ache in her throat. She stands watching long after he has disappeared from view.

THE LOST
Dorothy Crossan

I know I'm not as much help as I could be, as much as Rose expects, but at least we know that Ayo was here. If only we can find out where she is now. We hope someone has taken her to safety. Rose has brought Ayo's medicine with her, as it is now three hours after her time to take it.

The crowd is shifting disagreeably, pushed aside as Japhet forces his way towards me. 'Madame, Madame, come quickly.' He reaches out his left arm to clear his way, but he's still looking back over his right shoulder. We are near the edge of the market, where the stalls run out and there's just the beach stretching out towards Benin. There are no tourists here. The sea is volatile and capricious. The waves don't break until they're almost on the shore, the surf tumbling fiercely, the power of the sea driving down into the beach, the sand sucked back under the waves and spat up into the air to sting like rain.

Where Japhet is indicating I can see a group of men, far along the beach, on the shoreline. The traders around us are also looking, a hush falling on them as they screw up their eyes to see through the haze of heat and sand. Rose steps forward to see more clearly, her left hand shading her sight against the sun, the other holding her headscarf in place as it flicks in the breeze. Beatrice has grasped my arm, her fingers constricting, her nails digging into me, her other hand at the crucifix around her neck. She is looking to me for comfort. After what she has done, she can expect none from Japhet or Rose.

Beatrice frowns as sparks of fear flicker amongst those around her. The crowd draws back sharply like a sudden intake of breath and then there are just Rose, Japhet, Beatrice, and me, facing the beach, and the men. Rose is pulling her scarf tighter around her head, her cheeks hollowed.

It was eight this morning when Rose, my maid, and Japhet, the compound caretaker, rang my front doorbell. I dragged my slightly hungover body to the door. I had been thinking I could have a lie-in, but the sound of the bell reminded me that for many people the 25th of December is just another day.

I was surprised to see them there. Rose has her own key to the back door and generally lets herself into the kitchen to start her cleaning while I am still asleep. Japhet takes his duties seriously, taking care of the people in the compound as much as the gardens and grounds. He will always take the time to say how wonderful it is to work for the British High Commission or to ask how I am enjoying my time in Nigeria, although he rarely allows me to distract him from his work for long, whether he is deadheading the hibiscus or sweeping broken twigs from the car park. I've heard Rose call him Baba, the word for father, a sign of their close friendship.

It had to be something out of the ordinary to bring them to the front door. One look at them confirmed it. I could see Rose's pallor, her arms dangling at her sides, the material of her skirt so badly tied it was gaping open at her thigh, her scarf slipping back unheeded on her head, showing her hair. She looked up and I had to concentrate hard to make out what she said. 'Ayo done gone.' I thought I knew what she meant, my limited experience of death denying me a response beyond the clichéd 'No.' But I didn't get the answer I expected. 'Ayo, she missing. Six today morning, Madame, I get up. Three my children, not four: David, yes, Esther, yes, Samuel, yes, Ayo, no.'

I tried to force my brain awake. 'What do you mean, missing? How could that happen?'

I felt a tug at the sleeve of my dressing gown and turned to Japhet as he snapped his hand back to his side as though he had never touched me.

Before he spoke he turned to Rose and she nodded. Japhet barely whispered, 'Ju-ju.'

Rose and Japhet waited nervously in my sitting room while I got dressed. When I came back in Rose was perched stiffly on the arm of a chair, Japhet standing by the window, warily eyeing my LP covers propped against the record player. I know they're not the only thing he disapproves of: I saw the way his eye ran over the empty wine bottle on the sideboard as he came in.

I would much rather have made myself comfortable on the sofa but I know better than to try to get away with such informality with Rose. I pulled out a dining chair and sat at the table, placing a pad of paper and a pen in front of me. I'd already faltered by answering the door in my dressing gown with last night's make-up smudged under my eyes.

I nodded to the chair opposite me and Rose pulled it far out from the table and sat formally on it, almost in the middle of the room, her hands on her knees. She looked round at Japhet for encouragement and then began.

'Beatrice is a bad woman. She is with many men. I tell her she bad lesson for children. She say I worship the devil.'

She whispered the last word. Rose is devout, if confused. A practising Muslim, she also draws on an eclectic jumble of Christian doctrine and tribal enchantments for her beliefs.

'She tell me she get poison from ju-ju men and kill my children. She say Ayo has not far to go.'

After only two months in Lagos, I know that just saying 'ju-ju' is enough to whip up fear for days, feeding on the village superstitions barely buried within all but the most hardened city dweller. I wanted to dismiss it but it's not so easy. Everyone I've met here has a story of ju-ju men, sometimes charlatans or magicians, often a tale of a threat followed by sudden unexplained illness or even death.

Rose's breathing was almost into hiccups, her face patchy and swollen by the upsurge of emotions bubbling just under the surface.

I tried to calm her. 'I don't believe Beatrice would really do anything to hurt your children.' And I meant every word. Beatrice and Rose are neighbours in the servants' quarters. They argue from time to time and I have seen them fight before, shouting across the perimeter wall, circling each other on the paving by the garages; a lot of bravado, once waving sticks, but no physical contact, ever. 'It sounds like you hurt her feelings and, wanting to hurt you in return, she said the worst thing she could think of.'

'But Ayo done gone.'

And my stomach chilled. Ayo is the Yoruba word for joy and, at three years old, joyful is what she is, with her hair twisted into plaits that stand on the top of her head like antennae. Rose has already asked me to take Ayo home with me in two years when my posting ends. Ayo is not well. Rose thinks I'm rich enough to fix her, my white Ford Fiesta being proof of my great wealth. She's not to know that a few months ago I was sharing a room in a South London hostel, trying to stretch my secretary's pay to the end of the month.

I didn't know what to do, so I played for time while I thought. 'What have you done so far?' Rose looked puzzled. I tried again. Sometimes it's just the order of the words that confuses, sometimes it's the words themselves. 'When you saw Ayo was gone, what did you do?'

'I go for call Japhet to the room. I aks Esther, she oldest, I aks her if she know where Ayo and she say no, she just wake. No one know where Ayo.' Rose's face was quivering. The rest of her quite still except for her hands. She was digging the fingernails from her right hand deep into the flesh below her left thumb.

'The police. Did you think of the police?' Even as I said it I knew it was a hopeless question.

Japhet answered, 'The police for people with money.'

I marked the page in front of me as if ticking off a list and then put down my pen. I had no idea how to help them.

'Was there something particular you wanted me to do?'

Japhet stepped forward from the window. 'I ask a friend to go to the taxi stand and get the taxi drivers for help. I give them this address, Madame. If they bring news, they bring it here.' He was looking so worried, as though he'd taken a terrible liberty.

'That's fine, Japhet. That's absolutely fine.'

As soon as they'd gone I rang Annabel, to get it over with. She lives in the same block, in the flat next door but one, but we always phone because, as she says, 'It doesn't do to be seen trotting back and forth for no good reason.' As personal assistant to the High Commissioner, Annabel sees the rest of us, the secretaries, as her junior staff, and she insists on being consulted on anything important. She thinks that at twenty-two I am too young for this posting, and I can't deny that I wouldn't have managed so far without her help. I had never even crossed the Channel before I came here. I am not just foreign in this extraordinary place. I feel as though I am staring out at the world from inside a Perspex box.

Annabel found Rose for me even before I arrived, and helps me make sense of the strange social rules of Lagos life. In her two previous postings she honed her three-pronged survival code: stick to your own kind, trust no one, and don't get involved.

Even though I knew what she would say before I started, I couldn't avoid telling her what was going on. She was bound to find out anyway. Beatrice is Annabel's own maid.

'You really mustn't get involved, Vivienne. You and I may think it quaint to believe that ju-ju men have magical powers but to them it's deadly serious.'

'I know, but Rose obviously thinks I can make a difference, and I don't want to let her down.' It's no good to try to reason with Annabel so I tried to distract her. 'It's like when she brings me Ayo's medicine to check the doctor hasn't made a mistake. I've no idea if it's right or not but I tell her it's fine and she's happy. It makes her feel better that I've approved it. I tried to tell her I didn't know what I was talking about but she kept coming and eventually I gave up.'

'And now she's beating a path to your door with every little problem, asking favours.'

Annabel finds my recognition that Nigerian staff are real people somehow distasteful. She regularly regales me with fearful anecdotes of ex-pats who had got too close to their staff and found their lives crumbling around them. 'There was that Jonathan Wakehurst,' she once recalled with particular satisfaction, 'used to let his steward have a beer in the evening. One morning he woke up and his entire house had been cleared out. Everything. All gone.'

I tried to keep my tone reasonable. 'I don't think this is a little problem.'

'All the more reason to keep right out of it. These little palavers pop up all the time. It'll all get sorted out one way or another without you putting your two penn'orth in, believe me.'

I gritted my teeth so loudly I could have sworn she heard it. She cut in with her most businesslike tone.

'Now, did Rose make you any breakfast?'

'Of course not.'

'Then I'm sending Beatrice along to do you some eggs on toast. If the Christmas dinner at the High Commissioner's is anything like last year, the turkey won't even be cooked until after four o'clock and everyone will be roaring drunk from too much wine on an empty stomach. I'll knock for you at noon and you'd better be ready. I'll need your help with the greeting and seating.'

I know I'm supposed to consider it a great treat to help with the High Commissioner's Christmas lunch party but I can't help thinking it's just a different kind of cheap labour. Annabel's been tutoring me on what's expected: wandering around the garden with a plate of canapés uttering such crass entreaties as 'Can I tempt you?' while fluttering our eyelashes at the diplomats and government officials who are the honoured guests. But my sulky thoughts didn't last long.

'I want for help find Ayo,' Beatrice told me earnestly as she made my breakfast twenty minutes later, the white steward's uniform that Annabel insists upon straining open between the giant plastic buttons, her feet swelling out of the shiny pink stilettos that she'd found in someone's bin six weeks ago and haven't been off her feet since. 'I know she need the medicine every day. Rose not allow me for look, but Ayo's going is not by me.' But as I watched she folded her left hand into a fist and held it against her mouth as though to force her words back down her throat and I knew she was lying. It was indeed her fault that Ayo had gone missing.

I got her to tell the truth by promising to make Rose let her help. We walked down the short path to the servants' quarters at the bottom of the compound garden. It was the first time I'd been there. Two concrete blocks face each other across a small courtyard, four doorways on each side. Across the end of the courtyard a third block with two marked doors leading to a communal kitchen and bathroom.

Rose was sitting on a doorstep hugging her knees, staring at nothing. She looked up as we came around the corner and for a moment her face lifted. She must have thought that I had good news but then she saw Beatrice and stood, folding her arms in front of her, her expression defensive. I told her Beatrice wanted to help find Ayo, that she had come to explain how Ayo's disappearance had nothing to do with ju-ju. I don't think Rose wanted to listen but she is my maid and in the short time I've been here I've learned that this is enough for her to do what I ask. Just as I know it is because I am her Madame that she has turned to me for help. And I thought the way to help was to stop Rose thinking that Ayo had been taken by ju-ju men.

Rose held aside the red plastic curtain that marks the entrance to her room. Inside it was dark and smelt of last night's boiled rice, but clean and tidy apart from a grey cardigan on the floor at the foot of one of the two low beds. Rose reached for it, revealing a jagged split dividing it along the back. 'Rat,' she explained, embarrassed, folding it to hide the bitten edges, and I watched more closely where I put my feet.

Rose and Beatrice speak to each other in English, not just for my benefit: their different tribal languages are almost as foreign to each other as to me. Once seated on the beds, Beatrice spoke hesitantly, guiltily.

'I tell Ayo, yesterday night, about Father Christmas. How he wear a red suit and has white beard. That he bring all good children present for Christmas Day. I tell her no present for her. She not good Christian child. Father Christmas not come to her.'

Shocked, Rose opened her mouth to speak but Beatrice put her hand up to press against Rose's lips and continued quickly, 'I know I say I call ju-ju but I not do such a thing, ever.'

I nodded in her support as Beatrice tried to take Rose's hand but Rose pulled away, her arms still crossed around the ruined cardigan. Not taking no for an answer Beatrice took hold of Rose's elbow, forcing her arms to unfold and the cardigan to slip back to the floor. She looked into Rose's face earnestly. 'So sorry.' She was leaning forward, seeming to say it with her whole body as she softly added, 'Truth,' and Rose relented enough to let her take her hand, pain still written across her face. They are not, as the Nigerians say, sisters same mother same father, but their servant's life makes them sisters nevertheless. I felt that I had achieved something good. But Ayo was still missing.

Maybe I should have followed Annabel's advice, but when the taxi driver, responding to Japhet's appeal, rang my bell and told me about the little girl who had been seen at Bar Beach market, that might be Ayo, I couldn't just pass the information on to Japhet and leave them to get on with it. It's not too far to walk to the market but it's quicker in the car and I was hoping we'd be bringing Ayo home.

At first they wouldn't get in the Fiesta. They just looked back at me blankly until I realized that they weren't happy to be driven by a white woman, and I was again exasperated by their rules. 'Can any of you three drive? No. Then just get in, for heaven's sake.'

The journey was short but fraught. Rose and Beatrice sat tense and silent in their seats. Rose in front, her eyes scouring the roadside as though she might tell whether Ayo had come this way; Japhet making incongruous conversation: 'So, Madame, are you having good Christmas?' I tried to give a light answer but the driving took all my concentration. It hasn't rained for three months. The combination of direct sunlight on the dust-streaked windscreen and its glaring reflection off the white bonnet gave me only a limited view of the road. Unlike the city centre the buildings of Victoria Island cling low to the ground and offer little shade beyond their walls, but at least you can see where the potholes are when it's dry.

The road was packed with battered cars and trucks, and bicycles with boxes on the front, on the back, even balanced on the handlebars, accompanied by the standard cacophony of beeping horns, frenetic yelling, and clashing music. I was relieved at the absence of my rear-view mirror, which fell off weeks ago. It's better not to see the mayhem behind me but to concentrate on unravelling the anarchy in front.

I'm not sure exactly when Japhet gave up his attempt at conversation. I know I thanked God when the low bungalows pulled back from the sea and the wooden shacks marking the edge of the market came into view.

The stalls are not set out in any order but range across the beach between the point where the road ends and the sea begins. Rose, Beatrice and I started at the road end, working our way along the stalls asking the stallholders and traders if they had seen Ayo, while Japhet went to check along the beach. We thought Ayo had come to the market to look for Father Christmas. Rose brings her here sometimes to look at the children's clothes and toys. The taxi driver's information said that the little girl was dressed in red and seen walking in the market and then sitting alone on the beach laughing at the waves. Japhet thought it couldn't be Ayo because she doesn't have a red dress, but Rose was sure, with a mother's dread and hope, that it was.

We caused a bit of a stir. It must have been obvious I hadn't brought any money, with no bag and no pockets, and it must have been obvious that we were worried, that we had something important to do that wasn't shopping, but it didn't put them off. If anything there had been even more jostling and shouting than usual. A throng of traders clustered round me, overladen with beads, bones carved like ivory, wood blackened to sell as ebony, and cloth of every colour. The tinny sound of snowbound Christmas songs all but swallowed up in the general fervour of heat and noise. The sun burning the bridge of my nose and making me wish I'd brought a hat.

The stalls straggle along the beach in tangled rows and it was soon difficult to tell which stallholders we had spoken to and who we had missed. The traders were interested and wanted to help. Perhaps they wanted to help too much. One woman told Rose in great detail how they had definitely seen Ayo cycling home. But Rose patiently explained to her that this couldn't be. Ayo is too small and has never been on a bike.

We had covered about two thirds of the market when Japhet called out to me, looking along the beach at the group of men, who are just standing there, watching us watch them.

And now we are caught in this stalemate. Beatrice is pushing hard up against my left side. She is leaning so far into me that I can hardly balance. She's rubbing her crucifix and muttering Hail Marys. She seems to be working herself up into a kind of fit. Rose is chanting under her breath in a pattern of words, over and over again. I don't know what it is but it sounds like Arabic. She has her eyes fixed on the men. They move a little nearer and then stop about 150 metres away, standing close together. I know what they are. They're ju-ju and they're waiting. We're all waiting, but I don't know what for.

Beatrice is breathing very heavily, right by my ear. Unlike Rose, Beatrice's emotions flow freely. She has begun to sob between snatches of Hail Mary.

Japhet and Rose and Beatrice move in behind me, and behind them are the market people. I look back to them. Beatrice has taken Rose's hand again. I'm not sure Rose has noticed. They are looking at me with a plea in their eyes. Someone has to go and find out what these men want; whether they know anything. Beatrice looks terrified; even Japhet looks alarmed and I know Rose's feelings about ju-ju. She wouldn't even let me have carvings of them in the house. I'm beginning to think it's going to have to be me.

Their breathing combines with the heat and the low thrum of shuffling and whispering. I feel forced forwards and held back at the same time. I want to go home. But Rose and Beatrice and Japhet are looking at me, so sure that I know what to do. This is why they came to me. I mustn't let them down. I start walking, trying not to think about what I'm doing. It just seems the only thing to do. As I step from the shelter of the last stall the sand-laden wind whips my skin.

Ahead of me are three men wearing leather belts and garters under their knees covered with feathers and what look like animal tails hanging down to the ground. They have strings of coloured beads twined around their necks. In front of them is a fourth hidden under a mass of long straw coming from the top of his head down past his knees. It could be a performance, but the straw is thick and shabby. This is no dance for tourists; this has the feel of something done before – some kind of ritual, or test.

As I get nearer the straw man starts to spin round. He is chanting and now and then he pauses, keeping time with his feet, looking at me, and then past me to where Beatrice has stopped, just a little way out from the last stall, her pink stilettos poking out of her stretched white pockets. Japhet and Rose have come a little closer. Rose looks determined. It is Japhet who is holding her back.

The straw man is spinning faster but at the same time he is moving diagonally towards me. The other men are fanned out irregularly behind him. Now that I am near enough to hear the tangled pounding of their low chants and stamping feet, my heart is beating from the outside in, drumming against my eyes and in my fingers. I look back again. What would they think if I was to run back to them now? But I can't and I turn back to the men.

I've stopped, but they keep coming. They have closed up together now in a disorderly V with the straw man a little ahead of the others. He is only a few feet in front of me when he stops. Even if he straightened up he would still be smaller than me. The way he is bent over makes him look almost as wide as he is tall. The noise comes to a jarring climax and then a low moan from all four as a twisted bony hand emerges towards me from the straw. It is holding a tiny naked black doll with trailing stringy hair. Its plastic skin smeared with dirt and sand.

He waves the doll in front of me, just out of my reach, twisting it in an exaggerated figure of eight. I don't know if he is begging me or daring me to touch it. I look back to Rose. She is shaking her head and I don't know if she is telling me not to touch it or not to stop. I cautiously reach out my hand towards the doll. Two of the other men move forward and I can't make myself keep my hand out. I recoil and the straw man jumps, lifting his feet off the sand so they disappear for a moment under the straw, then slamming them back down hard, and again he holds out the doll.

I feel fear crawl up through my body and try to batten it down, making myself reach out again to the doll. I start to close my hand around it but just as I almost get hold he pulls it back into the straw. For a moment I don't know if I have done right or wrong but then he crouches down on the sand and when he stands there is a bundle at his feet: the body of a small child.

Rose makes a noise somewhere between a scream and a howl and runs forward, stumbling, her scarf sliding unnoticed from her head. She snatches her hands at the empty air as she falls to her knees in the sand, then scoops Ayo up into her arms and her shuddering silence feels louder than any rage. The straw man disappears behind the other men and they move backwards, back along the beach, their feet pacing in time, chanting and moaning like they are singing a lament. I look around as Japhet comes forward. Surely we must stop them leaving. Beatrice is still rooted to the spot on the beach where she stopped but she has her hands up at her head now, her fingers twisting in her hair. Even from here I can see how she is shaking.

Rose stands up and turns back to me. She walks past cradling Ayo in her arms. There is no doubt that she is dead. The girl's body is slightly grey, no colour in her face or lips, salt on her cheeks. Her arms are looped through the sleeveholes of a red polka-dot dress covering up her blue cotton frock. Both dresses look soaking wet. Japhet picks up Rose's scarf and follows her along the beach folding and refolding it as he goes.

What are they doing? Don't they need to know? Was it her heart, or was it the sea? How did the men come by her body? Did the men try to save her, or was it them, did they hurt her?

'Rose? Wait. Don't we need to know what happened?'

Rose stops but doesn't turn towards me. 'Why? Will Ayo not be dead?'

I walk round in front of her, and put my hand on her arm. She must be in shock. I shake my head slowly to Rose in answer to her question, but also in disbelief that we will do nothing. 'Someone must know the truth?'

Her eyes are clear. I can see she is puzzled by my behaviour. She shrugs off my hand and continues walking.

This makes no sense. With no other idea of what to do, I follow Rose and Japhet to the edge of the market. My sense of purpose is gone. Rose is leading us now. Beatrice is still standing where we left her. She tries to reach out to Rose but neither Japhet nor Rose acknowledges her. Tears are pouring from her eyes as she tries to wipe them from her cheeks with the flats of her hands. I can't think of anything to say to her but I can't leave her here. I tap her arm and she flinches. I give her a push to get her walking through the market and follow Japhet and Rose, and Ayo.

Out of the corner of my eye I see a flash of red with white polka dots and I find myself in front of a stall covered in children's clothes. I look around to Beatrice and I see that she has seen it too: an identical dress to the one that Ayo was wearing. An elderly man is standing by the stall. He is watching Beatrice and me.

'The dress. The red dress came from you?'

He is twisting his hands. 'I do not wish to have trouble. I give her the dress. I thought her mummy was here. I would have kept her safe if I knew.' Now he is tugging his beard. 'I didn't aks for no ting. She crying. Then she see me and she smile. She aks me for present. She wipe her nose on dress so I give it for present and she stop crying.'

His hair and beard are white. He is wearing a red cotton kaftan with silver embroidery.

I try to make him feel better. 'I know you would have done things differently if you had known what would happen.' And behind me Beatrice begins her racking sobs again.

At the car Rose and Japhet get in the back with Ayo on Rose's lap. I'm worried that Rose will start screaming at Beatrice, but she doesn't even look up. She is staring out of the window, her tears running down over her chin on to Ayo's head. I get Beatrice into the front seat and she sobs noisily all the way back.

The journey home seems quieter. If anything it's hotter and the heat seems to have melted the worst of the noise. Or maybe we just have too much to think about. The steeringwheel has got so hot I can't keep my hands on it and have to steer in quick bursts holding the wheel between my fingernails. I do it absent-mindedly; concentration is impossible.

When I pull into the drive Japhet goes to take Ayo from Rose to help her out of the car but she twists away, unwrapping her blouse. She tucks her daughter's body against her own, twisting the legs around her waist, enfolding her in the material and holding her close as though to keep her warm. She walks slowly along the path to the quarters whispering into the bundle at her chest.

For a moment I stand uncertain on the path watching Rose disappear around the corner of her block. I feel something pulling me from the inside. I take a step after her, but then I hear the jagged sounds of grief begin and I turn away. I still need to do something: to help.

I appeal to Japhet. 'It might be Beatrice's fault Ayo wandered off but she didn't really mean to do her harm.'

'Beatrice called on ju-ju and they came.'

'That's not what happened, Japhet. Ayo went looking for Father

Christmas and, in her eyes, she found him. Whatever happened next was . . .' But I don't know what to say. Coincidence? Bad luck? Fate? Is that so different from ju-ju? I don't finish. Instead, I try to change the subject. 'What will happen now, to Beatrice?'

'She will go. No one will want her now.' He shakes his head as he turns but then he pauses. 'Thank you, Madame.' And I wonder, 'For what?' but I say nothing and he follows Rose's path to the quarters.

Beatrice is still sitting in the car sobbing. I hold the door open for her and she looks up at me. 'Red dress make her happy?' Then she is crying hopelessly again and I give up and leave her there with the car door open, taking the keys with me.

I go to my flat and close the door against the heat and the noise. I can't bear the sound of grief. I put on the air-conditioning and turn the radio up until I can't hear it any more and I sit alone for a moment, trying to think, wondering what else I could have done, until I realize there is nothing else I can do but get changed for Christmas dinner and wait for Annabel.

THE DOUBLE ROOM
Courttia Newland

Friday

She knew he'd be trouble the moment she laid eyes on him. Not in a general sense, but for her. She knew he'd be trouble for her. He sported the type of look that she found instantly attractive. Thick blond hair, curling at the front like the crest of a wave. Thin-yet-sharp eyes, blue as the sea that followed. Long thin nose, tanned skin, huge shoulders and to top it off he was tall – he had to be at least six feet three. She watched him enter the lobby with the sour-faced woman by his side, head swivelling from left to right to take in the grandeur. From then on, it was impossible to quiet the sensation. Lust. It had happened enough times for her to recognize the feeling. She knew this man would cause her to do something bad.

Serena watched the couple approach the reception desk, smiling in her perfunctory way as the sour-faced woman took the lead. The woman was a head shorter than the attractive man, yet she was older – a great deal older. Heavy bags formed dark pouches beneath her eyes. Skin wrinkled and puckered like old fruit. There was no doubt about it: the woman had the face of a bitch. While Serena had time to admit her thoughts might be a little uncharitable, she knew she was as right about the woman as she was the man. Some people had faces shaped by their personalities. Faces that couldn't hide what they truly were. She'd worked the reception desk at Hoskins for almost two years and believed that, over time, she'd become adept at watching people.

'Reservation for one double room, please.'

'Certainly, madam. Under what name?'

'Stephanie. Stephanie Rivington.'

'Just checking reservations for you . . .'

The woman was as haughty as Serena expected. She would've disliked the toad if she didn't already have an advantage. When Sour-Faced Stephanie told Serena her name, she looked her square in the eye to see if she knew, though Serena hadn't reacted. They were trained not to do so and she was good at her job. She simply let her eyes fall on her computer, her fingers on to the keys, tapping the name into the space provided.

Stephanie Rivington was CEO of a textiles business worth millions. She'd recently floated the company on the stock market and, despite the market chaos that was 9/11, shares were still going strong. Serena had read about her in the local paper whilst on lunch break, thrilled to find a woman from the North West doing so well. She was proud of this power-dressing person she'd never met. Ever so slightly envious. Serena had dreamed of being someone like that – back when she was younger with no responsibilities.

'Here it is, madam. Would you like to pay now or when you check out?'

'When I check out, of course.'

'Could I have a look at your credit card for ID purposes, madam?'

Stephanie nodded and dug around in her handbag. While her attention was diverted, Serena shot a glance at the attractive guy. He was strolling around the huge lobby with a childlike gaze of wonder, admiring the crystal chandelier, running his hand along the marble vase and sniffing the bouquet within, inspecting the ancient elevator doors like a repairman. Serena was staring so hard he must have felt it, for he turned as if tapped on the shoulder by an invisible finger. Before she knew what had happened they were looking into each other's eyes. She was stunned rigid. The man was beautiful. He smiled. The left corner of her lip gave a limp twitch, but she couldn't respond because –

'There you are.'

Stephanie handed over the card with an amused expression, as though seeing and knowing all. A faint blush lit Serena's cheeks as she took it, checked the signature, found the room key, then handed it over. Stephanie was watching her like a scientist would a lab rat.

'Room 416. Take the lift to the top floor and follow the signs from there.'

'Thank you.'

Stephanie walked away from the desk. The attractive guy was still wandering around the lobby and that's when the first thing happened, the thing that made her realize everything wasn't as cut and dried as she might have guessed. As the man inspected green glazed wall tiles with a curious finger, Stephanie came up behind him, grabbed his arm and tugged hard enough to make him stumble. Serena barely held back her gasp.

'Come on, stop playing around, will you? I'm too tired for your rubbish tonight.'

Stephanie called the lift, which had been waiting on the ground floor for that very thing. The doors parted. They stepped inside. Stephanie turned sideways on, fixing the jacket of his suit and wiping invisible dust away, while the attractive man . . . did nothing. Stood inside the lift like an android whose power had failed, eyes blank, that same smile on his face, this time directed at the empty space before him. At no one. Stephanie finished her fussing and turned Serena's way just in time to catch her horrified gaze. And she grinned. A big, self-satisfied, got-you-there grin. She knew Serena had been so attracted she hadn't seen the truth.

Before anything else could happen, the doors closed.

'Oh my *God*.'

One of the porters was pushing a set of suitcases across the lobby, close enough to hear. He looked up.

'Whassat, gorgeous?'

She was too flustered to notice the compliment and tell him to leave it out like she always did.

'Nothing . . . Nothing.'

Serena returned her gaze to the monitor, outrage burning her face. If she were completely honest with herself, after seeing that, she knew exactly what she'd do.

Serena saw them only once more that night. Sitting in the massive restaurant area behind a huge table not interacting with any other diners, even to say hello. Serena was such a reliable figure at Hoskins she was allowed to take liberties where the other staff wouldn't dare. (Besides, it had long been rumoured that Martin the duty manager fancied her. It was true they'd fucked in the laundry room, but only twice and that was ages ago.) So, instead of sticking by the reception desk like she was meant to, Serena convinced one of her colleagues that she had errands to run. While engaging in idle chat with the chefs and servers she found that she could spy on the couple without arousing suspicion.

Stephanie was cutting the attractive man's food into minuscule pieces. Serving him impatiently, shovelling forkfuls into his mouth. Wiping surplus away from his chin like a mother does a toddler while the attractive man stared sightlessly into the faces of other diners.

And she was rude. Serena would have thought that her actions promoted love and good care, but Stephanie managed to perform them with easy disdain. When he didn't eat as fast as she liked, she pinched his arm and cajoled him. When he dribbled, she slapped his thigh hard enough to make him wince. Serena watched fellow diners get up and leave in silent protest, often staring at the couple in anger. One of the guys behind the bar made a move to go over and say something, but his manager grabbed him by the arm and shook his head. The barman fell back, his jaw rigid and his tanned face browned by anger.

Serena couldn't take much more after that. She went back to her desk trying to tell herself she was wrong about Stephanie's motivations.

It was unusually quiet for a Friday night, so there was time to look through the signing-in book until she found the woman's name, tracing her finger across the columns until she found the one marked 'Company'. She memorized the name, got on to the Internet, typed the name into a search engine and waited to see what came up. There were a few more check-ins after that, so it took awhile before she could thoroughly scan the list. After half an hour the rush died down. Serena went back to the computer. Finding what she wanted, she double-clicked. Stephanie's company website emerged.

There was lots of information about different textiles and how long the company had been running, but that wasn't what Serena was looking for. Clicking on a link marked 'CEO', she was rewarded with a picture of Stephanie and some vague biographical information. Disappointed, she went back to her search engine and tried again, this time typing Stephanie's name. Up came a host of articles featuring the woman CEO in pages from the *Financial Times* to *Marie Claire*. Serena trusted good old *Marie* to cover the angle she was looking for and clicked twice on the link, feeling optimistic.

She was correct in her assumption. The article began with the sentence: 'Attractive CEO of Bard Textiles, Stephanie Rivington has a lot to be proud of right now. This thirty-something powerhouse is ambitious, single . . .'

And that was all she needed to know. Serena had wondered how a married woman could brazenly flaunt her weekend with a younger man like this. Check in under her own name and even put her real company down in the correct column. Now she had the answer. What she couldn't understand was why. Why would she want to spend the weekend with an obvious simpleton? Didn't she care what anyone thought? Then again, she heard herself question, how bloody obvious is he really? Had me fooled enough to fancy him, and I'm not nearly as old as her . . .

It was the truth. When his older companion wasn't deriding the young man, when he was alone, he was something to be admired, there was no doubt. She even saw her initial thoughts reflected in the smiles of the bellboys (those that were that way inclined, at least) and some of the female kitchen staff as they stood by the buffet tables. Yeah, there was no doubt about it, the guy was sexy as hell. Enough for her to be his nursemaid in exchange for a weekend of fun? No. Serena didn't think so. But for a Plain Jane bordering forty with no romantic ties and a business doing so well she didn't have time for a partner . . . For a little bit of sex then back to the office like nothing ever happened . . . Serena saw it happen all the time. Admittedly, it was usually men with young secretaries or working girls in tow, but sometimes there *were* women . . . Though none as strange or cold as Stephanie. Thinking about the woman and her treatment of the mentally ill young man made Serena's skin crawl. Her earlier decision, the one she'd made while looking into Stephanie's eyes as the lift doors closed, became cemented into choice.

She would have him, Serena told herself, feeling her own little imp begin to dance. She would have him and nobody would know it but her . . .

Saturday

She entered Hoskins to begin her new shift early that evening. Her thoughts had circled around how she'd do it for most of the day, glad her three-year-old daughter was at her parents' so she had time to think. She strode into the lobby, smiling and accepting the usual compliments about how well she looked, then settled down behind the desk and immediately began checking in. Saturdays were always the busiest night by far, so there wasn't much time for staff small talk (which she loved), or skiving off (ditto); it was straight down to work, make no mistake. The steady flow of check-ins, room-service orders and complaints about faulty showers and the like kept her busy enough to temporarily forget her plan. However, close to midnight, when everything slowed to normal speed, Serena remembered what had scarcely left her all day. She couldn't recall the number on the key, so she looked it up on the computer. Room 416. Top floor. Begging a break from Martin the duty manager, she decided to have a snoop around.

Hoskins was a truly massive building. The four-star hotel was once a national insurance firm housing four floors, five hundred offices, six main conference rooms and employing almost two thousand people. Back then its clients were mostly big businesses of the fifties and sixties, though by the early seventies the tide began to turn. In the latter half of the decade, after the insurance company filed for bankruptcy, Hoskins took over the once-vibrant building and transformed the offices into bedrooms, the ballroom into a dining area, while retaining much of the original décor. Nowadays it was almost impossible to walk into the building for the first time without feeling a sense of awe and a little disquiet. First-timers often got lost in the labyrinthine lengths of corridor. In some sections of the building, even when the hotel was packed, it was possible to go up to half an hour without seeing anyone.

If she was truthful, walking the corridors at Hoskins sometimes scared Serena. She tried not to do it by herself but, of course, in this instance she had no choice. It helped that two years in the building had corrected her navigation to a point where she knew every corridor, every short cut, every turn. Moving through back staircases and service lifts until she reached the relevant floor, she blanked her eyes and slowed her pace, putting doubts out of mind. A sign above her head informed that the room she was looking for was at the far end of the corridor. Her plan was to knock and ask if everything was up to their requirements, if Stephanie or her companion needed anything. They would say no. Then she would leave. She knew the curiosity was meaningless, but she wanted to see him again so she would. Serena was a woman who always got what she wanted, whatever what she wanted may be.

These vague thoughts spun as she moved along the corridor in a trance, her face serene, picking 'em up and laying 'em down one after the other with her eyes on the door, only the door. So it was a shock when the body suddenly slammed into hers with the force of an HGV, knocking her into the opposite wall, making her gasp as her right shoulder connected, then sag when pain finally reached her, collapsing on to the carpet with a moan. Her vision swam in front of her eyes, went dark. Bright sparks appeared like stars in a desert sky. Serena took a deep breath, trying to calm her breathing and let the moment pass. Soon, she became aware that someone was moaning, moaning like a child who had just committed some terrible deed.

Before she even raised her head, she knew who it was.

He was huddled against the far wall crooning in a low voice, face pressed into the green tiles, body shaking. The suit he'd been wearing was gone, replaced by an unironed T-shirt and faded blue jeans, making him seem more like a teenage student than a grown man. Looking at him, seeing what he really was, rather than whom she'd dreamt, helped Serena forget her pain. She got to her feet, turning around to see if anyone was watching. No one was there. Scanning the vicinity, it was immediately obvious how they'd clashed. The corridor was shaped in a vague sort of T, with Serena walking the horizontal point, the attractive man the vertical. They were each so preoccupied with where they were going neither had seen the other until it was too late. Rubbing her bruised shoulder while looking at his, Serena thanked her lucky stars he wasn't some homicidal maniac. He was so tall and broad, she shuddered to think what he'd be like if he turned that brute strength against someone.

'It's OK. Look, don't worry about me, I'm fine. Hey! Hey, look at me! Look, I'm OK, there's no need to panic, you didn't hurt me. I'm just a bit bruised, that's all . . . Hey!'

Gently as she could, she grasped his chin with delicate fingers and turned his face around until he could see that she was all right. She smiled and felt a return of her lust as he looked at her through big blue eyes that seemed deep enough to dive into. She couldn't help herself, tracing her fingers across his chiselled cheekbone to the cleft chin as he took in her own features, confused. They stared at each other, two shades of beauty face to face. His whimpers receded into nothing, his mouth working in rapid fits and starts.

'Soh . . . soh . . . sorry . . .'

'It's OK. I said it was OK, didn't I?'

She snatched another cautious look up and down the corridor before taking the plunge, nerves dancing. Grabbing the back of his head and leaning forwards she planted a kiss on his lips, holding it a minute before opening her mouth just a little and pulling away. She smiled.

'It's OK. Truthfully it is.'

When he didn't react, she frowned and looked a little harder, trying to note even the slightest form of expression; but there was nothing. She was just about to let him go and give up the chase, when he leant forwards by his own power and returned the favour, then looked into her eyes just like she had his. It was her strangest, most innocent kiss ever.

'We should get out of here,' she said, almost to herself as much as her new friend, fully aware that this was her only opportunity. 'OK?'

No answer, just that lifeless stare. Even though the man had the ability to talk and communicate, it seemed as though he didn't use it much. Which was fine with her. All the men she'd been with in the past talked too much anyway.

'So what you doing out of your room at this time of night?'

The storeroom was a little musty, but warm. Only three people in the building had the key. She wasn't meant to be one of them, but she'd nicked Martin's and had a spare cut ages ago.

'Not gonna talk? Well, you could at least tell me your name, then. It's weird being intimate without knowing each other's names.'

She shrugged off her purple Hoskins jacket and placed it on a box of spare menus, followed by her blouse. It was very important that there were no stains.

'Have it your way, then. I suppose it wouldn't be the first time for me. The not talking takes some getting used to though.'

He was standing with his back against the shelves, a hand unconsciously by his crotch – not moving, just poised as though in wait. She knelt down in front of him, unbuckled his belt, and pulled down the jeans and boxers, then took him in hand. She stopped, looked up at him. His head was arched back so far all she could see was the lumpy bouncing ball of his Adam's apple. Serena frowned as she tugged back and forth.

'Do you talk to *her*? You must do, innit, you must say something or the other. Why are you with her anyway? I'm talking about Stephanie. Honestly, she's twice your age, not even very attractive and she treats you like shite. You shouldn't let her do it, you know.'

He was hard.

'*Very* impressive!'

She giggled. God, she was bad, but she loved every minute of it. She kept talking, even though he was breathing deeply and probably couldn't hear a word she was saying by now. In between sentences she took token licks, warming him up.

'A gorgeous guy like you . . . shouldn't have to take that kind of abuse . . . You . . . should . . . be . . . stronger than that . . . Next time . . . she's mean to you . . . you should be mean to her . . . She deserves it . . .'

She had to speed things up. They'd been lucky so far, but if she wasted any more time they'd be caught and she'd be sacked and she had a daughter to feed, so she couldn't have that. Serena took him halfway in, moving her fist along with her head, massaging his balls with her left hand while she did it. She was an expert, or so she'd been told. It wouldn't take long. Two minutes later he was moaning in a voice louder than any she'd heard so far. Her mouth grew sticky and warm. She got to her feet, held up a finger, searched in her jacket pockets. All she had was some scrap paper, so she used that to spit into, folding carefully, making sure nothing spilt. They had to leave no traces, particularly as she planned to corner Martin again some time in the near future. He wouldn't be pleased if he found out what she'd done.

'You OK?'

The man was panting and looking at her like a puppy gazing at its mother. She pulled up his jeans and buckled his belt, kissed him on the lips, then gave him a hug for good measure. He didn't hug her back, but she didn't mind. She'd had him. Not in the way she'd really wanted, but probably the only way she could. She guessed he wasn't very good at the penetration bit anyway, the way he was and all. And if the truth be known, Serena was already losing interest. She just wanted to get him out of the storeroom, back to his real partner.

Stephanie. Serena smiled at the thought of the CEO.

'So you remember what I said, OK?' Her voice was tinged with pleasure as she led him out of the room, checked to make sure everything was as it was, then locked the door and led him away. 'You don't have to take her shit. If someone hits you, hit them back, that's what me mam always taught me and I think she was right. Don't stand for it. You're a big hardback man. All right?'

He was staring at her, blank as a whitewashed wall. She sighed and led him up the staff stairs to his floor.

'Go on. Go to your room.'

He stood there, a smile on his face. He reached for her hand.

'No!' Despite her fear, she couldn't help a coy grin. 'Stop it, you . . . Go on, go back to Stephanie. She'll be missing you by now.'

He reached again. This time she slapped his hand away.

'*No!*' She pointed down the corridor. 'Back. Go . . . back.'

He looked at the floor, down-mouthed. She felt guilty and more than a little exasperated. He wasn't worth losing her job over. He had to go. She was wondering how to get the message across when he suddenly began to walk away, quickly, without looking back, taking long strides.

'See you tomorrow!'

He didn't turn. She closed her eyes. When she opened them, he was gone. She left the corridor.

Martin went mad when she got back, saying she'd taken half an hour more than her lunch break, but she promised she'd add it to the end of her shift. That kept him sweet enough to pinch her arse when no one else was around and she let him do it, glad he was still showing an interest. They had been quite friendly at one point, 'friends that fuck' as she'd put it, before he started seeing some white girl from Rusholme and seemed to lose his appetite for Serena. Apparently the white girl wasn't enough of a serving as he'd been sniffing around her again for the last week. Serena had decided to keep him on a loose leash and only reel him in when he was needed. She knew what game he was playing. Even though she was up for taking part, she smarted at the knowledge that he would never make her his girlfriend, even though she didn't want him either. Sex with Martin was largely for her self-esteem.

Her friends wondered why she constantly dated white men. She was drop-dead gorgeous, had a great body and was a right laugh, too. They weren't being racist (so they said), but didn't she ever, for once in her life, want a shapely arse, full lips, dark skin, in bed beside her? She had a black daughter so she had to know what that felt like. Didn't she ever miss the feel of a black man?

To be truthful (and she had told no one this), Serena pondered that question on many a night. Yes, she did like black men: Denzel, Wesley, Tyrese, D'Angelo, Maxwell and many more made love to her – in her imagination. The trouble was, there weren't many decent ones. Most of the ones she'd met she wouldn't touch with anyone's bargepole and she couldn't say why, just that she never seemed to click with them in the way that she did with . . . others. And it wasn't that she was ashamed to be black. If anyone thought that, they couldn't be more wrong. Her dad had made sure she knew her history, both the Caribbean and African stuff and not just slavery either. But she was half and half. Her friends had to accept that. They saw her as black, but half of her wasn't and there was nothing she could do to change that. Nothing she *would*. Still, she couldn't help wondering why she hadn't been with a black guy since her ex. Why white guys – even mentally disabled white guys, for flaming hell's sake – seemed like so much of a better deal.

Serena wasn't used to critical thinking, yet she knew full well what the catalyst was. The attractive guy. It had only just happened and she already felt guilty. She wasn't used to it. Though she tried to take her mind away from the depths of self-analysis, the longer her shift went on the more impossible it became. The man was mentally disabled. She'd known that. She'd taken advantage. What did that say about her?

Serena was so deep in thought that the remainder of her shift went by before she knew it, even the extra half hour. She usually larked about with Martin for ten minutes or so before she left. Today she got her coat and sneaked from the building without a word to anyone.

Sunday

It was two a.m. Serena sat by her reception desk reading Toni Morrison's *The Bluest Eye*, which she'd started years ago and loved, but never quite managed to finish. She knew full well why she'd picked the book from her shelf like ripened fruit, yet she was finding it difficult to maintain enthusiasm. Part of the reason was the concentration needed to read at work, which was hard to find, despite the quiet of the approaching dawn. The rest was down to Stephanie and her mysterious companion. What she had done to him.

She'd checked the computer on her arrival that evening. They were still here. She hadn't seen them all night so there was no reason to be worried about the guy letting the cat out of the bag, or behaving strangely, but . . . She hadn't seen them all night. Breakfast and lunch had been delivered via room service (she knew because she'd asked the porters). They hadn't been seen together since the previous day.

The reception buzzer went off, loud in the quiet of the huge lobby, making Serena jump. She placed a hand on her breast to steady her heart, laughed and automatically reached for the phone, then caught sight of a light flashing in front of her. Her hand froze as though infected with sudden rigor mortis.

It was 416. Their room. It was their room and she had to answer it.

She picked the receiver up like a poisonous snake, almost unwilling to put it to her ear. You knew he'd be trouble, her mind was cursing. You knew and you still went and did it . . .

'Good morning, Reception . . .'

Say it just the way she was meant to, raising her tone at the end, just like they were any old customers . . .

'Soh . . . soh . . . sorry . . .'

'I beg your pardon?'

She was trying to buy time, looking around the lobby to see who might overhear. Martin had disappeared ages ago and was probably sleeping. The two graveyard-shift porters were in the staff room playing gin rummy and the cooks weren't due for another three hours. She was on her own.

'Sorry . . .'

The phone disconnected before she could say his name. *Shit.* She didn't even *know* his name. And what was that all about anyway, calling Reception, saying one word then putting the phone down? It was a cheek, a waste of her time. She wished he'd learn something else to say, for God's sake. Sorry was the only word she'd ever heard him speak and that was only when he'd –

'Oh, no . . .' She covered her mouth with a hand. 'Oh, Jesus, no . . .'

She stood up and removed herself from the reception desk. Made sure her key card was attached to her waist. Walked to the lift and pressed the call button. Stepped in and took Otis to the fourth floor. Stepped out and walked along the bare corridor until she was standing outside room 416.

All was quiet, while in her ears there was a roar that was her own voice, her own voice saying: 'A gorgeous guy like you shouldn't have to take that kind of abuse . . . Next time she's mean to you . . . you should be mean to her . . . She deserves it . . .'

And he was big, wasn't he? Big enough to hurt near enough anyone, but especially a middle-aged woman. The guy was mentally deficient, which meant he was open to suggestion, wasn't he? Look how easy it had been to lead him to the storeroom.

And she had goaded him into hurting Stephanie.

She knocked on the door, timidly at first, but with more strength when she heard nothing. She pressed her ear to the wood, straining for a voice . . .

'Hello . . . Hello . . .'

It was Stephanie and she sounded in pain. Serena had been right. Something had happened.

She slipped in her key card and watched the light change from red to green, then turned the handle and went inside. In contrast with the corridor there was a shadowy darkness in the room and she couldn't see very much.

The TV was on, showing a late-night cable flick Serena had seen a million times before. From the bathroom, located on the right side and the only other room, she could hear the sound of a shower, though the water was hitting enamel, not a human body. She turned that way in order to switch it off. The constant sound was giving her the creeps. Her eyes finally adjusted to the dark.

That was when she saw Stephanie Rivington.

She was handcuffed to the bedposts by both hands. All Serena could see of her face was eyes. Her mouth must have moved, because all of a sudden there was that strange croak of a voice, a croak that sent wriggles of sensation to the tips of her feet.

'You . . . Reception Girl . . .'

'Yes, Ms Rivington, it's me,' she said in her best hotel voice. 'Now, do you know where the keys to the cuffs are so that I can release you? Then I'll go back to my desk and we won't say any more about this, will we?'

'It was *him* . . . *He* did this . . .'

She was searching the cabinet beside Stephanie in a rush, wanting to leave. He obviously wasn't around, but she didn't know how long that would last, and she definitely didn't want him to think she'd get involved in this freaky sex scene. She wasn't into bondage anyway.

'Now, Ms Rivington, you know that's none of my business. Now, if you'll just tell me where the keys are . . .'

The light. She needed more light. Serena moved to the main switch and made to touch it.

'You fucked him . . . didn't you?'

She stopped dead.

'Last night . . . Went to the shops to get me some cigarettes . . . Didn't get back for ages . . . Came in with damp underwear . . . Wasn't me . . . Saw the way you were looking at him . . .'

Serena couldn't face her. Not and tell the truth, there was no way. In fact, she couldn't tell the truth at all. Not now, not ever.

'Ms Rivington –'

'Turn on the light!' The woman began to scream. At that point, Serena wanted to join in. 'Look at what he did to me!'

She almost left right there and then. Walked out of the door, down the corridor and through the Hoskins lobby never to return again. Because she didn't want to know. The selfish part of her didn't, not really. It was her conscience that made her raise her hand, press the switch and turn to face Stephanie Rivington. It was her conscience that screamed when she saw that Stephanie was naked and covered with blood from head to toe, blood that saturated the blankets to such a degree she couldn't understand why she hadn't smelt it before. Blood trailing down her forehead like thick, red perspiration, running along the slight curve of her breasts and stomach, pooling in the crevice of her genitals like a muddy puddle of rain. Blood transforming the white sheets of bedding into a deep and dark red that looked slick and wet as fresh paint. And while she stared at this woman who looked more like a horror-movie victim than a human being, the selfish and her conscience joined hands and hid in a place where all the bad things in her life curled up and eventually died. Then all that was left was the shock of what she was seeing, the violence she was faced with. She found herself shivering, unable to turn away from the nightmare image; unable to remember why she'd turned the light on at all.

'See . . .' Stephanie whispered.

The door clicked. Heart in mouth, Serena turned around and saw that the indicator was green. Someone was coming. Stephanie pointed at the door and began screaming as loud as her cracked throat would allow. Serena moved away from the door, wanting to bawl in fear.

'It's him, he's coming, it's him –'

'Shut up!' she found herself snapping before flooding with instant regret. 'Wait a minute, let me think . . .'

There was no time for thoughts. The door opened and there he was, standing in the doorway looking at her with a maniac's gleam in his eye. He frowned at the sight of her, stepping further into the room. His creased T-shirt was spotted with Stephanie's blood. When he raised his left hand she could see the tiny glint of the razor blade and wondered how he'd walked the corridors without being seen, before she remembered the time of morning. Still, she wished that Martin or somebody else had faced the guy down before he'd come back to this room. A voice burrowed its way through the roaring in her ears.

'Kill him, kill him, kill him quick –'

'Soh . . . sorry . . .' the attractive guy was saying.

Stephanie's fear prompted her own. As he lumbered closer Serena grabbed the nearest thing she could find, a huge vase, and threw it as hard as she could. While he ducked and fell to the floor with the impact, her selfishness emerged from its hiding place. Serena bolted through the open door, ignoring Stephanie's curses and ran, ran as hard as she could. She didn't dare wait for the lift, leaping the stairs and almost breaking her ankle in the process, down four flights that seemed to go on for ever, finally running into the lobby in a jumble of hair, eyes and Hoskins clothing. Martin was behind her desk by then, looking ready to let rip until he saw the tears flowing down her cheeks. She ran at him full pelt, hugging him hard and letting the dam burst, hearing the frown in his voice when he asked what was wrong.

When she calmed down, Serena told him.

Everything was surreal after that. The ambulance came, police came. They even called the fire department when it became apparent that the key to the handcuffs was lost. Sitting at the reception desk with a blanket around her shoulders, Serena watched the attractive guy being led towards a TSG van by two large police officers. He still looks sexy, she thought to herself, wondering how she could allow the thought, knowing that she hadn't learnt, not yet. The guy's head was bowed, his expression a mask of sorrow. He kept his eyes averted from the desk as though he'd been told not to look. Serena sipped on her coffee with two hands and watched him walk out of her life.

Ten minutes later, a bandaged Stephanie appeared, wheeled out of the lift by paramedics, then towards the lobby doors. The CEO looked. She waved a mummified hand Serena's way, but that wasn't enough for the receptionist. She shrugged off her blanket, putting down the coffee and following Stephanie. She smiled her sweetest smile at the paramedics, both male, and asked if she could have a quick word in private. They grumbled a bit, then agreed to let them speak for just one minute. Thanking them, she knelt in front of the wheelchair.

'Hi there . . .'

'Hello.'

Stephanie's croaking voice was long gone, though her vocal chords seemed strained and huskier than before.

'What are we like, then, eh?'

'Like high-school girls, I reckon.'

Her more than Serena, but the receptionist wasn't arguing.

'So . . . They give you any painkillers?'

'An injection,' Stephanie whispered. 'It does the trick.'

They smiled at each other. Serena touched her shoulder.

'I'm really sorry this happened to you, Stephanie. Truthfully, I am.'

'Don't worry about it,' the CEO was drawling in a distant tone. 'Serves me right for not picking someone nearer my own age.'

She gave a woozy smile and closed her eyes. Close up, Serena could see her cuts for the first time. None on her face or neck, but six or seven straight slashes taped with white plasters just above her hairline. Strange. The rest were presumably beneath the bandages wrapping her arms and legs. Serena leant as close as she dared.

'Look . . . I just had to tell you . . . I'm sorry about my role in all this mess, I really am. And . . . Look, I'm grateful that you didn't tell anyone about what I did. With him . . . I need this job, so . . . Thank you, Stephanie.'

The women appraised each other once more.

'A favour for a favour,' Stephanie replied, bursting into a sudden smile, her voice a husky singsong. 'I won't tell if you won't tell . . .'

That didn't sound right. What was she going on about? It was the drugs, Serena concluded.

'What d'you mean?'

Nothing for a moment, then Stephanie grabbed Serena's hand in one of her own and squeezed, even though it seemed to cause her pain.

'Allan's such a dependable boy . . . Open to any suggestions, as you well know, Ms Reception Girl . . . It's amazing the things I got him to do this weekend . . . He'd never held a razor blade before, can you believe it? Wasn't allowed to, I suppose . . . Ah, well . . . He'll have to learn to think for himself now, where he's going. After all, anyone could take advantage . . . Couldn't they?'

Serena snatched her hand away, looking down at Stephanie in disbelief. The CEO put a finger to her lips and smiled again.

'Goodbye, Ms Reception Girl . . .'

Then the paramedics were back, wheeling her on to the ramp and into the ambulance with a nod of acknowledgement. Serena was standing in the same spot some twenty minutes later, rigid as the north wind chilled the tears that soaked her cheeks.

'The Double Room' is from the collection *Music for the Off-Key*,
Peepal Tree Press, 2006

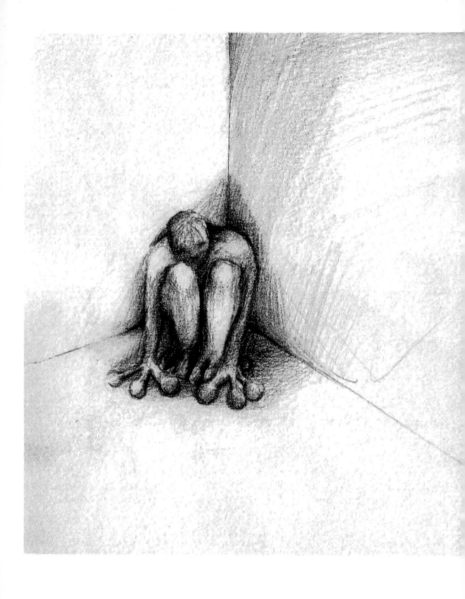

YOU JUMP YOUR HEART OUT!
Jamie Joseph

It's been exactly one week since Diane left and I'm watching a documentary about flying squirrels. I know it's been a week, because I checked the date on teletext this afternoon and counted back each morning from there. She wanted some time to herself, which has given me a great opportunity to catch up on all the stuff I can never do with her around. After all, it's not good to spend all your time with one other person, that's what everyone says. I tried to relay this to her as she was leaving. I said, 'Come back when you are happy with who you are,' and she gave me this wild-eyed animal look. I followed it up with a laugh to lighten the mood but she turned away, shaking her head as she picked up her bag. She scraped and banged it on the door before it shut and everything went quiet.

The first day was slow. For a while I just waited for her to call, to check in with me and make sure she was all right. As the days passed, I started to make it into some kind of routine. Checking the answering machine, cornflakes, coffee, TV, lunch, and then the dragging afternoons with those ridiculous two o'clock, three o'clock, four o'clock times. One afternoon, I found myself standing in the bathroom at three thirty-five, and then about twenty minutes later I was stroking the cabinet in the bedroom. The phone rang once or twice but the caller display was from work, so I left it alone.

Once you think about it, there aren't a million things you can start doing if you are worried about the phone ringing. But at the same time it got me thinking about how great it is having nobody here telling me what I have to do. I took the rubbish out yesterday and saw cars whizzing down the road, and counted five red cars in a row. In the afternoon as I did some washing-up, I wondered about the red cars. It seemed an odd thing to witness in the one moment I left the house, and then when I was drying the plates and everything was clean on the rack, I told myself that it would be odd if there was never a sequence of five red cars. I've grown accustomed to these tiny debates filling my head as I'm pottering around. I'd be moving papers from chair to table to chair and rearranging my books, while trying to decide whether it would be a coincidence if there were no coincidences in the world, or whether I am being ridiculous. I've caught myself thinking about simple words like 'denial' and 'without' and just picturing the words in front of me, occasionally saying them aloud and trying different pronunciations to see how they sound ('den-eel' and 'white-out', for instance). One evening a few days earlier, I watched *Out for Justice* with Steven Seagal just because the film review on teletext used the word 'meandering' and it got me thinking about meandering. It's not often you get so few demands on your time, and I've spent whole afternoons creating arbitrary criteria for what I will do next, like counting the number of TV ads on during the break to decide which channel number I will flip to.

The day before yesterday, I think it was, I was waiting for the sun to slide behind the buildings to give me the evening when I could open some wine and think about dinner and TV. I agreed with myself early on: two glasses of wine a day. People say that if you're spending a lot of time alone it's easy to find yourself drinking a lot without noticing, so I've tried to be careful. When I have my second glass of wine I use a second glass rather than refilling the first, because I figure it is the refilling habit that is dangerous, because you can lose count. It also leaves me with two empty glasses on the coffee table while I watch TV at night, which I can tap together to make a nice 'ting' noise, and also put the rims around my eyes like goggles and see how much of the TV I can see. You can see a lot more out of the bottom of tumblers than wine glasses because the stems on the wine glasses get in the way, but the tumblers don't make such a good 'ting' noise when you tap them together.

As I looked out of the kitchen window today, the afternoon was holding longer than I expected. It took ages for the sun to melt into the V dip between the rooftops, and even then it didn't give me the satisfaction I had anticipated. It was one of those humbling, majestic sunsets with streaming clouds and pink trails and swirls. The kind of sunset that reminds you of descriptions of Greek gods dragging away their fiery orb for the night and of scenes on holiday postcards and couples sitting on the beach and phrases like 'the best days of our lives'. I turned my head back to my messy little flat, and then got to thinking about the word 'inconsequential', which I quickly defined to myself as something that does not have consequences. I decided my life did have consequences but that they were not very big. Then I decided that nothing was inconsequential, because everything has an effect on something, which means it has consequences. So I decided inconsequential is a word that is used only in relative terms. Having clarified this, I didn't feel any better.

I wondered what Diane was up to and I considered phoning her, just to check in. But I just kept thinking about it, and only when the street lamps began to blink on did my mood pick up a little. After watching TV for a while I fell asleep and dreamed I was holding my breath under water and trying to count seconds in my head, but I kept forgetting how far I had got and had to start again. I got closer and closer to drowning, and I couldn't remember why I was counting. It was a dream that just went round and round, and it left me groggy and worn out when I woke up some time later.

Now it's deep into the evening, and I've been flicking through all the channels and getting more and more bored of the squashy up and down arrows on the remote. Frisbeeing it across the floor, I decide I'm determined to watch whatever comes on next. It's fun to have no idea what's coming up. If Diane were here now, we'd have plans, stuff to do, people to go out and meet, and on the off chance we would be watching TV it would be a particular programme, not the Russian roulette with broadcast boffins I'm playing. There is nowhere I have to be, no one constraining my time, and it feels good letting the evening run out in front of me like a kite on a line, twisting in the wind, letting it flutter. But the sofa has a way of grounding the feeling. I keep sliding down on to my back every few minutes, and have to hoick myself back up again. To keep my hands busy, I have a few slices of Cheddar sweating on the table to my left which I break apart and shape into cheese marbles and pyramids. I pop them into my mouth when I get bored playing with them. On the TV a few moments ago they announced the flying squirrel programme, and now I've got my socked feet tucked tight under the cushion at the other end of the sofa and I've curved my arm into an awkward triangle behind my head to lean back on. It doesn't seem to help, and I can't get comfortable. I am hot and sweaty and my stomach feels like it has risen up into my lungs. The sliding is starting already, but it doesn't really matter. It isn't like I have any reason to sit up straight with no one else here, the central heating roaring away full blast and the flat closed up for the evening. I've left the chain off, just in case. I lie there in my old ripped jeans and black sweater with its over-washed wool bobbling and budding and I think to myself once more, *You can do anything you want.* Picking up the TV listings I flick through it, page by page. My fingers are sticky and I find I can turn the pages just by blotting my fingers on to one page and pulling my hand across. I can't see the listings very well but it is nice to turn the pages.

As I look up at the screen, the camera sweeps and pans across enormous branches and thick leaves and a hushed voice makes me concentrate for the imminent flying squirrels. There's a close-up of a small squirrel with this wild look in his eyes, about to throw himself out there, trusting to the air, oblivious to anything else. Something pulls me out of my lethargy and I sit forward and brush the cheese crumbs from my sleeve.

The squirrel stops to look around for a second, turning to face the camera, looking for a moment right into the lens, and I can see his eyes like big brown marbles. Spanning all the difference in time and species he looks at me and I shout out, 'You go, little squirrel! You keep on going! You jump your heart out!' My voice sounds strange. Behind the squirrel a different branch shakes in the breeze and just as the squirrel is turning its furry head back towards the tree-trunk I feel this ripping inside me, as if my stomach has got caught on another organ or something. The pain is sharp and immediate. I fall on the floor, struggling for air, whapping my arm against the carpet to try to make it stop. Some crumbs of cheese fall off the table and land on my face. I look up with watery eyes for help from the squirrel who is now spread out as wide as he can go, almost black against the baby-blue sky, with each little finger and toe pointing out to form four star shapes in mid air. He is flying free with his limbs stretched out, while I lie on the carpet in the dark, curled up into a ball with the pain. I roll my torso around to try and out-manoeuvre the sensation, but it seems to make no difference. Closing my eyes, I feel the pain pull tighter. I can feel myself pushing at it and almost becoming numb to it, as if I am coming out the other side. It is like touching water that is so cold it burns, or like a knot inside me that somehow slips through itself. For a moment I'm not sure if the pain is so strong I can't feel it, or if it has just disappeared. And suddenly I am just sitting there on the floor, with the cushions scattered around me, feeling fine. I stand up and stretch a bit and walk around the coffee table a few times and nothing is even sore. It's weird.

Fuck this, I think. I'm not going to die here with nobody knowing anything about it. I pick up the phone and hit redial.

'Helloooo!' I sing out.

'Max, what is it?' Diane says.

'Don't be like that! Listen, some strange stuff has been happening to me, Di. I don't know, some *strange stuff.*'

'You can't call me, Max. We've talked about this. I told you how things had to be.'

'Yeah yeah, but listen. This is really strange and I thought you'd want to know. I just got this really sharp pain in my stomach. It really freaked me out.'

'Are you OK?'

'Well, yeah, I guess I'm feeling fine now.'

'So what's the problem?'

'It came on so suddenly, Diane! It came out of nowhere.'

'But you're OK now?'

'Yeah, but it was out of the fucking blue! It came so suddenly and it's gone completely, that's what's so strange!'

'Well, Max, I . . . y'know . . . what do you want me to do? I'm sorry you had this pain in your stomach, but it's gone now, yeah?'

'Well, yes, but it might come back any time.'

'Christ. Look, what can I do about it, Max? I'm not a doctor. If you're worried call a doctor.'

'Yeah, well Diane, look – what if something happens and I can't get to the phone? What then? What if I'm on the floor, having a heart attack or something, and I can't get to the phone?'

'Well, then . . .'

'Well then what? What if that happens?'

Diane pauses before replying. 'Well then.'

'What the fuck does that mean? You want me to die, is that what you're saying?'

'God. Look, Max, you're a grown man. I can't be there. It's just not working. I'm sorry you hurt yourself, but it sounds like you're OK, right? If you think there's a problem, call a doctor.' She's silent again, then says, 'What on earth were you doing?'

'What was I doing?? I was just sitting there watching this programme about flying squirrels and I had this searing pain in my stomach. It floored me, it dropped me to the ground.'

'Flying squirrels?'

'Yeah, you know, the ones with the flaps of skin that jump from trees.'

'What?'

'You know the ones. They run out on branches and jump to another branch. You'd have liked it.'

'Yeah, well . . .'

'They jump without looking, they throw themselves out there. It takes guts. They just go for it, and it works out. Do you see? They go for it and it almost always works out!'

'Have you been drinking, Max? Have you been eating cheese again?'

'Diane, don't you see? They have such brown eyes, they are so certain about it. They aren't scared of things, they don't pull away when things get difficult. They stick to their resolutions and see out the bad times. They put trust in it, and go at it with all their hearts. Otherwise, they'll never make it. It's the doubts that pull them down, and if they can believe in it, they always make it.'

'Goodbye, Max.'

She hangs up, and leaves me to pick up the cushions and to rearrange them on the sofa. I roll the bits of cheese on the carpet together with some fluff to bind them, and throw them away. The conversation ran away from me again, and nothing seemed to come out right. I sit down and watch more of the damn flying squirrel thing, and I pick the remote control up and get it stuck by jamming it down the side of the sofa. When the squirrel thing is over I have to get up and turn the TV off at the mains.

All the next day, I feel a bit better. By the evening I'm busy trying to fill the kettle exactly to the 'one cup' line. I got pretty close the first try, but then I tried to add a few more drops and it's too much and I have to pour some water out and start again. I try boiling the kettle to see how much the water level goes down when the steam leaves, but it's hard to tell. I need a ruler. But in looking through the drawer for the ruler, I find a magnifying glass, and I think maybe I could look at some small things through the magnifying glass and see how they look. I try boiling the kettle a few more times and just then I hear a loud bang, and suddenly the lights go out. Stumbling around, I bang my hip on the table, and kick a pile of unopened post on the floor, which sends it skittering off into the darkness. I pick up the phone, to see if it's still working. I'm not sure if this phone will work without electricity, but it seems to be. The phone sits in my hand, with the constant ever-ready 'burr' sounding. I contemplate it for a moment and think how light it feels, and I hit redial.

'Diane?'

'Max? Look, I thought we had agreed –'

'I've had a power cut!'

'Max!' She sighs, and there is silence for about ten seconds. 'Go on, then, tell me about your power cut.'

'There's not much to say. I guess all the clocks will be wrong now. I'll have to check. I'll have to find some candles and set them up. Do you know where the candles are? Why don't you come over and help me go through the clocks? We can light candles and it will be all shadowy and dark! It will be like when we went camping in the Cotswolds!'

There's a silence again, then she says, 'Did you check the fuse box?'

'Do you remember how I got my arm stuck in that fence after you told me I couldn't reach the water?'

'Yes, I remember.'

'And I couldn't get it out?'

'I remember.'

'And we had to get the farmer to come and help?'

More silence.

'Hello? Diane?'

'Yes, I'm here.'

'How are you, Diane? What's new?'

I can hear her breathing down the phone.

'You've been going to work, haven't you, Max? You haven't just been sitting at home?'

'Of course I've been going to work.'

She starts making a strange, high, humming noise every few seconds.

'Why did you do this to me, Diane?'

I pick up the ruler and tilt it back and forth until it catches some light and I can measure the eight centimetres between the edge of the table and the chair. The phone is silent, but I can't think of anything to say.

'I saw the second half of the flying squirrels programme, Max.'

Her voice sounded higher than usual.

'Yeah?! Why don't you come over so we can talk about it?'

'You were right, I did like it.'

'I knew you would. I always know what you're going to like.'

'You said they looked confident, Max, and they never had any doubt and they stuck with their resolutions and didn't run away. You said it was about them not being frightened and not wavering in what they were doing. But I thought they looked scared.' She stops for a second, and huffs down the phone. 'They looked like they couldn't stand the branch they were on and they had to leave it or they'd die. They looked like they were stuck up a tree and couldn't get down the way they came up, and all they can do is throw themselves out there, and hope gravity won't catch up with them before they land on another branch. Max, they have to jump, they have no choice. They know they have to get off the branch they're on, that it's all wrong, and that it's better to jump and hope and reach out than to stay there. And if they are lucky they will land on another branch, on another tree, before too long . . . Max? Are you there?'

'What are you saying?'

'You know what I'm saying.' She paused, as if that would make it clear. 'You'll be all right, Max.'

She hangs up and leaves me walking around in the dark holding the handset. There is wine in the cupboard and I find a pint glass under the sink which takes most of a bottle. I also find some candles in the drawer beside the magnifying glass, and some matches. Each time I try to strike the match it goes out. I can't see anything until this big fizzing flare lights up my hand, but I can't hold the match still. It takes me six tries to get the candles lit.

In the bedroom I rummage around under the bed with blind fingertips to try and get hold of the box file I know is under there, along with some old socks and bags. Once I've got it, I carry the box file to the kitchen, wiping the dust off it, and lift out all the old pictures of Diane and me. There are a lot of pleasant pictures of us at parties, with arms around each other smiling, or over-flashed and holding bottles of beer with big grins and standing next to people I don't recognize. Under those prints, I find a black and white picture of us in Paris, sitting on a bridge, affecting serious expressions and dressed up in scarves and pouts, holding our cigarettes up like models. I'm looking to the right, and she looks across me to the left. I remember the guy we had take the picture, how he let out a sigh as he leant down to rest his brown briefcase before taking the camera from my hand, and how we'd kept cracking up and ruining our serious faces, and asking him again and again, 'Désolé, encore, encore!' There is another one of us playing football in her brother's garden, just before the ball hit her in the face and gave her a nosebleed. We got her nephew to take pictures and he only managed to catch us shoulders up, so a lot of the picture is trees and sky. There is a picture of us on the beach, with me doing a handstand and her mid cartwheel with her legs bent and splayed, and another of me with my cheeks puffed out while she sits on my shoulders and laughs. I can't remember those being taken and as I try to find the memory, glugging away at my glass with my elbows heavy and sliding on the table, my mind is pawing through ten other forgotten moments. Dancing in our living room with the lights off, giggling awkward sex on a coach to Bristol, her holding the flat door open for me and shouting as I try to find my shoes. These things just spill out over me. Walking home together as sunrise looms, throwing salt and vinegar Hula Hoops in the air to catch in our mouths. Sitting across the table in winter and chopping vegetables, next to steamed-up windows and bubbling pots. Brushing the hair from her forehead and trying to tuck it behind her ear, and watching as she redoes it properly so it stays in place. It gets me thinking about her asleep, her light whistles and whinnies, and suddenly everything is flushing out of me, hot tears and memories as I drink my wine like water, placing all the photos out on the table until they cover it in a messy montage. Looking at the faces gets me thinking about all the people we had asked to take pictures of us, watching us through the viewfinder, and the snapsnap moments they'd snatched of us. It is these people I rely on now, on the kindness of strangers, with my memories printed through their eyes.

After a while I head back into the bedroom and stand around next to her side of the bed leaning against the wardrobe. I grab hold of the few odd T-shirts she has left and try to squeeze them in my hands as tight as I can. A coat hanger pings off the rail and taps against something plastic on the floor. I reach down and discover her old Discman, with her Beach Boys CD inside, and head back to the kitchen fumbling the little buds into my ears. While I'm opening some more wine and pulling out a second pint glass, I get down all the green mugs she bought. They are a good weight for throwing, heavy enough to hurl. The music in my ears is loud and I'm screaming, 'I wish they all could be California girls,' as I smash the fuckers against the wall. The song skips as I shake and after a while I'm standing there and can't remember what I've just been doing. A bit later I'm on my hands and knees in the bedroom, getting out all my CDs and grabbing all the big Bob Dylan ballads I always thought I'd play at this moment but they sound too slow and I have to keep changing them, keep doing something else, and instead I put in old drum and bass CDs with busy foreground high hats and deep bass lines, with titles like *Medicine*, *Earth*, *Colours* and no words, only pure sound, so I can concentrate on ripping up the T-shirts she has left. I think maybe the scissors are in the drawer with the magnifying glass and go back to look for them, but the candles in the kitchen have gone out. My ears hurt and I cut myself on the bits of ceramic, stumbling around the fridge. Sliding on to the tiles, I listen to my breath heaving and sighing and I vomit a little. I can remember exactly her wild look as she left, and I think about the squirrel looking straight at me on the TV and about the fragments of green ceramic lying around me and how perfectly shaped they all are, like leaves. In the darkness, the wet floor seems almost translucent. I see myself with my toes wrapped around the branch as I balance, just waiting for the right moment to spring off, to let go, and then dropping through the leaves with my legs and arms stretched out into a star shape but my eyes and mouth closed, falling, falling, until gravity finally gets hold of me, and pulls me to earth.

NOTES ON CONTRIBUTORS

Lisa Appignanesi

Lisa Appignanesi's latest novel is *The Memory Man* (Arcadia, 2004). Amongst her other fiction are the bestselling *The Dead of Winter* (Bantam, 1999) and *The Things We Do for Love* (Harper Collins, 1997). She has recently edited a collection of writings, *Free Expression Is No Offence* (Penguin, 2005), which arose from the English PEN campaign against religious-hatred legislation. She is currently writing a non-fiction book, *Women and the Mind Doctors*, for Little, Brown / Virago. Lisa has a doctorate in Comparative Literature, was a founding editor of the publishing company Writers and Readers, and has been awarded a Chevalier de l'Ordre des Arts et des Lettres. She is Deputy President of English PEN.

ON WRITING

Q: What is the first thing you remember writing as a child, and how old were you?
A: Doggerel, just for the love of the rhymes. About eight.

Q: How do you respond to editors recommending changes to your work?
A: With a trusted editor, editing is necessary, even if one chafes. Particularly with a long book, where inevitably there will be some looser parts. It's not so much what they ask you to do, it's where they point to and say something's not working there.

Q: What have you learned from other writers?
A: Everything.

Q: If you were stuck in a lift with the managing director of Waterstone's, how would you pass the time?
A: It would have to be a long ride. I'd like to ensure a wider range of books in the shops, more from small publishers and independents who can't give huge discounts – and that's just the beginning. Are we going up and down a lot?

T. C. Boyle

T. Coraghessan Boyle is the author of nineteen books of fiction, including, most recently, *Talk Talk* (2006), *Tooth and Claw* (2005), *The Inner Circle* (2004) and *Drop City* (2003), all first published in the US by Viking. He received a Ph.D. in Nineteenth-Century British Literature from the University of Iowa, and his MFA from the University of Iowa Writers' Workshop. He has been a member of the English Department at the University of Southern California since 1978. His books are available in more than a dozen foreign languages, and his stories have appeared in most major American magazines, including *The New Yorker*, *Harper's*, *Esquire*, *Playboy*, and *The Paris Review*. T. C. Boyle has received numerous literary awards. He lives near Santa Barbara with his wife and three children.

ON WRITING

Q: What is the first thing you remember writing as a child, and how old were you?

A: I remember quite distinctly the cover illustration for James Joyce's *Ulysses*, which I first read at the age of two, prior to translating it into Mandarin Chinese.

Q: Do you have any peculiar rituals or superstitions you subscribe to while working on a novel?

A: As for rituals, many writers do indulge in them as a way of fending off the failure of will and inspiration. Personally, I adhere to the voodoo / Santeria regimen. That is, I bleed a Rhode Island Red rooster into a shallow dishpan each morning, submerge my naked feet in the blood and type until the blood begins to cool. Then I shut down the computer and go out to play tennis.

Q: How do you respond to editors recommending changes to your work?

A: Rarely does this happen because I am a bit of an anal-retentive perfectionist nutcase. I do very much worship at the altar of the copy-editor, however, especially when trying to sort out small inconsistencies in longer works. That said, no one noticed an essential logistical error in my new novel, *Talk Talk*, until a fan who had obtained an advance copy messaged my website. (In plenty of time, fortunately, so that I was able to make a quick and convincing fix.)

Q: Do you find writing more satisfying now, knowing that you have a wide readership?

A: Not only satisfying, but humbling. If before I was able to write in a void, now I know – especially from the palpitations of the fans at the various T. C. Boyle sites – that all I produce is eagerly awaited. Humbling and daunting too – but far better than being steadfastly ignored.

Q: What advice would you give to a first-time novelist?

A: Come from a very wealthy family.

Courttia Newland

Courttia Newland is the author of three critically acclaimed novels, *The Scholar* (Abacus, 1997), *Society Within* (Abacus, 1999) and *Snakeskin* (Abacus, 2002). He has co-edited *IC3: The Penguin Book of New Black Writing in Britain* (Hamish Hamilton, 2000) and has been published in many anthologies. He has written seven plays, including *The Far Side* (Tricycle), *Mother's Day* (Lyric, Hammersmith) and *B Is for Black* (Oval House). His latest books are *The Dying Wish* (Abacus, 2006) and *Music for the Off-Key* (Peepal Tree Press, 2006). His first radio play, *Hands*, was recently broadcast on BBC Radio 4.

ON WRITING

Q: When did you seriously consider yourself to be a writer by profession?
A: When my first book was published.

Q: Do you think in writing you have a moral responsibility to uphold a cultural or universal code of ethics?
A: No. Only your own.

Q: What do you think about the growth of creative writing courses?
A: They're great! It makes the art of creative writing seem less of an elitist career choice.

Q: Have any specific rejection slips made you more or less determined to get your work out there?
A: I try not to let good or bad rejections affect me.

Q: What advice would you give to a first-time novelist?
A: Write, write, write!

Kate Pullinger

Kate Pullinger's books include the novels *Weird Sister* (Phoenix House, 1999), *The Last Time I Saw Jane* (Phoenix House, 1996) and *Where Does Kissing End?* (Serpent's Tail, 1992), and the short-story collections *My Life as a Girl in a Men's Prison* (Phoenix House, 1997) and *Tiny Lies* (Jonathan Cape, 1988). Her most recent novel is *A Little Stranger* (Serpent's Tail, 2006). Kate's most recent radio play was *The Egyptian Collection* for BBC Radio 4. Her multimedia online novel, *Inanimate Alice*, won the first prize for Digital Art 2005, sponsored by the Museum of the Twenty-First Century (MAXXI) in Rome and Fondazione Rosselli. Kate teaches fiction for the MA in Creative Writing at the University of East Anglia, is Reader in Creative Writing and New Media at De Montfort University, and is a Royal Literary Fund Fellow. She can be found at www.katepullinger.com

ON WRITING

Q: How do you know when you've finished the final draft of a story or novel?
A: I need help with this, as I am prone to wishful thinking. I decide something is finished when, in my heart, I know it isn't. My agent will then read it and come back to me with comments and questions, and this, along with the time I've had away from the manuscript, will renew my energy and enthusiasm for the project. So, really, I rely on my agent and editor to help me figure out when something is really, truly, finished.

Q: Do you ever look at all the books in a second-hand bookshop and ask yourself, 'Why add another one?' And if so, what's your reply to yourself?
A: That way madness lies.

Q: What have you learned from other writers?
A: Everything! I learned to write by reading. I continue to learn to write by reading. I figure out how to live by reading, frankly.

Q: Have there been certain readers' responses that make everything worth it?
A: For me the highest compliment possible is 'I couldn't put it down'. This never fails to make me feel very happy.

Q: What advice would you give to a first-time novelist?
A: Spend your time thinking about writing; don't waste a moment thinking about 'being a writer'.

Dubravka Ugresic

Dubravka Ugresic was born in Croatia, Yugoslavia in 1949. She has held posts at American and European universities, and her work has been translated into many languages. She is the author of *The Ministry of Pain* (Saqi Books, 2005), *Thank You for Not Reading* (Dalkey Archive Press, 2003), *The Museum of Unconditional Surrender* (Phoenix House, 1998), and *The Culture of Lies* (Weidenfeld and Nicolson, 1998). She has received numerous awards and has been compared favourably with Vladimir Nabokov, Joseph Brodsky, Milan Kundera and Virginia Woolf. Dubravka entered self-imposed exile when Croatia's late president, Franjo Tudjman, proclaimed Croatia to be 'paradise on earth' in the early 1990s.

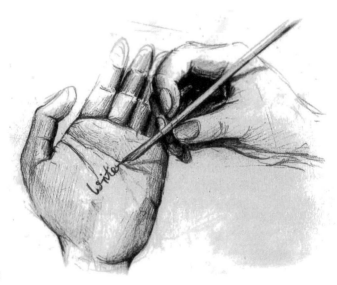

NEIL BAKER is a freelance writer and journalist. His work has been published in *Vogue, GQ,* the *Independent,* and *The Times,* among others. He has just completed the two-year Certificate in Creative Writing at Birkbeck. 'When the Fat Man Sings' is his first piece of published fiction.

JOHN BRAIME lives in North London. He is currently working on a novel about an elderly conjuror. [John is an editor of *The Mechanics' Institute Review.*]

DOROTHY CROSSAN is currently studying for an MA in Creative Writing. In a previous career she worked for the Foreign and Commonwealth Office, including a posting in Lagos, Nigeria.

HARRIET FISHER works as a teacher at a large college in North London. She has written mainly short stories but is currently working on her first novel about a young girl, her family, the lies she has come to believe in, and a hot summer. She lives in East London with her husband.

GRAHAME GLADIN has been making his living as a construction worker for the past twenty years. His interest in writing took him back into full-time education in 2000, where he began scriptwriting for radio and film. He's currently writing his first novel, *Higher Ground,* a story about the building of a London skyscraper.

EMMA HENDERSON has worked as a copywriter, a teacher and, for the last six years, as a hotelier in the French Alps. She is currently studying for an MA in Creative Writing at Birkbeck, finishing her first novel and working on her second.

CHRISTINE HSU was born in Skokie, Illinois and has a BS in Radio-TV-Film from the University of Texas at Austin. Currently she is working on a collection of short stories. [Christine is an editor of *The Mechanics' Institute Review.*]

MARIKO IWASAKI was born in San Francisco. At the age of six she came to live in the UK for five years, during which she picked up the English language and was also first exposed to creative writing. She has worked as a financial journalist for a US newswire company.

KAVITA JINDAL has worked in corporate public relations and the arts in England, Hong Kong and India. Her second collection of poetry, *Raincheck Renewed*, was published by Chameleon Press in 2004. In addition to writing a novel set in India, she is working on short stories, poems and song lyrics.

JAMIE JOSEPH was born in London and studied at the University of Warwick and the University of Tokyo. He has been writing fiction for a number of years and now works in academic publishing.

SARAH JANE MARSHALL lives in London writing reports on global health issues for the government. She has worked as a journalist for the *Sunday Times* and news editor for the United Nations. Her life in Kenya managing a livestock ranch and wildlife reserve provided the inspiration for her first novel.

CHRISTINA PAPAMICHAEL was born in Athens and raised in London. She began writing seriously after achieving some measure of success with her freelance work, in particular for the BBC's disability website *Ouch!*. Currently working on her first novel, she is nevertheless entranced and inspired by the elegance of short stories.

LAURA PETERS is a twenty-four-year-old English Literature graduate from Margate in Kent. She hopes to start a career in publishing at the end of this year, and is currently writing her first novel – a children's story, called *Mrs Gonzaleeny and the Birdcatcher*. [Laura is an editor of *The Mechanics' Institute Review*.]

AMY POPOVICH was born and raised in California, residing most recently in San Francisco. She has worked in magazine publishing and graphic design. She is currently working on her first novel, about the globalization of the American Dream and the culture of homeless youths living in Golden Gate Park. [Amy is an editor of *The Mechanics' Institute Review*.]

ROBERT ROYSTON grew up in Johannesburg and worked there as a journalist and publisher's editor. He now lives and works in London. He has had a play performed at the Gate Theatre and two stories in *The London Magazine*.

LENYA SAMANIS is currently living in London and is finishing her first novel, *Yen*.

VICTOR SCHONFELD is a film writer-director-producer whose productions have generated fury and awards internationally. A number of his films (*Loving Smacks*, *It's a Boy!*, *Shattered Dreams*, *The Animals Film*) were the pioneering works on their subjects. He is a US/UK dual national completing his MA in Creative Writing at Birkbeck. He is currently working on an American thriller novel, set in the world of Ivy League universities. [Victor is an editor of *The Mechanics' Institute Review*.]

FRANCA TORRANO is a Creative Writing and BA English student at Birkbeck. She lives and works in London and is currently working on a collection of short stories.

MAGGIE WOMERSLEY was born and brought up in West Sussex but has spent the last four years basking in the urban grittiness of Stepney, East London. She is currently working on a collection of short stories about drunkards and alcoholics.

Illustrators

KIT JILLY DING is currently a BA student in Illustration at Camberwell College of Arts, London.
Email: jilly_ding@hotmail.com

LUKE HORNUS received a BA Honours in Illustration at Kent Institute of Art and Design. He is working as an illustrator.
Email: lucky_warchild@hotmail.com

PEDRO LINO has an MA, with Distinction, in Illustration from Camberwell College of Arts, London, and a degree in Communication Design from the Faculty of Fine Arts, University of Oporto. He works as a freelance designer / illustrator / animator / director.
Email: pedrolino@gmail.com

FADI MIKHAIL is currently a third-year BA student in Fine Art at the Slade School of Fine Art, London.
Email: fadihany@yahoo.com

FLORE NOVE-JOSSERAND is currently completing an MA in Fine Art at the Slade School of Fine Art, London.
Email: flore.novejosserand@gmail.com

ANGELA SVORONOU has an MA in Fine Art from University of East London, an MA in Photography from London College of Communication, and a degree in Painting, with Distinction, from Athens School of Art. Her work has been included in a variety of exhibitions.
Email: angelasvoronou@gmail.com

Founded in 1823 and based
in Bloomsbury, Birkbeck
extends educational
opportunities while achieving
world-class research results.

Educating busy Londoners

Are you serious about creative writing and want to develop your artistic skills?

Birkbeck, University of London invites you to apply for our **MA Creative Writing** course for the 2006/07 academic year. This postgraduate degree will help you extend and experiment with your existing writing skills and develop to a professional level your own genre of fiction. The course culminates in the annual publication *The Mechanics' Institute Review*, which is widely distributed throughout the trade.

The course is taught by leading practitioners, including the novelists Russell Celyn Jones (Course Director), Julia Bell and Candida Clark. It is supported by visiting professionals (e.g. literary agents, publishers) and has master-classes by internationally regarded writers (Hari Kunzru and Maggie Gee in 2006).

With the option of studying part time over two years, or full time over one year, all classes are held in the evenings, enabling you to pursue the course without giving up daytime commitments.

Located in central London (WC1), Birkbeck is ranked as one of the leading centres of teaching and research excellence in the UK. Our tutors are not only experts in their chosen fields but they are also specialists in supporting students with work and family commitments.

Applications must be supported by a portfolio of creative writing (fiction) of approximately 5,000 words in length.

Further information and application forms are available by calling the Course Administrator on 020 7079 0689. Alternatively email: awhiting@bbk.ac.uk or visit: www.bbk.ac.uk/eh

Visit www.bbk.ac.uk or call 0845 601 0174 to find out about the full range of part-time and full-time study opportunities at Birkbeck.

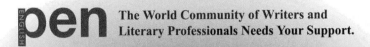

pen The World Community of Writers and
Literary Professionals Needs Your Support.

*"Among the world community of writers, PEN is a benign and vital force,
dedicated to the free expression and exchange of ideas."* Ian McEwan

Help us Defend the Right to Write.

We welcome all those who believe in the
Importance of Literature and Oppose
Political Censorship.

For further information about English PEN and its work
please visit our website   or email us at
www.englishpen.org   enquiries@englishpen.org

Tales of the DeCongested is a monthly event set up to promote the short story and provide a platform for new writing.

Fuelled by submissions of no longer than 3,000 words, the event consists of six or more authors reading their work.

The audience is attentive with agents, editors and enthusiasts all ending up in the pub afterwards to mull over the evening's tales.

Despite support from Ali Smith, Stella Duffy and Candida Clark, we are always looking for new submissions.

Tales of the DeCongested is held on the
last Friday of every month on the
2nd Floor Gallery Space at Foyles,
113-119 Charing Cross Road
(nearest tube: Tottenham Court Road).

For more information and submission guidelines
see: www.decongested.com